THE EARTH
AND
ITS ATMOSPHERE

View from an altitude of about 100 miles showing one and a quarter million square miles of the world's surface (corresponding to two fifths of the continental land area of the United States). This photograph is made up of 310 prints from a 16 mm motion picture film shot from an Aerobee rocket which was fired by the Naval Research Laboratory of Washington D.C. at White Sands proving ground, on the 5th October 1954.

The horizon extends approximately 2800 miles from Omaha, Nebraska, on the left, to the lower part of the Gulf of California (Mexico), on the right. It is not part of a great circle so its curvature is not the true curvature of the globe in a plane through the centre.

The hurricane which is centred near Del Rio, Texas, is about one thousand miles in diameter. An interesting meteorological feature is that the surface winds beneath it were easterly and had nominal velocity.

THE EARTH

AND

ITS ATMOSPHERE

Edited by

D. R. BATES, F.R.S.

Professor of Applied Mathematics
The Queen's University of Belfast

BASIC BOOKS, INC.

Publishers, New York

B
—
B

First Printing, 1957

Published in the United States by

Basic Books, Inc.

Library of Congress Catalog Card Number: 57-14982

CONTENTS

* Now at *The Rand Corporation, Santa Monica, California*

PREFACE

THE first half of the twentieth century saw remarkable advances in the geophysical sciences: technical developments made various new types of observation and measurement possible; a deepened understanding of the fundamental laws of nature gave the necessary basis for the interpretation of many of the complex phenomena concerned; and the practical importance of some of the fields greatly stimulated research. Much progress is expected to result from the intensification of effort throughout the International Geophysical Year. THE PLANET EARTH has been compiled in response to the widespread interest aroused by this vast enterprise, its main purpose being to provide the educated public with a background of knowledge which will aid them in appreciating the significance of some of the work being done. In addition, it is hoped that specialists will find that the book forms a light but useful introduction to branches of geophysics which they themselves have not studied.

My sincere thanks must be given to my Assistant Editor, Mairi Stuart, for her invaluable help in the preparation of the manuscripts for publication.

D.R.B.

July, 1957

CHAPTER ONE

The International Geophysical Year

S. CHAPMAN

THE INTERNATIONAL GEOPHYSICAL YEAR is the name of a great research enterprise, shared by many nations, with the aim to increase our knowledge of the planet we all inhabit, the Earth. This enterprise entails a concentration of effort that few nations, if any, would be willing at present to maintain steadily. Although called the International Geophysical *Year*, the period is actually a year and a half, beginning on July 1, 1957, and continuing till the end of 1958. The adjective *geophysical* is used because it is the physical aspects of the Earth that will be studied.

Of course, there are many other important aspects of our planet —geographical, geological, biological, economic, political. They too may be involved in the International Geophysical Year, but incidentally. As regards geography, the only large part of the Earth that still offers great scope for exploration is the Antarctic continent. The International Geophysical Year, or IGY, is an outstanding period in the history of geographic as well as geophysical Antarctic research.

GENERAL SCOPE OF THE ENTERPRISE

What are the physical aspects of the Earth? They concern all its parts, the atmosphere, the oceans and the solid land. They are numerous and interwoven. In the space available here only an outline of the vast field of geophysical observation and research can be given.

The atmosphere, the region of weather and climatic change, intimately affects our daily life and our food supply. Though long studied, its changes, their causes and mechanism, still present many baffling mysteries. Time was when the properties of the air—

such as its pressure, its temperature, its humidity, its winds, its rainfall—were measured only near the ground. Now they are explored in height, by instruments borne aloft by balloons or rockets. Many surprising features have been revealed; among the most recently discovered of these are the *jet streams*, swift meandering rivers of air somewhat comparable with the rivers in the oceans, of which the Gulf Stream is the best known. This upward exploration of the atmosphere is essential if we are to understand and properly predict the changes of the atmosphere near the ground. It is all the more necessary now that air transport, moving to ever higher levels, has become so important.

In investigating the complicated changes of the atmosphere, it is vital to have *simultaneous* observations, on a wide scale and for a sufficient period. Owing to the large area of the globe covered by water, this is a difficult undertaking. In the North Atlantic Ocean there are a few weather ships that are floating meteorological observatories, but over other immense areas of ocean the weather data are very scanty. It is the *simultaneity* and great geographic extension of atmospheric observations that will give the IGY its special value for weather science in its broadest sense. There would be much less value in the same kind of observations, made at the same places, for periods as long, but not simultaneous.

The water of the oceans is more sluggish than the fast wandering air; but its changes of temperature, and its slow but far travelling currents, do greatly affect the atmosphere. The currents are ultimately generated by the sunlight heating the water unequally in different places. They transport warmth and cold to other regions. The evaporation from the seas starts the grand cycle of rainfall and snowfall, on which agriculture depends. The heating and evaporation also alter the salt content and density of the sea-water, and influence its teeming living population, from which we draw so much of our food. The movements of the sea and air currents are much affected by the Earth's rotation. Properly to understand either the oceans or the atmosphere we must gain a greater knowledge of both, again by widespread simultaneous observations. Hence the IGY includes an extensive programme of oceanographic research, on the seas and along their borders.

But also a higher region of the atmosphere, above 60 miles, is engaging attention, although it is above the level of our weather changes and air transport. In this region, called the *ionosphere*, an important part of the air consists of electrically charged particles, positive ions and negative electrons. In the lower atmosphere, except in thunderstorms, these electric particles are few and insignificant. The ionosphere is of interest to mankind especially because it affects radio communication, which it can both help and hinder. It is ionized, or rendered electrical, mainly by ultra-violet light from the Sun, which it absorbs and thus prevents from reaching the ground. The Sun also adds to the ionization by streams or clouds of gas which it sends forth; much of the gas is guided by the Earth's magnetism so as to enter the atmosphere (with high speed) especially in polar regions, where it produces the northern and southern polar lights or aurorae. At times, when such solar particles are streaming densely into the outer atmosphere, aurorae are especially brilliant and widespread; and the ionosphere is highly disturbed, so much so that we speak of the event as an *ionospheric storm*. These storms occur most often when there are many and frequent spots on the Sun, and when violent eruptions of light occur among the sunspots; they are called *solar flares*, and are part of what may be termed *solar storms*. When these solar storms take place near the edge of the Sun's disc, great prominences or visible outpourings of solar gas can be seen. Much of this gas falls back on to the Sun, but also much escapes, and when it passes over the Earth, as this moves along its orbit, an ionospheric storm is produced, with brilliant aurorae. During solar storms the Sun also sends out intense radio waves of short length.

Because of the great influence of solar storms upon the ionosphere, and thereby on radio communication, solar observation is being stepped up to new levels of intensity and detail during the IGY. The aim is that always at least one solar observatory will be watching the Sun; as the rotation of the Earth carries each observatory in turn away from the Sun, from day to night, one or more other observatories will take up the watch. Clouds may obscure the Sun from view at some observatories at a particular time, but it is hoped that the observatories taking part in the watch can ensure continuous observation. Thus the astronomers as well as the scientists who study the Earth play an important part in the IGY.

The ionosphere is a fairly recent discovery of science, dating from the development of radio communications. Until then we had no knowledge of the disturbances it undergoes, following solar storms. But the aurorae, which mainly shine from the ionosphere—above 60 miles up—had already been linked with the solar storms. They had been linked also with disturbances in the Earth's magnetism; these likewise are called storms when intense. Our human senses give us no indication when magnetic storms are in progress, but they have been recorded at magnetic observatories for over a century. After they had been recorded for some years they did begin to impinge on human activities, when telegraphy, especially by long distance cables, was developed. Thus solar storms affect communications whether with or without wires, by magnetic and by ionospheric storms. Like the aurorae, these storms are most intense in high latitudes, though they affect the whole Earth simultaneously, and sometimes develop with remarkable suddenness, all places becoming affected within a single minute. Observation of magnetic storms and the aurorae are important parts of the programme. Like the observations of the lower atmosphere and the oceans, whose changes are linked together, and should be studied simultaneously, so also with the observations of ionospheric, magnetic, auroral and solar storms—they are most valuable when they are made simultaneously, continuously, and as widely as possible.

There are other phenomena of the upper atmosphere, which as yet have no direct influence on human concerns, that are being studied in the same widespread co-ordinated way during the IGY. In this great detective attack upon the physical mysteries of our planet, it is well to neglect no clue that may help to unravel its secrets. One of the clues to what goes on in the ionosphere is the gentle light called the *airglow*, that shines from that high region, though it is far fainter than the aurorae. Careful preparations have been made to study this light from the sky in many parts of the globe during the IGY; the information so gained will tell us more about the chemical and electrical processes that make the air in those rare regions shine of itself.

Other clues to the interlinked complex of physical events on the Earth and the Sun are provided by the study of the cosmic rays. These perpetually pour with high speed into the Earth's atmosphere from outside; some of them can penetrate the whole atmosphere, perhaps pass through our own bodies, and even embed themselves many yards deep in the land or the oceans. They represent a flow of energy that is weak compared with what we receive daily from the Sun; but the particles that come in have exceptionally great individual energy for their size, energy far exceeding what the ingenuity of man has yet been able to impart to charged atoms by his most powerful cyclotrons, betatrons, cosmotrons and other devices. Some scientists have thought that the cosmic rays come from the far depths of space, others speculate that many of them gain their great energy from processes going on in the solar system, linked with storms on the Sun. Certainly their inflow, usually very nearly constant at any one place, is sometimes altered during solar storms or magnetic storms by 10 per cent or more; other storms, equally intense, do not affect the cosmic rays. Without any thought of a possible direct usefulness to mankind, the connection of cosmic rays with magnetic and ionospheric storms presents a challenge to the atomic or nuclear physicists that they take up eagerly. Hence the cosmic rays are being investigated during the IGY, along with the other phenomena mentioned.

These many physical properties of the atmosphere and oceans may all change notably, from day to day, from month to month, and from season to season. Owing to their interconnection, observations of them all gain in value if made for the same period. That is the main reason for having a concentration and expansion of effort in these several Earth sciences and in solar observation, during the IGY.

The geologist is concerned with aspects of the Earth whose changes are on a far longer time scale. If he studies the rocks ten years hence he will find them almost the same as today, or ten years or a century ago. In geology and in geography there is not the same need for observations in widely different parts of the Earth, all at the same time.

However, there are some problems of the almost fixed solid body of our globe that are receiving attention during the IGY. The greatest of them all concerns the size and shape of the Earth. The different continents can be surveyed, and their shapes found— though an accurate survey is no easy task, when extended over a land mass so large that the curvature of the surface is important; one standard of direction, the vertical, is affected by influences that deflect the plumb line—that is, the mountains and depressions, and the different densities of rocks and waters; also the varying moisture and refraction of the air affect measurements of differences of level across long lines of sight. But it is still more difficult to extend the survey across the oceans that separate the continents; hence their distances from one another, their disposition over the globe, are known with less accuracy than if the Earth's surface were all land.

Two and a half centuries ago, sailors could determine their latitude by their sextants, but they could find their longitude only by dead reckoning from their log: if they were in an ocean current they might not know it, and if so they might wrongly estimate their position. How far wrong they might be is shown by the shape of South America on maps of that date, 1700, when the development of modern science had already made good progress; Cape Horn was placed more than 10° too far west. This was remedied by the invention of reliable chronometers, enabling the navigator to know the time of his home port or of Greenwich; thus he can calculate his longitude by comparison with local time found by his sextant observations of the Sun or stars. A further improvement was provided when radio time signals were introduced, giving a closer check on the chronometers.

Astronomers have been and still are the world's providers of accurate time. They compare the local time found by their own star observations with the time signalled from other observatories; thus astronomers in different continents can determine the differences of longitude between them. They must make allowance, however, for the time of passage of the signals, small as that is. The time of passage depends somewhat on the state of the ionosphere. Hence our knowledge of the size and shape of the Earth is bound up with ionospheric studies such as are being made during the IGY; and this period, in which the ionosphere is being studied as never before, will enable astronomers to advance our knowledge of the distances between the continents. They will also photograph the Moon, in new and highly ingenious ways, from their different observatories, and use the results to improve the measurement of the size and shape of the Earth.

Some scientists think that the continents have changed their positions relative to one another and to the bulk of the Earth, as if they were huge rafts of rocks, plains and mountains, floating and slowly drifting on a denser layer, partly plastic. Such speculations may be checked by measurements of our globe at different epochs; only extremely high accuracy will suffice for a reliable comparison, and then only over a long period, perhaps a century or centuries. The IGY may for the first time in history provide sufficiently precise data about our globe for such a future comparison.

Other long-term comparisons of our globe at the present epoch with its state at later epochs may be of value, without, as in this case, involving extreme accuracy of measurement. One of these concerns glaciers. If these diminish, by increased melting or reduced snowfall, then there will be more water in the sea and the sea level will rise. Too much melting of the snow and glaciers might submerge some of our greatest cities. During the IGY, glaciers and snow cover will be measured in many parts of the world, both on the ground and from the air. It is not so necessary as in the other branches of geophysics mentioned, that such a survey should be made during the IGY; but at least in the Antarctic the presence of scientific expeditions with other aims enables the glacier and snow studies to be made with less effort and expense than if expeditions went out with this as their sole or main object.

The visit of observers to the Antarctic, and to remote islands and other places seldom visited by scientists, is being used likewise for some other kinds of investigation for which simultaneous concentration of effort is not essential: earthquake records and measurements of the Earth's attraction, or gravity, are examples. They will fill in gaps in our knowledge of the globe, for regions where such knowledge is lacking or scanty.

HISTORY AND ORGANIZATION

After thus briefly surveying the scope of the IGY, let us consider how this immense enterprise has originated and developed.

It is by no means the first attack upon the great physical problems of the Earth. Indeed it follows a long series of such efforts, extending from the distant past. As early as the third century B.C., the famous natural philosopher Eratosthenes, of Alexandria in Egypt, believing the Earth to be a globe, first measured its size. After the fall of Greece and Rome came the so-called Dark and Middle Ages. A few centuries ago learning and science revived again in the Old World, mainly in Europe. The large scale study of the globe then began to be renewed, especially among the seagoing nations. In the nineteenth century *international* scientific co-operation started to develop vigorously. International unions or associations were formed by scientists in many branches. Some sciences can be studied in any laboratory, but others need co-ordinated observations in different parts of the world. This is evidently necessary in the Earth sciences, and it is so also in astronomy, whose study requires observatories in both the northern and southern hemispheres, and in different longitudes. For the full development of the Earth sciences and for astronomy, international co-operation is essential.

The first large international co-operation in the study of the Earth was an enterprise called the International Polar Year, which occupied 13 months of 1882–3. Its main object was more *arctic* knowledge of meteorology, magnetism and the aurorae. Britain sent an expedition to Fort Rae in northern Canada, other European nations occupied arctic islands, and the United States established an arctic observatory at Point Barrow for the year. It was a successful enterprise, and much enhanced scientific knowledge of the polar regions.

Fifty years later, in 1932–3, a second International Polar Year was organized, mainly for arctic studies as before; but an increased programme of weather observations was instituted also in lower latitudes. The observations included ground weather, magnetism and the aurorae as in Polar Year I, though with improved instruments. Further, two important additions were made. The atmosphere was measured not only at the ground but also by instruments carried upwards some few miles by balloons, and able to signal the results obtained to the ground by small radio transmitters. This made a real advance in arctic weather science. The other addition was that radio scientists laid the foundations of our knowledge of the arctic ionosphere at Tromsö in northern Norway, where there is now a permanent auroral observatory.

In April 1950 Lloyd Berkner, one of the pioneers in the exploration of the ionosphere, proposed to a small group of Earth scientists meeting socially in Washington, D.C., that a third Polar Year should be organized, not after 50, but after 25 years. One of the main reasons for the proposal was the advance made in many techniques of measurement since 1933, especially through the stimulus afforded by the second world war and the development of radar.

Berkner's proposal was brought before international scientific bodies later in 1950, and their support led in 1951 to its adoption by the International Council of Scientific Unions (ICSU), an important co-ordinating body for unions in many branches of pure science. This body in 1952 appointed an international committee to organize such a third polar year, and also invited the nations belonging to the Council, and others, to set up national International Polar Year committees. Later in 1952 the scope of the enterprise was widened to embrace the whole Earth, and its title was then changed to International Geophysical Year. The organizing committee sent out to many nations a summary of the work it was hoped to do, and renewed the appeal to form national committees. Its first full meeting was at Brussels in 1953, when it considered 26 national and international reports received from the nations and the international unions that had already begun to develop their plans. A second full meeting was held in Rome in 1954. To that meeting came a Russian delegation, with the news that Russia had set up a national IGY committee, and had thus accepted the invitations sent in 1952, and renewed in 1953, to join in the IGY, as she had done in the two Polar Years. The Russian delegation announced their intention of seeking the adherence also of the government of China, which came in 1955. By October 1954, thirty-six countries had agreed to take part in the IGY. Since then the number of nations taking part has risen to over fifty. Seven international scientific bodies, for geodesy and geophysics, astronomy, radio sciences, geography, physics, biology, and the World Meteorological Organization, are giving their co-operation in the enterprise. In 1955 and 1956 the international committee held further planning meetings, at Brussels and Barcelona.

The programmes of observation are paid for by the nations making them; the relatively small funds needed for the central international planning are provided by them and by ICSU and UNESCO. The whole enterprise has been estimated to cost more than 40 million pounds sterling, or over 100 million dollars. The largest contribution from an individual nation is being made by the United States, whose Congress has voted about 30 million dollars as a direct support for its programme. Much more is involved in auxiliary aid, such as naval and air transport. The Antarctic section of the programme, in which twelve nations are taking part, is one of the most expensive sections of the whole. Exploratory expeditions of advance parties to survey and select possible sites for the IGY stations began in 1954, and stations were set up and occupied already in 1955, one being at the South Pole itself.

B

The countries that are setting up one or more Antarctic stations are Argentina, Australia, Britain, Chile, France, Japan, New Zealand, Norway, Russia and the United States. Regional IGY conferences have been held in several parts of the world to co-ordinate the IGY programmes in the main sections of the globe.

SPECIAL FEATURES OF THE IGY PLANS

The IGY is a period of concentrated effort, but even a year and a half is rather a long time to keep it up at the highest pitch. Hence there are special periods within the IGY itself, in which the fullest possible observations are being made, by countries, or at stations, that are unable to maintain the full programme throughout the IGY. These periods include three Regular World Days each month, fixed beforehand, and cover also some predictable events like eclipses and meteor showers. For weather observers there are longer special periods, namely six World Meteorological Intervals, each lasting ten days—one such Interval in each quarter year.

But the onset of solar, ionospheric, magnetic and auroral storms cannot be predicted long ahead. Several are expected to occur during the IGY, which will be near the epoch of sunspot maximum. The close watch being kept on the Sun will indicate some days before when there is a special chance (though not a certainty) of such storms—notices of World Alerts then being issued from a central predicting agency. These are distributed within each participating nation to its own stations concerned with the geophysical observations. By this means it is hoped that all stations will be fully ready to observe the storms if they do occur. When the continuing developments on the Sun render it suitable, a Special World Interval is declared about twelve hours in advance, to continue until terminated by the predicting agencies; during such Special World Intervals the most intensive ionospheric, magnetic and auroral observations are to be made. This should make it possible for any of those aurorae which on rare occasions become visible even from the tropics, to be properly observed, in many parts of the world for the first time: in the past these remarkable events occurred without warning, and we have only very poor and haphazard observations of them.

Another special feature of the IGY is concentration of measurement in *space* as well as in *time*. The Earth's surface is too great, and too much is covered by ocean, for it to be possible to cover it with a good network of observing stations. Hence, especially in meteorology, there are special regions for intensive and more complete observation, such as the Arctic and Antarctic, the tropical belt, and the meridians 70°–80°W (N. and S. America), 10°E (Europe and Africa), and 140°E (Eastern Asia and Australasia). Including islands in high southern latitudes, no less than twenty-one Antarctic stations are planned, which will lead to a major advance in our knowledge of this seldom-visited region.

In many of the fields of IGY observation the measurement techniques have been much improved since Polar Year II; perhaps the most striking of all these advances lies in the rocket exploration of the upper atmosphere. Immense efforts and very versatile skills have been devoted to the design of instruments of many kinds, that can record the changing properties of the tenuous upper atmosphere during the swift passage of the rocket through it. These have revealed the nature of the solar radiation in the ultra violet and X-ray part of its spectrum, all absorbed at high levels; this knowledge could scarcely be acquired in any other way. In the IGY rocket programme the United States is playing the major part, but Britain, France, Australia and perhaps other countries, may also contribute to it. The U.S. plans include the firing of over 200 rockets from land, ship and balloon, at U.S. continental stations, at Churchill in Canada, in the Antarctic, and from ships in the Pacific Ocean and the Arctic and Antarctic seas. In 1955 the United States made the sensational announcement of its intention to fulfil a hope expressed by the international committee for the IGY, that satellites might be launched to study the outer atmosphere at greater heights, and over longer periods, than is possible with rockets. These satellites will be launched from Florida, and are expected to circle between latitudes 40°N and S, between heights of 300 and 1500 miles; they should add much new knowledge of the atmosphere at these great elevations. Russia also intends to launch satellites.

CHAPTER TWO

Origin, Age, and Possible Ultimate Fate of the Earth

GERARD P. KUIPER

THE CONCEPT of the Earth having a distinct origin is probably as old as civilization itself. Each of the ancient peoples seems to have had its own traditional legend on how the Earth came to be— but they shared in a common belief that the Earth was created from something totally different. This belief seems natural. The Earth and the stars, like all things living, show changes; living beings are born and pass away; hence, this must be the fate of the Earth.

If one examines the problem of Earth origin scientifically, one is at once confronted with some difficult questions. Are the changes which the Earth unquestionably shows, really signs of ageing— that is, are they, at least in part, progressive; or are they merely periodic, seasonal or of much longer period, which leave the Earth in the long run and on the average, essentially unchanged?

Consider the broader aspects of geology, the science concerned with the structure and the changes of the outer 10 to 20 miles of the solid body of the Earth. Many of the changes that geology examines appear at first sight progressive or *secular*. Mountain chains are found to form by uplift, folding, or volcanism. After-wards they are downgraded and all but wiped off the face of the Earth by erosion. Whole provinces may slowly rise, while others subside. Seas on the continental margins become part of the continent; continental areas subside and become sea. An amazingly complex pattern of change unfolds as the study progresses. But are these changes truly secular, at least in part, or are they merely local aspects of a quasi-cyclic reworking of the continental blocks?

Or consider the oceans, which cover 71 per cent of the Earth's surface. Large quantities of water evaporate each year, falling as rain or snow on oceans and continents. Most of the continental water runs off and joins the ocean again. Another part evaporates. Does this mean that the water circulation is merely cyclic and that the oceans are secularly unchanged; or is there a net quantitative gain or loss of water or some of the many substances dissolved in it?

Or, finally, consider the atmosphere. Its entire oxygen content passes through living matter, the *biosphere*, every 3,000 years or so; its carbon-dioxide content every ten years or so. Such changes are so rapid that they must be cyclic. But are there slow secular changes as well? Do volcanoes and fumaroles add significantly to the atmosphere? Do the additions of argon and helium from radioactive sources in the crust cause a gradual build-up, and is the present atmospheric content explicable in terms of such and other processes, acting over a finite interval?

We shall return to some of these questions below, after information from other sources has placed them in better perspective. It is useful to examine first what may be learned from viewing the Earth in its astronomical setting. Then the Earth becomes just one of a family of eight co-equal planets, Mercury to Neptune, moving about the Sun in an array of orbits that shows great regularity. The orbits are nearly circular, are situated close to a common plane of symmetry, and the planets move all in the same direction about the Sun. This system is so far from chaotic— so far from what random forces operating over very long times would produce, that we may have here an indication of the finite age of the solar system and possibly even of the general mode of origin. Very difficult and laborious studies of the dynamics of the planetary system, however, have not been able to prove or deny that the system is dynamically stable for ever. But something else can be said with certainty.

Since the Sun moves between the stars, taking its beautiful and fragile planetary system along with it, it cannot have done so for an infinite time. Close encounters with other stars would have disrupted the system, at least to the point of destroying the regularity of the orbits. Neptune's very nearly circular orbit places a million million years as the upper limit to the age of the planetary system.

A much lower age limit is found from the studies of stellar structure and energy production. This puts the age of the globular clusters in the galaxy at up to about $6\frac{1}{2}$ thousand million years; and since the Sun, being a star in the disc of the galaxy, is almost certainly younger than the globular clusters, its upper age limit is about 6 thousand million years. The Earth and the other planets cannot be older than that.

THE AGE OF THE EARTH

There is no doubt, then, that the Earth has a finite age. Its upper limit is roughly 6 thousand million years. It is of interest now to review the evidence which may make this age more precise.

The presence of radioactive substances is one of the most compelling arguments for accepting a finite age of the Earth; and it allows a fairly accurate measure to be made of an important event early in the Earth's history. Each of the radioactive elements may be regarded as a clock running off with its own unalterable pace—unaffected by heat or cold, chemical change or compression. These clocks must have been wound at some finite time in the past; otherwise they would have built up an infinite amount of decay product. Nuclear physics is well enough advanced to rule out the possibility that these clocks were wound up inside the Earth itself. Therefore, the Earth must have formed, at some time in the distant past, from matter that at a still earlier epoch, was dense and hot enough for the synthesis of heavy elements to have occurred.

The principal radioactive isotopes* present in the Earth are U^{238}, U^{235}, Th^{232}, Rb^{87} and K^{40}, which, respectively, decay into Pb^{206}, Pb^{207}, Pb^{208}, Sr^{87} and A^{40}. The lives† in units of one thousand million years are 4·5, 0·7, 15, 5 and 1·3 respectively. It is precisely the fact that the lives are comparable to the age of the Earth itself that helps to make these substances useful as time clocks. Something more is needed, however. The decay or daughter products must remain with the original or parent substance and be identifiable as such, so that the ratio of the amount of the parent to the amount of the daughter may be measured and the age of the rock computed. This means that if a rock at one time has melted,

* The letters are the chemical symbols for the elements concerned, (U, uranium; Th, thorium; Rb, rubidium; K, potassium; Pb, lead; Sr, strontium; A, argon): the superscript on each indicates the mass of the nucleus of the particular isotope.

† The life of a radioactive isotope is defined to be the time that elapses before half the amount originally present decays. In scientific literature the more precise term *half-life* is used for this time.

the age measurement will include only the interval since solidification. That is, measured rock ages count from the time of their most recent melting. Since remelting of rock within the crust is quite common (formation of metamorphic rock), with or without the intrusion of new lavas, it is not surprising that the oldest rocks located on the Earth are not as old as the Earth itself. They are about 2·7 thousand million years old. This, then, is a *minimum* age for the Earth. Rocks of this or nearly this age, have been found on at least three continents, Africa, Australia, and North America. The rocks in question are pegmatites, intrusions into sedimentary and volcanic rocks. Erosion did take place, therefore, already some 3 thousand million years ago, and igneous rocks must have existed previously to produce these sedimentary rocks.

Before we consider the measurement of the age of the entire Earth, it is useful to consider the related problem for the meteorites. Meteorites (Chapter 15) are fragments of asteroids, broken off in the rather frequent collisions that occur within the asteroid belt between Mars and Jupiter. The structure and composition of the meteorites show conclusively that the parent bodies have for the greater part been molten and that the interiors cooled very slowly. Now the iron meteorites contain practically no uranium and thorium, so that the lead found in them cannot have formed by radioactivity after the asteroids solidified. The lead-isotope ratios Pb^{206} to Pb^{204}, Pb^{207} to Pb^{204} and Pb^{208} to Pb^{204} represent therefore the lead composition at the time of solidification; Pb^{204} is the non-radiogenic lead. One may now use these isotope ratios to subtract the non-radiogenic component from the lead in stony meteorites, which do contain uranium and thorium. When that is done, the age of the stony meteorites since solidification is found. The result is about 4·6 thousand million years. An almost identical age is found from the K^{40} to A^{40} ratio. The epoch of the asteroid solidification time is therefore known with some assurance.

It is of great interest that the age of the solid Earth mantle, found by the same method, is also 4·6 thousand million years. This age, then, refers to the time of solidification of the Earth, and its major differentiation into a core, mantle, and crust, the process that V. M. Goldschmidt has called the 'primary geochemical differentiation'. The age of the Earth is higher, by the time interval it took the Earth to melt. Strictly speaking, the time of solidification should be added also, but it is presumably quite short compared to the melting time. Since the epochs of solidification of Earth and asteroids were nearly coincident, it is reasonable to assume that the epochs of initial formation were also nearly coincident. This view is confirmed on other grounds in the next section. From the known composition of the meteorites an estimate can be made on the mean composition of the asteroids. It can then be computed how long it would have taken them to melt, if the melting reached its optimum 4·6 thousand million years ago, and if the melting were due to heating by its own radioactivity, which at that distant epoch was much more intense than it is now. On this basis a pre-melting age of about a thousand million years is found. It is therefore probable that the Earth and the asteroids formed between 5 and 6 thousand million years ago.

We note, in passing, that this age gives a full explanation of the amount of the argon isotope A^{40} in the terrestrial atmosphere. This argon cannot be 'original' or cosmic, because cosmic argon is primarily A^{36}, of which only a trace is present on the Earth, consistent with the small amounts of neon and krypton present. The A^{40} was formed from the roughly known amount of the radio-active potassium isotope K^{40} during the period of melting plus subsequent additions from the remelted parts of the crust.

The age of the Earth is also in general agreement with the present rate of recession of the Moon from the Earth as a result of tidal friction. This rate gives a time scale of about 4 thousand million years since the Moon was close to the Earth; but the numerical constant is quite uncertain owing to the uncertain distribution of shallow seas in past geologic periods. No accurate age check can thus be provided.

The rate at which salt is added to the sea, together with the total salt content of the oceans, gives a rough value on the age of the Earth since the oceans formed. It is of the same order of magnitude as the more accurate ages already quoted.

With the high age of the Earth thus reasonably well fixed, it is not surprising that studies of the crust, the oceans, and the atmosphere, referred to earlier, have difficulty establishing progressive changes. Most of the data considered refer to the last 10 per cent of Earth history, beginning with the Palaeozoic era.

THE FORMATION OF THE PLANETS

As we have seen, the age of the Earth appears to be 5 or 6

thousand million years. The age of the meteorite-forming asteroids is very closely the same. The maximum age of the Sun is about 6 thousand million years. Since the Sun cannot be younger than the planets, their ages must be essentially the same.

The most natural explanation of this approximate equality of ages is that a single grand process led to the formation of both Sun and planets. Such a process might still be of two kinds. Either the planetary material separated from the solar material after the Sun got as compact and hot as it is today; or the separation occurred beforehand. There are several good arguments for the latter to have occurred; the most direct argument is based on the present compositions of Earth, meteorites, and Sun. The Earth and the meteorites have a deuterium to hydrogen ratio of about $1/6000$ while for the Sun the ratio is too low to be measured (which means that it is less than $1/100,000$). The solar abundance of lithium is also relatively very small. Both are explained by the high temperature of solar matter, which has consumed deuterium and lithium in thermonuclear reactions. Apparently, then, the matter that formed the Earth and the meteorites never participated in this thermonuclear process; i.e., it separated from the solar matter before the Sun got hot (well above a million degrees Centigrade). Since the contraction of the Sun to a normal star lasted about 80 million years, the ages of Sun and planets must be considered to be equal within a margin smaller than this amount.

It is important to gain some insight on how solar and planetary formation shared in the combined process. There are several ways of approaching this problem, but the most direct and convincing is perhaps one based on a comparison of planetary and solar compositions. There is little doubt that initially these compositions were nearly equal. The compositions of the Sun and the stars in the solar neighbourhood are very closely the same; and so is the composition of interstellar matter, from which the stars are supposed to have been formed. It is true that there are some minor differences between the great majority of the stars and the roughly one per cent of 'oldest' stars, which are apparently as old as the globular clusters. The difficulty which astrophysicists have experienced in establishing any composition differences at all, emphasizes the statement that, at least among the stars belonging to the disc of the galaxy, the differences are remarkably small. Since a contracting interstellar cloud, or *protostar*, has no way of separating its elements spatially, it must be presumed that the *protoplanets* were essentially of the same composition as the Sun. However, the present planets differ greatly in composition from the Sun. The only reasonable explanation is that the protoplanets have lost the deficient elements. Examination shows that for the terrestrial planets (Mercury to Mars) the deficient elements are in the first place hydrogen and helium, which make up about 99 per cent of solar or cosmic matter by weight and which are almost completely absent from the Earth; the inert gases other than helium (neon, argon, krypton, xenon), which are also almost totally absent; and such fractions of the other elements as might have existed as gaseous molecules (methane, ammonia, water vapour, etc.) rather than solids. It may be assumed, then, that the terrestrial planets formed from masses of solar composition, some 500 times more massive; and that somehow the gaseous constituents were subsequently lost. For the Jovian planets (Jupiter to Neptune) relatively smaller but still manyfold losses are indicated. Very rough figures are thus arrived at for the protoplanet masses; they are about one thousandth that of the Sun for the terrestrial planets and about one hundredth that of the Sun for the Jovian planets. By combining several arguments it is possible to fix these quantities with fair precision; but the rough figures cited will suffice for the present discussion.

The picture to which we come, then, is the following. The Sun and the planets formed from a contracting protostar; a small fraction of the mass (some 6 per cent, as found by closer study) was left behind and led to the formation of the planets; the remainder formed the Sun. The formation of the Earth and its sister planets was thus incidental to the formation of the Sun. This picture suggests that one should examine the general process of stellar formation for additional clues. One then finds that, owing to minor initial motions within the protostars, the ultimate product of a protostar is usually not a single star, but a binary or multiple star, which is able to take up most of the angular momentum (which must be preserved) that was contained in the original protostar. The angular momentum is crucial in this problem because of the enormous linear contraction that a protostar must undergo before a stable star can result; the contraction factor is about 10 million. The slightest initial motions within the protostar will, by conservation of angular momentum, assume large proportions before the contraction process is complete. The study of protostar evolution, with the resulting interpretation of the binary and multiple stars, leads to an estimate of the fraction of stars that will be attended by planetary companions. It is a few per cent. There are therefore probably several thousand million planetary systems in the galaxy alone.

The planets were formed from gaseous protoplanets of solar composition and very considerable mass; these in turn, must have developed from a rotating nebula the 'solar nebula', surrounding the Sun. This nebula, left behind while the main mass of the Protosun continued to shrink, was of very low temperature. The Sun became luminous only towards the end of its contraction period; during the first several million years, when it was comparable in size to the Mercury orbit, its radiation to space was feeble and mostly in the infra-red part of the spectrum. The nebula lost heat by radiation to interstellar space and its temperature dropped to values less than 50 degrees Centigrade above the absolute zero. This caused the nebula to assume the shape of a thin disc, because the thickness of the disc is a measure of the temperature of the gas, just as the thickness of our atmosphere is a measure of its temperature (it is also dependent on composition and the force of gravity, as was true for the solar nebula). A further consequence was an increased mean density. This density gradually became so large that gravitational effects between parts of the nebula became comparable in amount to solar tidal effects which tended to keep such parts from combining. A general gravitational instability set in and the nebula broke up into discrete clouds, the protoplanets. From the theory of gravitational instability and the composition constants found from other evidence, one can estimate the temperature of the nebula at the time and in the region where the Protoearth formed. It is about 40 degrees Centigrade above the absolute zero.

THE FORMATION OF THE EARTH

Protoearth was thus formed as a disc-shaped, largely gaseous mass, at a very low temperature and at a time when the Sun was still dark. The initial mass was about 500 times the present planetary mass; the initial diameter was about 0.15 astronomical units or nearly 1800 times the diameter of the present planet.

At the low temperatures prevailing, the composition of the cloud was hydrogen, helium, neon, methane, ammonia and water-vapour as gases, though most of the last named was frozen out. The solid condensate consisted essentially of the materials now contained in the Earth, with much water-snow and some ammonia-snow added. The initial condensations must have been finely divided, like interstellar grains; but they grew in diameter much faster than the grains in interstellar space, proportionally to the vastly greater density. Soon the condensate began to fall and spiral in toward the centre of the protoplanet and eventually formed the planet there. Apparently, however, a secondary condensation nucleus formed, which became the Moon. The stellar analogy of this process is the formation of a double star, with two unequal components. The Moon is too large to be regarded as a true satellite; instead, it forms with the Earth a double planet.

As this process of core formation was going on, the Sun gradually completed its Helmholtz-Kelvin contraction process. The duration of this process is found to be about 80 million years, if proper allowance is made for the fact that the Sun was less bright on its way, and therefore released its gravitationally-won energy very slowly initially. After the Sun got bright, the entire aspect of the solar system changed drastically, and with it the Protoearth.

The tenuous gas between the protoplanets became ionized, and the ionized particle streams that emanate from the Sun swept interplanetary space clean, much as in modern times they sweep away the ionized parts of cometary envelopes, and cause the well-known straight comet tails. These tails are driven away with accelerations several hundred times the force of solar gravity.

After interplanetary space was cleared, the protoplanets themselves came under the attack of the powerful solar ultraviolet and particle radiations. Exospheres* formed in the outer parts of the gaseous envelopes, and very efficient escape of gases to space began to develop. That the escape was efficient can readily be seen from the mass and dimension cited for the Protoearth. The mass to diameter ratio was 5/18 of the present ratio and it is this ratio which determines the velocity of escape. Since the Sun was nearly of the present brightness, the exosphere temperature will have been comparable to that found today. At present hydrogen and helium escape efficiently. These gases would have escaped very efficiently then, and since they accounted for 99 per cent of the

* Cf. page 107.

total mass, the mass of the Protoearth could rapidly reduce. Whether or not the escape became increasingly efficient and gradually extended to heavier gases will have depended on the changes in the mass to diameter ratio. For a circular disc of nearly uniform surface density, the mass is proportional to the square of the diameter and the ratio in question will descrease as time goes on. The opposite will be true for a protoplanet whose mass is strongly concentrated toward the centre. There is, therefore, no difficulty in principle to understand that the Protoearth lost even most of its heavy inert gases, krypton and xenon. In fact, the abundances of the inert gases, neon, argon (A^{36}), krypton and xenon, can be used to determine empirically how in a general way the ratio mass to diamcter of the Protoearth evolved; these gases are dependable sources of information because they must always have been part of the atmosphere. One finds that the ratio first decreased, from the initial $5/18$ to about $1/40$ of the present value, before it increased to the modern value. This means that the Protoearth was initially not strongly concentrated toward the centre and that nearly all the gases were lost when the exosphere was still several hundred times as high above the Earth centre as it is now.

The duration of the escape process must have been considerable. One can show that only the energy of the absorbed solar radiation can have caused the escape. From the known solar radiation and the dimensions of the Protoearth one finds a time of at least several hundred million years and perhaps even a thousand million years.

EARLY CONDITION OF THE EARTH

The condensate that collected at the centre of the Protoearth will have gradually heated up, principally as the result of three effects: compaction, which led to the release of gravitational energy; radioactivity, at that time some 15 times more intense than at present; and the formation of the Earth's iron core, once melting began and gravitational separation of molten silicate and molten iron became possible. The period of melting resulted in Gold-schmidt's primary geochemical differentiation, the formation of core and mantle, and probably already some continental crust. Evidence for an early beginning of the continents is found in their present distribution over the globe, which can probably be interpreted as having been caused by a current system in the mantle of the Earth, operating at a time when the Earth still had a rapid rotation. If this explanation of continental distribution is correct, it is probable that the currents occurred in a partially liquid mantle rather than in the subsequent frozen mantle. As we saw in an earlier section, the time it took the Earth to melt can be estimated to be of the order cf a thousand million years. Thereafter the mantle solidified, from the bottom on up, because of the compara-tively large increase with depth of the melting point of silicates. After solidification, the mantle could no longer transport internal heat by convection; and, because conduction of heat over large distances is extraordinarily slow, the temperatures in the deep interior could not be appreciably lowered thereafter. The molten iron core remained molten and the inner part of the mantle re-mained close to the temperature at which solidification had taken place. Only the outer 500 miles or so of the Earth were able to cool distinctly below the freezing point. With the freezing of the mantle, about 4·6 thousand million years ago, geological history began. But it should not be overlooked that there was also a pre-geologic history of about a thousand million years.

It may cause surprise that the melting by radioactivity of the Earth (and the asteroids) appears to have happened only once. For the Earth the explanation appears to lie in the upward move-ment of the radioactive elements caused by the process of solidifi-cation. The radioactive atoms have comparatively large dimensions and do not fit into the crystal structure of silicates. During the freezing process they are continually rejected and eventually join the light residue that solidifies last. This residue will float to the top of a molten mass and this property appears to have resulted in the present condition that most of the radioactive elements are now concentrated in the uppermost 20 to 50 miles of the Earth, either in the continental blocks or in pockets and veins of low-melting point materials in the upper parts of the mantle. This relocation of the bulk of the radioactive substances has rendered them 'harmless', in the sense that the heat they produce can now largely be disposed of by conduction to the nearby outer surface. Not entirely however: while the Earth as a whole is out of danger of remelting, the buried pockets and veins continue to cause local troubles on and just below the skin of the Earth. These skin effects are known as volcanism and mountain formation. In the latter process the bulk of the lavas appears to remain below the outer crust and often to act as hydraulic fluids in the transmittal of the forces; at least, such is suggested by the frequent association of mountain formation and igneous activity. These last remarks are preliminary to the discussion of the ultimate fate of the Earth, made at the end of this chapter.

THE EARLY ATMOSPHERE

The condition of the early atmosphere affects such problems as the nature of the earliest sediments and the origin of life on this planet. We shall briefly examine what one might expect on the basis of information gained on the processes of origin. The abundances of the inert gases measure the fraction of the proto-planet gases that remained with the Earth, depending on molecular weight. Of the initial amount of neon (weight 20 units), only one part in a hundred thousand million appears to have remained; of the heavy gases, krypton (weight 84 units) and xenon (weight 131 units) only one part in ten million. Therefore, of the initial supply of methane (weight 16 units) and ammonia (weight 17 units), less than one part in a hundred thousand million must have been left. The actual situation was even more extreme, because these molecules would not have reached the exosphere intact but have been dissociated photochemically at lower levels in the en- velope.

At the time the protoplanet envelope had dissipated by escape to space, essentially all original methane and ammonia must therefore have been lost, with a small fraction converted to other carbon compounds and to nitrogen gas. The amount of nitrogen gas so produced and retained is quite insufficient, however, to account for the present nitrogen content of the atmosphere. The data on the escape of the inert gases show that less than one part in 1000 can thus be explained. All the rest must have been produced from subsequent exhalations of the crust.

The conclusion on the origin of the present atmosphere, based on seemingly trustworthy evidence (the abundances of the inert gases), poses a serious problem, however. How could the Earth have lost its protoplanet envelope so completely? Because of the importance of this question for the theme of this book and because this matter has not yet been developed elsewhere, a brief discus- sion is given here.

For a non-rotating Earth no solution seems possible. With the present exosphere temperature, the escape of the heaviest inert gases, krypton and xenon, would have become insignificant within about 30 Earth radii, since the molecular weights are 21 and 33 times that of helium. Now the part of the envelope within that distance probably contained at least one part in several thousand of the initial gaseous mass. Yet for krypton and xenon only one part in ten million is now present. Therefore, for a non-rotating Earth the present atmospheric composition cannot be understood.

One may next consider the other extreme case, a primitive Earth rotating so rapidly that it was on the verge of instability; its equator then moved with a velocity just below the free circular velocity. The atmospheric fringe able to rotate with the Earth would then have been quite thin and its gaseous content could have been a very small fraction of the protoplanet envelope. If it be assumed further that the adjacent higher layers also moved in essentially free circular orbits about the Earth, none of this outer material could have joined the planet later. It is true that it could not have escaped as a single mass either, but the lighter gases could have escaped by 'evaporation' from the entire outer envelope, and the small quantities of the remaining heavy gases would gradually have become ionized by solar ultra-violet radiation and driven away by solar particle streams.

A second effect could have been an important contributory factor. While the envelope was being lost to interplanetary space— from where it was swept outward by solar radiations—the Earth itself was heating up and undoubtedly emitted large quantities of steam and other gases. If the rotation of the Earth were very rapid, and hence the vertical density gradient in the atmosphere very small, part of the exhaled gases could have streamed across the boundary of free circular velocity, carrying along a corresponding fraction of the gases of the pre-planetary envelope. In this manner the envelope gases surrounding the Earth proper could have been diluted; this second mechanism appears to require, as does the first, a primitive Earth in very rapid rotation.

Now the requirement of a very rapid rotation for the primitive Earth agrees qualitatively with the usual concept on the early tidal history of the Earth-Moon system. It remains to be determined whether full quantitative agreement can be obtained. The problems involved are unusually complex because both the masses of the

Moon and the Earth and their mutual distance must have continued to change as long as accretion of solid matter occurred and the mass distribution within the inner gaseous medium shifted.

In summary, then, the abundances of the inert gases in the present atmosphere show that only minute quantities were derived from the original envelope. It is also fairly clear that the genesis of the new atmosphere must have started well before the outer envelope had vanished. The exhalations forming the new atmosphere were presumably similar in composition to those exhaled by the present crust, though the proportions may initially have been different, in the direction of greater reduction; while the rates will have been vastly greater than at present, particularly during the pre-geologic era of heating.

Some idea of the evolution of the new atmosphere can be derived on the basis of the processes operating in the present atmosphere. Ammonia, water vapour and methane are decomposed photochemically, in this order, in the higher layers of the atmosphere, to which solar ultra-violet radiations can penetrate. These processes are in part irreversible because hydrogen will be convected and diffused upward and be lost at the exosphere level. Nitrogen and oxygen cannot escape and must accumulate or be used in chemical combination. Carbon dioxide and carbon monoxide are now prominent constituents of volcanic gases and must have been throughout geologic history, on the basis of the vast quantities of carbonate rock produced during geologic time. If the present rate of oxygen production by photolysis from water vapour be compared with the average rate of volcanic carbon monoxide production, one finds that the latter was somewhat too great to permit oxidation of all the carbon monoxide to carbon dioxide. On that basis no free oxygen would have been present in the atmosphere till photosynthesis by plants appreciably increased the oxygen production rate.

It is possible, but not certain, that the oxygen production rate from water vapour could temporarily have become higher than at present as a result of a self-regulating process to which H. K. Paetzold has called attention. In the absence of oxygen (and ozone) the ultra-violet light able to decompose water vapour would penetrate to great depth in the atmosphere, where water vapour would be abundant, provided atmospheric ammonia were less abundant than water vapour. Increased oxygen production could result until

c

free atmospheric oxygen and hence ozone developed; this would immediately cut back further oxygen production. A steady state with a trace of atmospheric oxygen may thus have developed during part of geologic time. Paetzold has also pointed out that an atmospheric oxygen content of only one part in 100,000 would already suffice to produce an ozone layer equal to half the present atmospheric ozone content, resulting in effective shielding of ultra-violet radiations dangerous to cells.

POSSIBLE ULTIMATE FATE

In considering the ultimate fate of a living being one need not consider his geological or astronomical surroundings. One need not examine whether his death may be brought about by the next ice age; by violent volcanic action, changing the entire landscape; or by the end of the Earth itself. Not so for the fate of the planet Earth. Its destiny is measured in time scales which are the same as for the Sun and for the stars; and possibly for the entire universe. In considering the fate of the Earth we must therefore analyse whether the planet Earth will 'die' of natural, inherent causes; or whether it will be 'violent death', imposed by the outside.

What would happen if the Earth were left to evolve with its own internal energies and forces, on the assumptions that neither its distance from the Sun nor the Sun itself would change? What would be the time scale of such evolution? When the tentative answer to this question has been found, it may be compared to the time scale of the evolving Sun and the evolving stellar system, to see which would act first.

If the Sun remains at the same brightness and if the distance of the Earth from the Sun does not change, the solar illumination of the Earth will remain the same and the temperatures of the upper atmospheric layers will also remain unaltered. The loss of gases from our atmosphere will therefore be limited to hydrogen and helium, which will be lost about as fast as they are formed— hydrogen from the decomposition of water vapour by solar ultra-violet light, and helium from the disintegration of radio-active substances in the crust. Because the rate of loss of water vapour by photolysis is small even during geologic periods, the depletion of the water reserves will be insignificant, so that the terrestrial oceans will not be lost. However, radioactive decay in the upper mantle and in the crust will diminish as time progresses, so that molten magmas in the upper part of the Earth will probably become increasingly rare. Mountain formation and volcanism will thus slow down and ultimately become insignificant. Erosion will gradually reduce the heights of mountains and of continents; continental shelves will build out over the ocean floors, and more and more land will be submerged. There is a real danger that the ultimate picture would be an Earth covered with a universal ocean. It is true that this ocean will not be of equal depth everywhere, because there will still be continental blocks and presumably also truly oceanic regions, where the crust is thin. However, the continental blocks will be thinner than they are now, because as the land masses are eroded away, the blocks will be somewhat lifted from the mantle in which they are floating plastically, which will permit further erosion to take place, until ultimately the continental blocks become in equilibrium with the oceanic regions. Their ultimate thickness cannot be estimated accurately because of the uncertain continental composition; it is perhaps two-thirds of the present thickness, say about fifteen miles. This situation would, of course, not destroy all habitation; certainly the inhabitants could build dykes on the borders of their flat continents and protect themselves from disaster by the sea. They could in fact reclaim a good part of the continental shelf by methods which are not unfamiliar to the Dutch. This would not give rise to further erosion.

The time scale of this flattening process is expected to be many times the half-life of the important radioactive elements and therefore at least ten thousand million years. Long before this somewhat monotonous destination would be reached, forces outside the Earth would have taken control. We must ask, what will the *Moon* do over a span of ten thousand million years? Will it have completed its ultimate recession from the Earth after which, as Sir George Darwin has shown, it must return to this planet, only to be destroyed by its gravitational effects when it comes within the Roche limit? This maximum distance for the Moon is about 40 per cent greater than its present distance. The period of rotation of the Earth will then have slowed down to about fifty days, and the month, which is the period of the revolution of the Moon around the Earth, will have increased also to fifty days. When this condition has been reached, lunar tidal friction on the Earth will have ceased to exist, but the Earth will be slowed down further in its rotation because of solar tides. The day will now become longer than the month and lunar tidal friction will set in again, this time causing both the day and the month to shorten, in such a way that the day will always remain longer than the month. This is the situation prevailing for Mars, where the small satellite Phobos revolves around the planet in 7 hours 39 minutes. As a result, Phobos spirals in towards Mars and the rotation of Mars is very slightly accelerated. However, the time scale of lunar tidal friction becomes enormously long as the point of maximum distance, 40 per cent beyond the present, is approached. Periods much longer than ten thousand million years are involved, and we must examine the operating times of other outside forces before we need be concerned about the ultimate fate of the Moon.

If one examines the evolution of the *Sun* one soon recognizes that here we find the critical phase of terrestrial evolution. The Sun is probably about 5·5 to 6 thousand million years old and for a star of solar mass this is an advanced age. Since the Sun contracted from a protostar, leaving the solar nebula behind, and settled to a star of its present dimensions, it has begun to increase its diameter and its brightness very, very slowly and has now reached the point where its brightness is 20 to 25 per cent greater than it was initially. This increase of dimension and of brightness will continue without let-up. The present rate is still slow, even on a cosmic scale, but the rate is slowly increasing and in roughly three to four thousand million years the Sun will have developed into what is known as a M-giant star. It will not be one of the very luminous M-giants like Betelgeuze or Antares; nevertheless, its dimension may swell to that of the Mercury orbit. Its brightness will also increase. The brightness to the human eye may not increase more than perhaps a factor of 10, but the total amount of radiation emitted will increase perhaps a 100-fold and this will have disastrous effects on the Earth. The mean surface temperature, which is now slightly above the freezing point of water, will become about three times greater, counted from the absolute zero, which is far above the boiling point of water. Slowly but surely the Earth will therefore heat up, until some 2 thousand million years from now the oceans will begin to boil. The heat will destroy all life as we know it. It will probably not lead to a loss of the water reservoir, since there is no reason why the temperature of the upper atmosphere, from which the escape to interplanetary space takes place, would be greatly increased. It is true that the solar radiation will have increased; but the temperatures in the uppermost layer of our atmosphere are caused by the amount of ultraviolet radiation, and its amount will not increase appreciably. While, therefore, the atmosphere will be filled with steam, the water vapour will not escape. The Earth as seen from the Moon or from Venus will have become enveloped in a brilliant-white cloudcover, hiding all surface detail from view. This condition will last as long as the Sun is in the subgiant to giant stage, which may be roughly one thousand million years.

Thereafter the Sun is likely to decrease in size once more, in a more rapid evolutionary process which will terminate in the white-dwarf stage. Some of the intermediate stages may be cataclysmic and cause the Sun to be temporarily quite hot; but if present information on steller evolution may be extrapolated, it is quite likely that the Earth will survive as a planet during all the vicissitudes of the Sun, until the latter has reached its white-dwarf stage. Somewhere in this development the water vapour will condense again and form new oceans; the temperature will continue to drop; and at a given time the oceans will start to freeze over, beginning at the poles and eventually reaching the equator. A hypothetical immortal observer on another planet would now be startled by the totally different aspect presented by the Earth. The veils have cleared away and the surface is visible again. But gradually polar caps will form over the land areas; they would gain in size until, millions of years later, they will have enveloped the entire land mass. The light of the Sun will grow dimmer and dimmer, and the last view our hypothetical observer would have, would be an Earth with frozen oceans and the land everywhere covered with snow. This layer of snow would not be as thin as the polar caps of Mars are: because as long as the oceans were not entirely frozen over, snow clouds would continue to add their deposits in the higher latitudes, which would resemble the Greenland ice cap (Chapter 10). A dismal picture indeed, broken locally at rare intervals by some volcanic action, which by this time would not yet have completely decayed.

Will this be the final destiny or will forces operating over still greater intervals of space and time change the terrestrial scene once more? Clearly, if the Sun would undergo a stellar collision, such would be the case. However, this is so unlikely that we need not consider it seriously. The white-dwarf Sun could conceivably enter a nebula with such low velocity that it would permanently acquire a part of it which, upon accretion on to the Sun, might rejuvenate it. This possibility does not seem to be too unlikely for serious consideration; but such an encounter would be due to chance and its circumstances could not be predicted. Therefore we shall not try to explore this chance adventure further.

Could, however, the entire universe reverse its present expansion, and during the ensuing contraction bring about a general heating which would thaw out the frozen Earth? Periodic solutions for the dimensions of the universe have actually been considered and do not seem to be entirely incompatible with present empirical data such as the mean density of the universe and the recession velocities. It need scarcely be pointed out that the rejuvenation of the Earth which would result from this hypothetical development would be of short duration. The universe would be on its way to a cataclysmic 'remelting' process, not in a chemical sense but in a nuclear sense. Nothing could be more dramatic than the dissolution of the Earth and all that is on it in the mad rush of stars and planets during the concluding moments of the present cycle of the universe.

CHAPTER THREE

The Deep Interior

K. E. BULLEN

In 1909, A. Mohorovičić while studying a Balkan earthquake found indications of a marked change of property some tens of miles below the Earth's surface. Later work by others showed that the change is world-wide and takes place at a depth of 20 to 25 miles below continental areas. The depth appears to be somewhat greater below large mountain ranges, and is appreciably less in oceanic areas.

The region of the Earth above the level of this change is sometimes referred to as the *crust*. The subject of the present chapter is the part of the Earth which lies beneath this crust. Since the mean radius of the Earth is some 3959 miles, a very large part of the Earth's volume is involved.

The use of the term 'crust' suggests that the Earth bears some resemblance to Robert Louis Stevenson's description of human character, namely, 'a paste-board portico covering up a deliquium of deadly weaknesses within'. Many geologists and others, impressed by the spectacular phenomena of thermal activity and lava flows from volcanoes, in fact once thought that the Earth consists of a thin crust enclosing an entirely molten interior. As will be seen, however, the rigidity in the Earth, in so far as it is revealed in observations of earthquake waves, actually increases downwards to a depth of some 1800 miles. Hence it is well to realize that the term 'crust' has only a conventional significance nowadays.

The Earth is approximately a spheroid with equatorial and polar radii of 3963 and 3950 miles, respectively. From these data, the volume is determined.

It first became possible to make intelligent statements about the interior when the Earth's mass came to be estimated. The volume being known, knowledge of the mass carries with it knowledge of the mean density.

Density, strictly speaking, means the mass per unit volume; the density of water is, for example, 62½ pounds per cubic foot. In the present chapter, the term will be used for what is properly called the 'relative density', or the density compared with that of water. On this usage, the density of water is 1, the densities of many rocks lie between 2 and 3, and the density of iron is about 7, at ordinary pressures.

THE EARTH'S MASS AND MEAN DENSITY

Newton's work on gravitation had enabled the masses of the Sun and the planets to be compared. The mean density of the Earth had been shown to be about four times that of the Sun and Jupiter, about 1·1 times that of Venus, and so on. But only the proportional and not the absolute masses had been determined.

Newton made the very plausible guess that 'the quantity of whole matter in the Earth may be five or six times greater than if it consisted all of water'. He had also pointed the way to finding the Earth's absolute mass by measuring the deflection of a plumb-line suspended at the side of a mountain of known mass. The measurements would enable the sideways gravitational pull of the mountain to be compared with the downward pull of the rest of the Earth, and thence the mass of the Earth to be deduced in terms of the mass of the mountain.

The first experiment on these lines was carried out in 1738 by Pierre Bouguer on the 20,000 feet Peruvian mountain Chimborazo, the mass of which was estimated from surveying and mineralogical data. The experiment enabled Bouguer to refute certain current theories that the Earth is a hollow shell, or a globe full of water, but was not precise enough to yield a good estimate of the Earth's mass.

In 1776, the English Astronomer Royal, Nevil Maskelyne, carried out a similar experiment on Mt. Schiehallion in Scotland, and estimated the Earth's mean density as 4½, a value which was later raised to 5 when the mass of the mountain became better determined.

In the meantime, John Michell had proposed a different form of experiment. It was known that the mass of the Earth could be deduced from the known value of the acceleration (32 feet per second per second) due to gravity on a falling body, if the universal constant of gravitation (See Appendix I) were known. Michell devised a method of finding the constant by measuring the mutual attraction of relatively small bodies in the laboratory. The actual experiment was carried out by Henry Cavendish who in 1798 obtained a value near $5\frac{1}{2}$ for the Earth's mean density. The correct value is now known to be 5·517, within one part in a thousand.

The observations of geologists and others have shown that the mean density of the Earth's crust is less than 3. It is further known that, with relatively minor exceptions, the density cannot decrease downwards in the Earth. Otherwise, the Earth would be in a state of gravitational instability which could not have persisted over the thousands of millions of years of its lifetime.

These various results show immediately that the bulk of the Earth must consist of material whose mean density is nearly twice that of most surface rocks, and that the density deep down must exceed $5\frac{1}{2}$.

MOMENT OF INERTIA

There are, however, infinitely many possible distributions of density in the Earth which would fit a mean density of $5\frac{1}{2}$ and also fit the requirement that the density nowhere decreases with depth.

By way of illustration, consider two solid spherical balls, A and B say, of the same size. Suppose that A has a constant density of $5\frac{1}{2}$ throughout, while B consists of an outer shell of density $4\frac{1}{2}$ reaching half-way to the centre and a core of density $12\frac{1}{2}$ occupying the remaining volume. Then it is readily checked that B has the same mass and mean density as A. And it is obvious that an indefinite number of other balls, all with different internal structures, could be constructed to agree with A in size, mass and mean density.

An interesting point about A and B is that, even if their outward appearances should be indistinguishable, it is nevertheless possible to discriminate between them without directly examining their interiors. One method of doing this is simply to find which would roll the faster down an inclined plane: a calculation based on purely dynamical theory shows that B would take about $3\frac{1}{2}$ per cent less time than A.

The crucial point of the calculation is that the *moment of inertia* (see Appendix II) of B is only about 0·84 times that of A. The moment of inertia of a body is connected with the degree of concentration of the mass towards or away from the centre. The smaller the moment of inertia of a body of given total mass and size, the greater is the central concentration, and the more readily can the body be made to spin or roll.

Knowledge of a body's moment of inertia thus places a further limitation on the possible forms of its internal structure. And just as dynamical methods can throw light on the moments of inertia of balls like A and B, so they can be brought to bear to determine the moment of inertia of the Earth, though of course this will not be a simple case of rolling the Earth down an inclined plane.

The method followed in practice includes a consideration of the dynamics of the Earth-Moon system. The Moon's attraction on the Earth's equatorial protuberance leads to slight changes in the direction of the Earth's axis of spin which reveal themselves in the phenomenon called the precession of the equinoxes (Appendix III). Dynamical theory gives an equation connecting the Earth's moment of inertia with the precession, which is measured by astronomers. With the addition of certain data on the Earth's shape, it has thence been shown that the moment of inertia is 0·83 of the value that would apply if the density were constant throughout.

This result shows that the Earth must resemble the ball B more closely than A in internal form, and, in particular, that the Earth's deep interior must indeed contain a great deal of matter whose density is appreciably in excess of the mean value of $5\frac{1}{2}$.

EARTHQUAKES

Any theory of the Earth's internal constitution must fit the important criteria provided by the now well-known values of the Earth's volume, mass and moment of inertia. But there still remain many widely different possible density distributions which agree with all these criteria. To narrow the possibilities, it is necessary to have recourse to more direct observations of the deep interior.

The more direct evidence comes outstandingly from *seismology*, the study of earthquakes. Every year there are many earthquakes large enough at the source (or *focus*) to send recordable waves (seismic waves) through all parts of the Earth, including the deepest. The waves on emerging at the surface are recorded by *seismographs* in observatories in many countries.

Seismographs are highly sensitive instruments which pick up ground motions far below the level of human perceptibility. Emerging seismic waves cause the ground to move relatively to what would have been its configuration had there been no earthquake. It is this motion which practical seismologists seek to measure. The waves, however, set in motion everything attached to the ground, including seismographs themselves. The design of a seismograph depends on the fact that, while an object rigidly fixed to the ground takes up the ground motion immediately, a body such as a pendulum bob lags behind because of its inertia. The motion of a pendulum relative to the ground is not quite the relative motion sought, since the pendulum takes up some of the ground motion. Thus the recording of seismic waves is not a straightforward problem. In the course of many years of evolution, it has now become possible, however, through the introduction of elegant practical devices, to infer many important characteristics of seismic waves to good precision.

The motion induced in a seismograph is recorded, normally with high magnification, on paper on a rotating drum. The paper after use shows a trace running usually for 24 hours, and is called a *seismogram*. The trace runs straight when there is no ground movement; but shows characteristic transverse displacements, lasting sometimes for several hours, when an earthquake has occurred. Through long accumulated experience, the seismologist is able to associate particular parts of the trace with waves that have travelled by particular routes from focus to observatory site. The corresponding readings constitute the raw material from which detailed features of the Earth's deep interior can be worked out.

It is interesting that the century in which experiments on the absolute mass of the Earth were first made was the century in which earthquakes first came to be intelligently studied in Europe. The same John Michell who worked on the mass of the Earth was also most prominent among earlier students of seismic phenomena. His interest appears to have been stimulated first by a series of earthquakes in England in 1750 and then by the great Lisbon earthquake of November 1, 1755. The Lisbon earthquake aroused interest in the scientific study of earthquakes all over Europe. Apart from its devastating effects in Lisbon where 60,000 people were killed, it attracted widespread notice because it coincided with All Saints' Day religious services, where people all over Europe saw chandeliers swaying like seismographs. By 1760, Michell had surmised that earthquakes were accompanied by wave motion through the Earth's interior.

In the century following the Lisbon earthquake, seismic studies were, naturally enough, largely concerned with appraisals of earthquake damage and geological effects, and with the preparation of catalogues of earthquakes. In due course attention came to be devoted to the physical measurement of ground motion due to earthquakes. The first known use of the word 'seismograph' occurs in writings of the Italian L. Palmieri, who in 1855 devised an instrument which detected earthquakes not felt locally. By 1892, John Milne, working in Japan, had constructed a seismograph which could be installed and used on a world-wide basis.

The present century has seen the setting up of some hundreds of well-equipped seismological observatories, covering most countries of the world. The seismograph has been further developed, and a great quantity of numerical data from seismograms has been amassed.

P and S Waves

In interpreting the data from seismograms, the theory of elasticity, concerned with displacements in a deformable medium, plays a prominent part. The theory shows how a body like the Earth can transmit waves from an earthquake focus. There are two broad classes of waves—bodily waves and surface waves. Surface waves throw valuable light on the Earth's crustal structure. The present chapter will be concerned, however, only with bodily waves, which are the ones to penetrate to the deep interior.

As in the case of light waves, use is made of the concept of *rays* in discussing bodily seismic waves. In a uniform medium, the wave-fronts spreading out from a point source are spherical, and the transmitted energy can be regarded as moving outward along the set of rays constituting the radii from the source. In the seismic case, the rays are curved, usually upward, because the Earth's properties vary with depth. Close to the very disturbed zone near the source of an earthquake, the ray concept is not valid, but it has led to important progress in interpreting seismograms some distance away.

The bodily waves are of two types, the primary or *P* waves, which travel the faster, and the secondary or *S* waves. The *P* waves, like sound waves, make the particles of the medium move in the line of a ray, while the S waves make them move transversely. In a fluid medium, the P waves are identical with sound waves, while the S waves are negligible unless the fluid is noticeably viscous.

Deformations in a body (brought about by wave motion or other cause) are called *strains*, and the associated forces (measured per unit area) are called *stresses*. For any given material, strains and stresses are connected by equations which contain coefficients depending on the material. For present purposes, it is sufficient to have just two such coefficients. These are commonly taken as the *incompressibility* (or *bulk-modulus*), which measures the resistance of the material to change of density under pressure; and the *rigidity*, which measures the resistance to distortion of shape.

For an ordinary material the two coefficients are determined by direct laboratory measurement. For the material of the Earth's deep interior, the coefficients are derived from seismic data. The material is called *solid* if the incompressibility and rigidity are both appreciable, and a *fluid* if the rigidity is negligible compared with the incompressibility. A solid can always transmit both P and S waves, but a perfect fluid can transmit only P waves, the S wave-velocity being zero when the rigidity is zero (see Appendix IV).

There can be many rays along which energy can be carried from the focus of an earthquake to a given observatory site. To begin with, there can be both P and S rays. Then some rays follow relatively simple paths, while others suffer complications such as reflection at the Earth's outer surface, or reflection or refraction at internal surfaces where there are sudden changes of property. And a ray of either P or S type incident against a boundary may generate both P and S reflected and refracted rays. Thus a seismogram may show many 'phases', each of which appears as a group of waves which can be associated with a particular ray. The unravelling of the various phases, and the building up of tables giving the times of travel along the rays in terms of the distances from the focus constituted a principal task of seismologists during the first 40 years of this century.

It transpires that the travel-times for a given distance agree quite remarkably for paths in different geographical regions. When allowance is made for the Earth's oblateness, the agreement in the case of the principal P waves is within some 2 seconds (possibly less) in travel-times up to twenty minutes. It follows that the Earth's interior is quite remarkably symmetrical about its centre; it appears that in fact the principal deviations from symmetry, other than oblateness, occur in and close to the crust.

If the velocity of say P waves were constant throughout the Earth, any P ray would be a straight line and the travel-time would be proportional to the length of the chord joining a focus and observing station. The P velocity could then be simply calculated by dividing the distance by the time. Actually there are substantial deviations from this simple proportionality, from which it follows that the P (and similarly the S) velocity varies with the depth. By an elegant mathematical process it has proved possible to determine the P and S velocity variations through much of the Earth's interior. Near the outside surface, the P waves are found to travel with a speed of about 3 miles per second, and they reach a maximum speed of about $8\frac{1}{2}$ miles per second at a depth of 1800 miles. The S waves travel through solid parts of the Earth at about two-thirds of the speed of P waves.

LAYERS OF THE DEEP INTERIOR

One of the early triumphs of seismology was the discovery and precise location of a *central core* in the Earth. At the end of last century, E. Wiechert in Germany had suggested the presence of such a core, and in 1906, R. D. Oldham established from seismic data that this was in fact the case. The part of the Earth outside the central core is called the *mantle*. In 1914, B. Gutenberg showed that the mantle is 1800 miles thick, so that the radius of the central core is some 2160 miles. More recent work of Sir Harold Jeffreys has shown these figures to be correct within 3 or 4 miles.

An idea of the way in which the discovery was made can be given by considering a hypothetical large earthquake with focus at the South Pole. From such an earthquake, P waves would be recorded at stations throughout the whole Southern Hemisphere and in the Northern Hemisphere up to about 15 degrees north of the Equator, i.e. up to the latitude of Aden. But between the latitudes of Aden and London, the observations of the P waves would be nearly (not quite) absent. Then at 52°N, they would again come in strongly and be well recorded from here to the North Pole. All Southern Europe and Northern Africa would thus be part of a 'shadow zone' for the particular earthquake. Examination has shown that such a shadow zone could arise only through the presence of a central core in which the P velocity is sharply reduced at the bottom of the mantle. The actual reduction is from $8\frac{1}{2}$ to 5 miles per second.

What happens is that the principal P rays which emerge at distances up to 105 degrees lie entirely in the mantle. Rays whose distance is 105 degrees just graze the boundary of the core. All steeper P rays strike the boundary, where the sudden velocity reduction causes them to be bent sharply downwards and to emerge at the surface at distances exceeding 142 degrees, leaving a shadow zone between 105 and 142 degrees.

It was also discovered early this century that S as well as P waves travel through all parts of the Earth's mantle, excepting the oceans and limited pockets of fluid volcanic matter. Hence the whole mantle is essentially solid.

On the other hand, there are no observations of S waves in the central core. This suggests that there is much molten material immediately below the mantle. Evidence from other sources, including measurements of the tidal deformation of the solid earth and astronomical data on the movements of the Earth's poles, confirm this suggestion. Calculations made by H. Takeuchi in Japan and M. S. Molodenski in Russia have shown that the outer part of the central core is much less rigid than the mantle. It is now practically certain that most of the central core is in a molten state.

Another major seismological discovery was made by I. Lehmann of Copenhagen in 1936. It had been known for some time that the shadow zone between 105 and 142 degrees is not a complete shadow—that relatively small P waves do emerge in this range of distance. These waves had been attributed to 'diffraction'—a proportion of the waves which grazed the core boundary were presumed to cling to this boundary for some distance before rising to the surface. And, in fact, the diffraction theory does explain some of the waves emerging in the shadow zone. But for others, I. Lehmann proposed the alternative theory that they arise through the presence, inside the central core, of an *inner core* in which the P velocity suddenly becomes large enough to bend rays sharply upwards. Her hypothesis was supported by B. Gutenberg and C. F. Richter of California in 1938. Then in 1939, when Jeffreys showed that the diffraction theory could not explain all the observations in the shadow zone, the existence of the inner core came to be firmly established.

The radius of the inner core is approximately 800 miles. For want of a better name, the thirteen-to-fourteen-hundred-miles-thick region between the inner core and the mantle has been called the *outer core*. It is the outer core which is almost certainly molten. The question of the fluidity or otherwise of the inner core will be considered later.

The interior of the Earth has been subdivided into further regions, though the subdivisions are not as precisely determined as the division between mantle and core. The following notation for these regions was introduced in the course of work on the Earth's density variation.

Just below the crust, called region A, there is a region B in which the P and S velocities change moderately as the depth increases. This is followed first by a region C in which there are relatively rapid velocity increases, and then by a region D' in which the changes become moderate again. In the lowest hundred miles or so of the mantle—the region D''—the velocities appear to stop increasing and to remain steady to the core boundary.

The outer core, called region E, is one of moderately increasing P velocity, while in the inner core, called region G, the velocity is not far from constant. Between the outer and inner core there are signs of a transition region F less than 100 miles thick. Work of Jeffreys on two earthquakes in the Solomon Islands and the Celebes Sea indicates that the velocity decreases with increase of depth in the region F, and then jumps suddenly by 15 to 20 per cent at the top of the inner core. Gutenberg's work implies a transition region in which the P velocity increases rapidly, but without any discontinuous jump, between the inner and outer core.

Table 1 gives details of the regions, based on the Jeffreys-Bullen seismic travel-time tables, prepared over the period 1931 to 1940. The velocity values are those calculated by Jeffreys. The depth of the boundary between B and C is uncertain by some 100 miles or so, and there are considerable uncertainties about the region F. On the other hand the boundary between D'' and E is very precisely located. The depths of other boundaries are intermediate in uncertainty. The depth given for the lower boundary of the crust needs to be much reduced in oceanic regions.

TABLE 1

Region	Name	Range of depth (miles)	P velocity (miles/sec)	S velocity (miles/sec)
A	Crustal layers	0–25	Widely variable	Widely variable
B		25–250	5·0–5·6	2·7–3·1
C		250–600	5·6–7·1	3·1–4·0
D′	Mantle	600–1700	7·1–8·5	4·0–4·6
D″		1700–1800	8·5	4·6
E	Outer core	1800–3100	5·0–6·8	Assumed zero
F	Transition Region	3100–3200	6·8–6·0	Not observed
G	Inner core	3200–3960	7·0–7·1	Not observed

DETAILED DENSITY DISTRIBUTION

The theory of seismic waves shows (see Appendix IV) that the velocities at a given depth depend principally on the local density, incompressibility and rigidity. The preceding discussion shows that the P and S velocities may be assumed known, to greater or less accuracy, down to a depth of 3100 miles. The two sets of velocity values thus provide two sets of restrictions on the possible densities and elastic moduli down to this depth. The densities etc., could in fact be simply deduced if values at depth were available of some third observed quantity depending on them.

As it is, there is no such third set of observational data directly available. But a variety of evidence can be brought to bear on the problem. First, seismic data can be further used to throw light on density changes due to increasing pressure in the Earth, these changes being connected with the incompressibility. Secondly, as seen earlier, important criteria are provided by the known volume, mass and moment of inertia of the Earth. Thirdly, the matching of P and S velocities in the outer part of the Earth against laboratory experiments on rocks indicates that the density just below the crust is close to 3·3.

By putting these and related sources of evidence together, it is estimated that the ranges of density in the mantle regions B, C

D

and D (D includes both D' and D'') are 3·3–3·6, 3·6–4·7 and 4·7–5·7, respectively. In the outer core (the region E), the range is 9·4–11·5. It will be noted that there is a sharp jump in density, in the ratio 1·65, across the boundary between the mantle and central core. This is one of the outstanding features of the Earth's interior.

The evidence so far cited does not enable the density below the outer core to be inferred. Additional evidence to be presented on page 43 indicates that the density at the centre of the Earth lies between 14½ and 18.

PRESSURE AND GRAVITY IN THE EARTH

The density calculations also lead to determinations of the distribution of pressure and gravity in the Earth.

The pressure of the Earth's atmosphere is about 15 pounds weight per square inch. This pressure is commonly taken as the unit of pressure in high-pressure measurements, and referred to as 'one atmosphere'. The pressure of steam in a locomotive reaches some 25 atmospheres. The pressure 5 miles below the surface of the Pacific Ocean is about 800 atmospheres.

P. W. Bridgman of Harvard has produced in his laboratory the immense pressure of 100,000 atmospheres. This pressure is reached in the Earth at a depth of about 200 miles. At the bottom of the mantle, the figure is 1⅓ million atmospheres; and at the centre of the Earth, between 3 and 4 million atmospheres.

The term 'gravity' is used in the present section to denote the acceleration 'g' which the Earth's attraction produces in a freely falling body. Over the Earth's surface, g ranges from 32·09 at the equator to 32·26 feet per second per second at the poles.

Values of g at points of the interior indicate the acceleration a body would have if there were hollows through which it could fall freely. Contrary to some expectations, the value of g does not on the whole diminish downwards in the mantle. Down to a depth of 1500 miles, the value fluctuates mildly, but keeps within one per cent of 32·4 units. At the bottom of the mantle, g reaches its maximum of about 33·5 units. Inside the central core, it then falls steadily to zero at the centre.

ELASTICITY

The principal elastic properties of the Earth are the incompressibility and rigidity, already defined. (Other properties such as

Young's modulus, of special interest to the engineer, can be simply deduced.)

In 1863, Lord Kelvin announced the then surprising result that the Earth is on the whole about twice as rigid as ordinary steel, and therefore much more rigid than most surface rocks. The calculation rested on measurements of the Earth's tidal straining, and showed convincingly that a large part of the interior must be well removed from the fluid state.

From modern seismology and the further results on density, it has been possible to add much detail to Lord Kelvin's result. Calculations indicate that the rigidity increases downward in the mantle until at the bottom it has nearly four times the value for ordinary steel. Then in the fluid outer core, there is a sudden drop to a small fraction of the mantle value. The question of the rigidity of the inner core will be discussed shortly.

The incompressibility likewise increases with depth in the mantle and also has nearly four times the value for steel at the bottom.

At the boundary between the mantle and core, however, the incompressibility behaves strikingly differently from the rigidity and density. Whereas the two latter change abruptly by large amounts, the incompressibility and also its pressure-gradient appear to be much the same on the two sides of the boundary. A detailed study of these features led me a few years ago to propose that the property of incompressibility is smoothly changing right through the Earth from a depth of 700 miles to the centre. This hypothesis has since been linked with work of W. M. Elsasser, L. Knopoff and others in theoretical physics, and appears to be a good approximation.

The hypothesis carries with it some interesting implications. The most important is that it implies that the Earth's inner core is solid in the sense defined on page 37. This result provides the simplest and most likely explanation of the rise in the P velocity found by Lehmann between the outer and inner cores.

A second important implication is that the density at the Earth's centre most probably lies between $14\frac{1}{2}$ and 18, as already stated (page 42). There is also a suggestion that the density increases in the inner core a little too rapidly to be consistent with constant composition. At the centre of the Earth the incompressibility may reach ten times that of ordinary steel, while the rigidity appears to lie between two and four times that of steel.

The hypothesis implies that the region F, if the seismic velocities suggested by Jeffreys prove to be correct, is one of rapidly changing density.

Finally, there is a suggestion of some slight accumulation of denser matter at the bottom of the mantle in the region D''.

Imperfections of Elasticity in the Earth

For all the inferences so far made, it is sufficient to treat the Earth as being in a perfectly elastic state. Such deviations as there may be from this state are quite trivial in their effect on the transmission of earthquake waves, except close to the crust.

But there remains the question as to how far there exist deviations from perfect elasticity which do not manifest themselves in seismic waves. For example, a material like pitch behaves nearly perfectly elastically under stresses of short duration as in earthquake vibrations, but flows like a viscous liquid under stresses sustained over a long period of time.

It is a fact that any solid subjected to stress will become imperfectly elastic when the stress differs from a symmetrical pressure by a sufficiently large amount. The value of this stress-difference in a solid when an irrecoverable distortion sets in determines the *strength* of the solid. When the strength is exceeded, the solid either fractures or flows like a viscous liquid.

An earthquake occurs when, at some point below the Earth's surface, the strength is exceeded and fracture takes place. Earthquakes, including very large ones, have foci at depths up to 500 miles, and distortional S waves are always at least as prominent as the P waves. This suggests the presence of considerable strength in the outer part of the Earth. The necessary stress-differences (due to thermal changes or other cause) must accumulate before the earthquake at a faster rate than viscous flow can remove them.

Gutenberg and Richter have classified the foci of earthquakes into 'normal', 'intermediate' and 'deep'. Normal foci lie within 50 miles of the outside surface, intermediate foci between depths of 50 and 200 miles, and deep foci between 200 and 500 miles. Eighty-five per cent of the total energy release in earthquakes comes from normal, twelve per cent from intermediate, and 3 per cent from deep focus earthquakes. Altogether, the average rate of energy release amounts to about 100 million kilowatts. The intermediate foci occur largely, and the deep foci almost exclusively, below points near the circum-Pacific border.

It is a striking result that of the many thousands of well-recorded earthquakes, none has had a focal depth greater than 500 miles. This result has been linked by Jeffreys with his theory of thermal contraction in the outer part of the Earth.

Recently there has been much interest in questions related to the possibility of plastic flow in the mantle. Various theories of solid convection currents in the Earth, of drifts of continents across ocean floors, and of related polar wanderings have been contemplated. The theories depend on how far the equations of perfect elasticity need to be modified to cater for stresses of long duration, and as yet there is no sharp quantitative test that can be brought to bear. One promising line of investigation is the study of the observed damping down of certain oscillations of the Earth's poles about the mean position. The damping arises from dissipation of energy in the Earth's interior and may be connected with imperfections of elasticity. When this mechanism comes to be better understood, it may be possible to throw some light on the possibility of flow inside the solid mantle. Data on the Earth's magnetism, to be discussed in Chapter 6 are also relevant.

COMPOSITION OF THE DEEP INTERIOR

Questions of the Earth's chemical composition are more conjectural than questions of the mechanical properties such as density, pressure, etc., but a number of important suggestions can be made on the basis of the numerical results discussed in previous sections.

The values of the P and S seismic velocities just below the crust, combined with surface geological evidence, make it highly probable that the region B consists of silicate rock. The mineral olivine, consisting of iron-magnesium silicate, is commonly thought to be a principal constituent, although another view is that the region is composed of eclogite, a rock of the same general chemical composition of, but denser than, basalt.

The region C appears to be a transition region in which either the high pressure brings about a change in crystalline form, or else there is a progressive change of chemical composition.

Work of F. Birch of Harvard indicates that the region D', in contrast to C and possibly B, may be one of nearly uniform chemical composition. Birch considers that there are distinct phases such as silica, magnesia and iron oxide in this part of the Earth.

There is as yet no generally accepted view on the composition of the region D'' at the bottom of the mantle. One theory has been that the region contains iron sulphide, but a number of objections have been raised against this theory.

For most of the present century, it has been held that the central core consists predominantly of molten iron, probably mixed with nickel. This view arose from early observations of meteorites, assumed to be samples of material from inside an exploded planet, and from the known fairly high mean density of the Earth's core.

An alternative view put forward by W. H. Ramsey in 1948 is that the outer core consists of material of the same chemical composition as that in the region D, but in a different physical state brought about by the huge pressure of $1\frac{1}{3}$ million atmospheres.

On the iron outer-core theory, it has been shown by Jeffreys that the terrestrial planets—Earth, Mars, Venus, Mercury— must have considerably different overall chemical compositions. On the new theory, these planets may have been originally of the same overall composition. The new theory is, however, still highly controversial.

The compressibility theory (page 43) suggests that the outer core is fairly uniform in composition, but that there may be some variation in the inner core. There is evidence that the inner core cannot contain much material that is denser than iron or nickel. The time is not yet ripe to speculate on the composition of the region F.

TEMPERATURE

It is well known that as one descends vertically in mines, the ground temperature rises. The rate of increase depends on the heat conductivity of the local rocks, an average figure being 30 degrees Centigrade per mile. If this rate persisted throughout the whole Earth, the temperature at the centre would exceed 100,000 degrees.

Such a rate could not, however, continue far into the solid mantle without causing the mantle to melt. It is in fact possible to use the known solidity of the mantle to set limits to the temperature at the bottom.

R. J. Uffen of Ontario has estimated that, on certain plausible assumptions, the whole mantle would not remain solid if the temperature at the bottom exceeds 5000 degrees Centigrade. One or two other authors would put the upper limit a few thousand degrees higher than this. The temperature in the core is nowhere thought to exceed the temperature in the mantle by more than about 500 degrees. On practically all current theories, the temperature at the Earth's centre thus does not exceed 10,000 degrees.

Further work of J. Verhoogen of California indicates that the temperature at the Earth's centre is not less than about 2000 degrees. While these plausible lower and upper limits to the temperature in the Earth's deep interior can be set, the actual temperatures cannot yet be assigned as precisely as the pressures.

Sir Francis Simon of Oxford and J. A. Jacobs of Toronto have used thermodynamical considerations to show how the central core can contain a solid inner core, if the whole core is largely composed of iron. Birch had previously suggested that the inner core may be composed of a crystalline form of iron. Jacobs suggests that an Earth, wholly molten at some stage of its history, started solidifying from the centre outwards, and also from the base of the mantle upwards, leaving a molten outer core trapped in between. This is an extension of earlier work of Jeffreys, which showed that solidification of the mantle must have started at the bottom.

CHAPTER FOUR

The Crust

J. TUZO WILSON

MAN'S HOME—the surface of the Earth—is a small and temperate shelter set in a vast and alien universe. The most remote oasis of the deserts is not to be compared to it for solitude. Well may mankind glory in its fertile plains, its snow-topped pinnacles, its mighty oceans, for they are rare examples of moderation in a universe where extremes of heat and cold prevail. Through space too vast to comprehend there is darkness blacker than midnight and cold which is nearly absolute. For the most part space is empty, but at rare intervals dust as tenuous as the aurora lights up to the fiery glow of another Sun, a furnace hot with nuclear fire.

Many theories suggest that around millions of other stars solar systems may revolve, but none can be seen. Within our own system no other place but the surface of the Earth is habitable. Certainly the other planetary bodies whose solid surface we can see—the Moon, Mars and Mercury—are not.

The utter contrast between the surfaces of the Moon and the Earth, whose environments in space have been so similar, is particularly striking. The Moon's surface is dry and without air. On it there are no continents, no long ranges of mountains, and no active volcanoes, but instead a multitude of meteorite craters of all sizes, which are almost lacking on Earth. Various reasons suggest that the Earth's surface was once like that of the Moon and that the Earth has developed its crust, its oceans and its atmosphere, while the Moon has remained unchanged.

On Earth the greatest miracle is life, but the combination of circumstances which have made life possible is hardly less remarkable. An abundance of water and the emergence of dry land above it are the unusual attributes of the Earth to which we owe our existence. This favourable environment has developed because of two circumstances unique in the solar system and of great rarity in the universe. One factor has been that for several thousand million years the Sun's heat has maintained most of the Earth's surface in the narrow temperature range of liquid water. If the surface had been too cold it would have become solid and inert; if too hot it would have vaporized. Extremes of heat and cold are inimical to life in any form, so that we can be sure that suitable conditions for any kind of creatures, even ones very different from those we know, are rare.

The second factor has been activity within the Earth. By good fortune, heat generated by the disintegration of radioactive minerals, combined with that given to the interior of the Earth during its early history, has provided energy for earthquakes and volcanism. Their activity has sufficed to uplift lands continuously above the eroding sea and maintain them as island homes. Moreover, it seems reasonable to conclude from the many sources of information which modern geophysical science has placed at our disposal, that the atmosphere, the oceans and the crust of the Earth have all been brought forth from the interior by volcanic and seismic activity during the planet's long history. Thus oceans and continents, with their vast ridges and trenches, valleys and mountains, have gradually been constructed on top of the original surface of the Earth. This now forms the base of the crust. It is hidden and only known to us from the echoes of seismic waves which it reflects. This view is a new one and not yet widely understood, but it seems forced upon us by our expanding knowledge.

Consideration of the rate at which gases, steam and lava are poured forth by volcanoes has led to the idea that the atmosphere, oceans and rocks of the crust have all been produced by volcanicity. Studies of their composition and abundances strengthen this view. A rate not much higher than that at which volcanoes emit lava today would have sufficed to build the entire crust during the age of the Earth, which has recently been proved to be 4·5 thousand million years. This has made it possible to recount the growth of the world to its present state instead of merely describing its appearance. Geological features which were once a catalogue of details to be memorized by students are now beginning to take their places in an ordered story of evolution. But it is still a difficult story to tell, and will remain so until there has been time to fill the gaps and remove uncertainties in our new kinds of information.

It is important to emphasize the embryonic state of our new ideas about the Earth, for in this brief account we cannot dwell on the uncertainties, nor do justice to all the conflicting theories and suggestions, which for the present form part of the new and evolving history of the whole Earth.

It seems simplest to begin with an account of the fracture systems which have controlled activity and guided the growth of the crust, then to discuss the rocks which furnish clues to many phases of its history, and finally to describe the great ocean floors and the growth upon them of submarine mountains, islands and continents.

EARTHQUAKES AND FRACTURES

The flow of lava and hence the building of the different parts of the crust is related to systems of fractures along which seismic and volcanic activity take place. Many parts of the Earth's crust have been fractured in the past. The faults mapped by geologists are scars that show where former displacements have occurred. Along active fractures, intermittent movements produce shocks called earthquakes, which are felt in the vicinity and recorded on sensitive seismographs all over the world. By studying these records and triangulating from the stations, seismologists can tell us when, where and at what depth any particular shock occurred.

To collate and publish the data on earthquakes collected by all of the world's 600 seismological observatories, there is an organization called the International Seismological Summary, under the direction of Sir Harold Jeffreys of Cambridge. This information has been analysed by B. Gutenberg and C. F. Richter of California, who have shown in detail how all the world's important earthquakes are arranged along one of two narrow systems. Most of the world's volcanoes lie along these systems also, so that it is natural to suppose that active fractures provide the relief of pressure and the channels by which volcanic materials escape from the hotter interior of the Earth.

The more active of these systems lies for the most part along continental margins and is here called the *continental fracture system* (Fig. 1). It is formed of two belts which enfold the world in the shape of a great T. The stroke of the T extends along the Mediterranean region through the Alpine, Turkish, Persian and Himalayan Mountains, through Indonesia, New Guinea and other islands to New Zealand. The stem of the T springs from a junction in Celebes to encircle the Pacific Ocean through the Philippines, Japan, Alaska, the Cordillera and Andes of the Americas, to Antarctica.

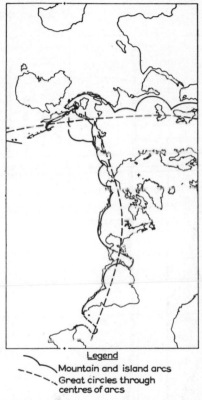

Legend
───── Mountain and island arcs
– – – Great circles through
            centres of arcs

FIG. I.   Continental fracture system.

The stem and western limb of the pattern each consist of a series of arcs joined end to end, which are but the surface expression of great conical fractures whose shape and position have been indicated by plotting the location of many earthquakes (Fig. 2). Several of the cones extend to depths of 450 miles, which is over one tenth of the Earth's radius, but deeper shocks have never been recorded.

The other principal fracture system is followed by the line of the mid-ocean ridges after which it is here named. (Fig. 3). The

mid-Atlantic ridge, along which Jan Mayen Island, Iceland, the
Azores, Ascension Island and Tristan da Cunha are peaks, is the
best known part, but the *mid-ocean fracture system* is continuous
and worldwide. M. Ewing of Columbia University has recently
pointed out that the mid-Atlantic ridge turns and continues beneath the Southern Ocean south of Africa to connect with the

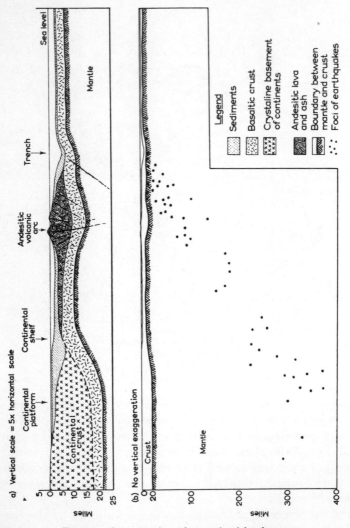

FIG. 2.   Cross section of an active island arc.

Carlsberg ridge in the Indian Ocean, and thence south of Australia to join the principal ridges of the Pacific Ocean. Its pattern is irregular and not made up of a series of arcs like the continental system. All of the earthquakes along it are shallow—that is, less

Legend

➤ Mid ocean ridges   Ocean depths less than 1500 fathoms

Land   Ancillary fracture

FIG. 3.   Mid-ocean ridges and ancillary fractures.

than 45 miles to their foci. Connecting these two principal systems and branching from them are many ancillary faults. Some of these are well known, both on land and on the sea floor, but the whole pattern has by no means been elucidated.

The movement on fractures takes place a little bit at a time, giving rise to earthquakes. The displacement in a single earth-quake is often several feet. For example, in the central zone of the San Francisco earthquake of 1906, the whole surface of the Earth on one side of the fault was horizontally displaced by 21 feet relative to the other side. Fences, roads and houses lying across the fault were torn apart.

Since only narrow belts about the Earth are seismically active, people in most parts of the world have never experienced a severe earthquake; but along the active fracture systems people feel them every few weeks. The following account of the great Assam shock of 1951, published in *Nature* by Captain F. Kingdon-Ward, gives some idea of the great forces released at the central region in a major earthquake.

'Suddenly, after the faintest tremor (felt by my wife but not by me) there came an appalling noise, and the Earth began to shudder violently. I jumped up and looked out of the tent. I have a distinct recollection of seeing the outlines of the landscape, visible against the starry sky, blurred—every ridge and tree fuzzy—as though it were rapidly moving up and down; but fifteen or twenty seconds passed before I realized that an earthquake had started. My wife shouted: "Earthquake!" before I did, and leapt out of bed. Together we rushed outside, I seizing the oil lantern which I placed on the ground. I was conscious of fearing that the tent would catch fire. We were immediately thrown to the ground; the lantern, too, was knocked over, and went out instantly.

'I find it very difficult to recollect my emotions during the four or five minutes the shock lasted; but the first feeling of bewilderment—an incredulous astonishment that these solid-looking hills were in the grip of a force which shook them as a terrier shakes a rat—soon gave place to stark terror. Yet my wife and I lying side by side on the sandbank, spoke quite calmly together, and to our two Sherpa boys, who, having already been thrown down twice, were lying close to us.

'The earthquake was now well under way, and it was felt as though a powerful ram were hitting against the Earth beneath us with the persistence of a kettle-drum. I had exactly the sensation that a thin crust at the bottom of the basin, on which we lay, was breaking up like an ice floe, and that we were all going down to-gether through an immense hole, into the interior of the Earth. The din was terrible; but it was difficult to separate the noise made by the earthquake itself from the roar of the rock avalanches pouring down on all sides into the basin.

'Gradually the crash of falling rocks became more distinct, the frightful hammer blows weakened, the vibration grew less, and presently we knew that the main shock was over.'

The cause of the formation of fractures is not absolutely known. Some authorities believe that great but slow convection currents of a plastic nature occur in the mantle, but there has never been any direct evidence for the existence of these or any agreement about their nature. It is not clear why this flow should create fractures, nor have these theories been developed to a stage where they can explain the details of the Earth's surface as seen by geologists. A better theory seems to be the much older one that the Earth is cooling and shrinking, and that as a result its outer parts crack in this rather special way. The emission of volcanic matter causes further contraction.

METHODS OF DATING ROCKS

Study of rocks and fossils has furnished the principal clues for deciphering the history of the land surface. To understand how this has been done it is essential to have some knowledge of the methods used for dating them.

Three groups of methods exist, structural, palaeontological and radioactive. The first two were developed a century and a half ago They have generally been used together to date stratified, sedimentary rocks, and they have provided a precise but only relative time scale for fossiliferous rocks. They depend upon working out the order of succession in stratified rocks, using fossils and lithology to correlate from place to place and to fit the successions into a standard time scale based upon the evolution of fossil life.

The last group of methods, which only became possible after the discovery of radioactivity sixty years ago, is still undergoing development. They can best be applied to igneous and metamorphic rocks and so are often difficult to correlate with the older methods, but they give absolute ages and they have already revolutionized our thinking about the greater part of the history of the Earth.

By using fossils a relative time scale was worked out for the younger rocks, and all sections of it were given names. The three main divisions have been called the Palaeozoic, the Mesozoic and the Cenozoic eras, each subdivided into named periods, epochs and ages (Table 1).

The palaeontological methods break down entirely for rocks older than five hundred million years because before that time few creatures had hard parts. For the older rocks, for all absolute dates, and for metamorphic rocks, radioactive methods of age determination must be used.

A typical method of radioactive age determination depends upon the slow decay of a naturally occurring radioactive element like uranium to its daughter element, lead. Uranium and lead have no

TABLE 1

Geological time scale

Events	Time (thousands of millions of years)	Geological Scale
Present Day	– – – 0 – – –	} Cenozoic era
	– – – 0·07 – – –	} Mesozoic era
	– – – 0·2 – – –	} Palaeozoic era
First index fossil	– – – 0·5 – – –	
	– – – 1·0	
	– – –	Precambrian
Change in rock types	– – – 2·0	
	– – –	
Oldest known rocks	– – – 3·0 – – –	– – – – – – – –
	– – –	
		No rocks preserved
	– – – 4·0	
Origin of Earth	– – – 4·5	

chemical affinity for one another so that there is no reason for any lead to have been present initially in a uranium mineral. If, therefore, chemical analysis shows that a uranium mineral contains several percent of lead, it is reasonable to assume that the lead is the decay product of the uranium. The rate of decay of uranium is uniform and known. For example, half of any quantity of the isotope uranium-235 decays to lead-207 in 7.1 hundred million years.

Thus the age of deposition of the mineral can be calculated from the ratio of lead to uranium. Several checks are possible to show whether alteration or additions have occurred.

It is this group of methods which have shown that the Earth itself was formed about 4·5 thousand million years ago, while the oldest rocks are 3 thousand million years old. The palaeontological method had given no clue to events during the first five-sixths of geological time, and the structural methods were primitive and not easily applied to ancient rocks which were commonly deformed. Thus it has been the development and application of radioactive methods during the past ten years which has completely changed our ideas about the age and early behaviour of the Earth. A. Holmes of Edinburgh and A. O. Nier of Harvard and Minnesota have been leaders in the development of these methods.

KINDS OF ROCKS

There are three principal classes of rocks. Those formed from lava are called volcanic rocks; those originally deposited on the sea floor and subsequently hardened are called sedimentary rocks; while those of either class which have been greatly recrystallized and altered are called metamorphic or plutonic rocks. The name igneous is often used to cover all volcanic rocks and some of the plutonic rocks which most resemble them.

Volcanic Rocks

Under this heading we will consider only those rocks which are known to rise as liquid lava along fractures. Their importance may be judged from the following simple calculation. In 1927 K. Sapper estimated the volume of all lava and ash poured out by volcanoes all over the world since A.D. 1500. The average rate of one fifth of a cubic mile per year seems moderate enough, but consider the implications. If this rate had been constant during the total history of the Earth, enough lava would have been produced to cover all the continents with 18 miles of lava, but the continental crust is only 20 miles thick and the oceanic crust is smaller. Since the present rate is probably lower than that which prevailed in the remote past, it is likely that enough lava has been poured out to provide material for the whole crust. However, the lava is modified by processes to be described, before being incorporated into the crust.

E

Andesitic volcanics—Andesite is the name of the most abundant type of lava emitted along the continental fracture system. It contains about 60 per cent silica (SiO_2), the remaining 40 per cent being made up of elements common in many rocks, aluminium, iron, magnesium, calcium, sodium and potassium. Most of the world's 480 volcanoes lie along the continental system and emit mainly andesitic lavas, with lesser quantities of more siliceous lava called rhyolite (about 70 per cent silica), and of less siliceous lava called basalt (about 50 per cent silica). It is these lavas, and chiefly andesite, which are believed to have supplied the materials out of which the continents have been built.

Basaltic volcanics—The only group of lavas found along the mid-ocean fracture system and on the scattered volcanoes of the ocean floors are the less siliceous basalts and certain variants formed during their crystallization. Unlike andesites, basalts are found in all parts of the world, for they are emitted by volcanoes of both systems although subordinate to andesites in the continental system.

The sources of lava—Basalts, without any andesites, flow from fracture systems which earthquakes show to be shallow, less than 45 miles deep, but andesites with a mixture of some basalt, flow from systems which earthquakes show to be up to 450 miles deep. It seems logical to explain this by suggesting that these lavas are derived from different layers within the Earth, the basalts originating in a shallow layer by partial melting of the mantle, while the andesites come from a deeper layer, bringing some basalt with them as they rise through the upper layer.

Plutonic Rocks

The coarsely crystalline rocks which have formed at depth within the crust are given the name *plutonic*. Some of these are igneous rocks which have formed from trapped lavas which have cooled slowly. Others are volcanic and sedimentary rocks which have recrystallized under high temperature and pressure to form metamorphic rocks, many of which are called *gneisses*. Gneisses derived from sediments are the commonest rocks of the continental shields. In some cases the products of these two processes are so similar that their particular origin may be obscure.

Among the igneous plutonic rocks, granite, granodiorite, and gabbro are the coarse-grained chemical equivalents of rhyolite, andesite and basalt respectively.

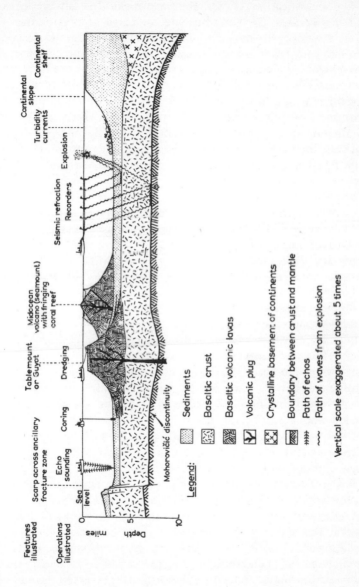

FIG. 4. Cross section of the oceanic crust illustrating various features and methods for investigating them.

Sedimentary Rocks

The classification of sedimentary rocks has always proved difficult, because they are variable mixtures of precipitates and material worn or broken off other rocks. Traditionally the classification into rock types has been based upon texture and composition. Gravel and conglomerates are coarse, silt and shale are fine, sands are intermediate in texture. Everyone knows the chief constituents of sandstone and limestone. Shales are clay with an admixture of sand and lime. Less well known are arkoses, which consist predominantly of feldspar with quartz and a little mica, and greywackes which are a mixture of quartz and mica sometimes with a little feldspar. Much less common are black shale and coal, salt deposits and iron formations.

For the purposes of broad regional description, such as are involved in this chapter, these classifications are not useful because several different rock types commonly occur together. T. D. Krynine and F. J. Pettijohn have shown that these associations are not random, and they have worked out genetic classifications, or *facies*, of rocks, based upon occurrence and origin.

Borderland facies—This facies is sometimes termed *graptolitic*, from the graptolite fossils frequently found in its shales, but more commonly *eugeosynclinal*, literally, 'more of a large earth downfold'. These sediments are those which are piled up along island arcs, swept into ocean trenches and accumulated in deltas and on continental shelves. They consist chiefly of shales and greywackes, the ill-sorted products of erosion of lavas and the finer material carried from continents. Since they accumulate along the borderlands of the continents in vast volumes and on the marginal ocean floors which are several miles deep, they form very thick sequences, often slumped and contorted (Figs. 2 and 4).

Rocks of this facies are by far the most abundant, but this is not readily apparent because most of them are below sea level and invisible until metamorphosed and uplifted into young mountains. By that process they are changed to plutonic rocks whose origin is disguised. Nor is the origin any more apparent when the mountains have been eroded to the gneisses of continental shields, although the average andesitic composition is preserved throughout. Thus there is a cycle among the rocks in which lavas are broken down by weathering to sediments and sediments are metamorphosed to plutonic rocks, some of which may be recycled by being eroded again to form more sediments.

Platform facies—As the level of the ocean has fluctuated and as eugeosynclines have weighed down the continental margins, shallow seas have often penetrated far inland over the continental crust. The North Sea, Hudson Bay and the shallow seas north of Australia are present day examples. Minerals derived from the crust are washed by waves, cleaned and sorted, until the beds laid down consist at the base chiefly of pure sandstone and grade up into shales and pure limestones. Evaporation and shallow water encourage the growth of corals where the climate is warm, and the formation of limestone. These platform rocks, widely exposed on every continent and full of fossils, are the stratigrapher's delight. They have come to be regarded as typical sediments, although they are in truth a rather special and ephemeral form which with the passage of time become eroded away and carried to more permanent resting places at the borderlands.

These platform rocks grade into the borderland deposits, and at the junction may be preserved as wedge-shaped basins which are frequently called *miogeosynclines*, literally 'less of a large earth downfold'.

Piedmont facies—After great mountains are uplifted, they are rapidly eroded. Torrents sweep coarse, ill-sorted and undecomposed fragments down into piedmont fans, into swampy basins on the inner sides of young mountains and into basins between ranges. These beds are predominantly red arkoses, but they also contain black shales, coal and occasionally copper-rich beds. Some examples are the Keweenawan rocks around Lake Superior, the Old Red Sandstone of Scotland, the Red Molasse of the Alps, and the Newark and Catskill series in the Appalachians. These rocks may be formed on top of miogeosynclines formed earlier in the same cycle.

THE OCEAN BASINS

The largest part of the crust is occupied by the world's ocean basins, which cover over 70 per cent of its surface, an area of 140 million square miles. Mapping this vast extent is an enormous and expensive task. It requires ships especially equipped and despatched for the purpose, since merchant ships have neither time nor facilities for exploration, and travel relatively restricted sea lanes. Most charts have been made by the world's navies, but other scientific work has been carried out by a hundred or so oceanographical expeditions.

Soundings by lead and wire reached the deep ocean floors a century ago, but until as late as 1920 our knowledge of submarine topography was very scant. When the time-consuming method of sounding with lead and wire was replaced by modern echo-sounding methods, it became possible to make continuous records of the time required for echoes to return to a ship from the sea floor. Properly scaled, these give profiles of depth. From them good charts have been prepared of many coasts and of the northern ocean floors. During the International Geophysical Year ships will be making great voyages to chart the unfrequented southern oceans.

Scientific study of the deep ocean floor was initiated by the great Challenger Expedition of 1872–6. In addition to making soundings, the expedition used dredges to collect grab-samples from the bottom. Later, corers were introduced, but they did not penetrate far until 1947, when B. Kullenberg of the Albatross Expedition devised a piston which used hydrostatic pressure to help draw cores into the barrel. With such a device the Russians have cored as deeply as 100 feet into the floor of the Arctic Ocean, while other oceanographers have collected over 1,000 long cores from the deep oceans.

Just as the sea floor reflects the signals of echo-sounding equipment and so reveals its depth, so do interfaces between layers of the crust reflect or refract back the stronger seismic waves generated by small explosions. Thus by dropping charges overboard at intervals, a ship or a pair of ships suitably equipped can receive these echoes and measure depths to layers within the crust. Other devices for studying the crust below the oceans are F. A. Vening Meinesz's method of determining gravity at sea, and Sir Edward Bullard's ingenious probe for measuring the rate at which heat is lost from the Earth by flowing out through the ocean floors.

On the Earth's surface there are two main levels, that of the land plains and that of the ocean floors. The latter cover much larger areas and are about 3 miles below the general level of the land. We can think of the ocean floors as being close to the original surface of the Earth, only separated from the mantle by an average of 3 miles of mud and lava flows.

Not only do the ocean basins occupy a larger part of the crust than do the continents, but the topography of their floors is grander—the peaks are higher, the canyons deeper and the ranges longer than any on land. For example, the Hawaiian Islands rise 33,000 feet from the floor of the Pacific Ocean: the mid-ocean ridges form a continuous chain tens of thousands of miles long. No valleys on land in any way compare with the great trenches hundreds of miles long lying off island arcs at depths of from 10,000 to 15,000 feet below the general floors of the ocean. The greatest known depth of 35,840 feet is reached in one of them, the Mariana Trench near Guam Island. Between these more striking features and covering much of the ocean floor are vast abyssal plains, deep, flat and extremely smooth.

It was once supposed that the deep oceans had remained dark, lifeless and unchanged, save for the finest rain of sediment, since the world began; but new knowledge has quite dispelled this view. Across the ocean floor geophysicists have now traced great fractures, scarps and rifts, have found scattered volcanic peaks and ranges, and have charted canyons cut by slumps and flows of mud on the continental margins. From time to time earthquakes unleash huge mud slides on the continental slopes. On its own tremendous scale the ocean floor is slowly active, and the great features raised upon it are preserved in unseen majesty from the eroding effects of the atmosphere, each portraying its origin more clearly than do similar features on land (Fig. 4).

The continental blocks—Over one quarter of the surface of the crust are reared the continental blocks. They are like solid rafts set in a solid sea. Nevertheless they may be said to float after a fashion, for their rocks are lighter than those of the ocean floor. In addition to rising 3 miles above the ocean floors their light roots of continental material sink to a depth of about 14 miles and depress beneath them the 3 miles of basalt lavas corresponding to the ocean floor. Thus the whole crust under the continents is 20 miles in thickness and is in hydrostatic equilibrium with the oceans.

The margins of the continents are flooded over by waters resting on the continental shelves. These may be anything up to 500 miles wide. Their edges are usually marked by a sharp increase in slope, frequently occurring at a depth of about 600 feet. It is believed that the shelves were cut to this depth during the last great glacial period when ice caps over much of the northern hemisphere lowered the oceans by this amount. The steep sides of the continental blocks are called the continental slopes.

Island arcs and trenches—Lying in most cases off the margins of continents are chains of island arcs, such as those off the coast of east Asia and in the West Indies. Seismically and volcanically they are the most active and mobile features of the Earth. Parallel with them along their convex sides are located all the deepest trenches in the oceans, so that together these features are part land and part ocean (Fig. 2). They appear to indicate where continents are growing, and we will leave further discussion of them and of continents until later.

The mid-ocean ridges—Apart from the continents, the greatest features rising from the ocean floor are the mid-ocean ridges whose extent has already been described (Fig. 3). The first discovered was the mid-Atlantic ridge, and it has only recently been shown to be connected with ridges in other oceans. These ridges are largely if not entirely composed of lava and volcanic debris and along them a concentration of shallow earthquakes has assisted in locating them and leaves no doubt that their volcanoes rise along a great fracture system. Great rifts and scarps which cut the volcanic rocks along the crest of the ridge show that movement and volcanism have alternated intermittently.

These ridges form a continuous system at least 40,000 miles long. They are often 200 miles wide and usually rise at least 10,000 feet from the ocean floor. Along the margins in some places are depressions, suggesting that the weight of the ridges has bowed down the crust on which they rest, so that in addition to the exposed parts they may have roots. No one has measured the depth or volume of these ridges, but it is very great and the volcanic activity that has built them is only sporadic and feeble. Clearly they have taken a vast length of time to accumulate—very likely most of the history of the Earth. The concept of unifomitarianism, that is, that the effect of natural laws on the Earth is constant, is a fundamental and sound one. The fact that these ridges are active and growing today suggests that this has been their behaviour in the past. The rates of growth, the scarcity of inert or abandoned ridges, and the impossibility that any ridges once formed could disappear, all suggest that these mid-ocean ridges are very old and fundamental structures of the crust.

The foci of the earthquakes along them are all at depths up to 45 miles, and none are deeper. A depth of 45 miles is well within the mantle and the temperatures there may be near the melting point of iron and magnesium silicates which probably constitute the mantle. The lavas along the mid-ocean ridges are basalt, which geochemists consider could be formed by partial melting of the mantle. It seems reasonable to believe that at times the fracturing below the ridges causes enough relief of pressure to allow pockets of lava to form. All these lavas have little gas, are not viscous and flow quietly out of the fractures. This accounts for the tranquil nature of the volcanoes on Iceland, Hawaii and other mid-oceanic islands. From such lavas have the mid-ocean ridges been built.

Ocean scarps—The fractures along the mid-ocean ridges, although they may be the chief ones, can hardly be the only ones on the ocean floor. During the past five years, R. Revelle, H. Menard and other oceanographers sailing from Cailfornia, have proved the existence of five great scarps running east and west for thousands of miles across the floor of the Pacific, spaced at regular intervals between San Francisco and the Galapagos Islands. These features, which are shown on Fig. 3, are marked by cliffs up to two miles high, by lines of volcanic peaks and by changes in the nature of the sea floor on their two sides. For example, the floor may be smooth on one side of the scarp and fractured and covered with submarine peaks on the other side.

I. Tolstoy has pointed out that a line of sea mounts and scarps extends across the Atlantic Ocean from near Gibraltar through the Azores to the south side of the Grand Banks. Doubtless other scarps will be found, but in many parts of the oceans deep sea sediments may have largely buried them.

Seamounts and guyots—Along these scarps and scattered elsewhere over the oceans are thousands of seamounts, that is, volcanic peaks which do not break the surface of the water. The pattern of their abundance and distribution is portrayed in the Micronesian Islands, the one region where such volcanic peaks appear as islands rather than submarine seamounts.

A curious feature of seamounts is that the summits of many of them (called guyots) are flat and uniform. This cannot be an original volcanic feature, and H. H. Hess of Princeton has suggested that these seamounts formed as island peaks, became inactive and were long ago cut down to a former sea level. At first it was thought that the sea was once shallower, but opinion now is that the crust was not able to support these loads, and that they have slowly settled to their present depths. On some, corals have been able to build reefs at a rate equal to the settling and thus preserve the islands in the form of coral islands or atolls. Although the bases of many guyots are hidden in sediments, their frequent straight alignment suggests their connection with crustal fractures.

Continental slopes, turbid currents and abyssal plains—That rivers deposit much mud is made apparent in the rapid silting of harbours. Finer silt is swept out to sea and there slowly settles. One of the Spanish captains wrote in 1518 of the Amazon, that it 'carieth such abundance of water and it entreth more than twenty leagues into the Sea, and mingleth not'; but the prodigious volume of the silt so carried was not measured until this century. Most of it settles close to shore upon the continental shelves and slopes, and indeed it is what they have largely been made of, as drilling for oil in the Atlantic and Gulf Coast shelves of the United States has shown.

When detailed charts were first made of continental shelves, it was seen that they were scoured and furrowed as by gigantic slumps, and great canyons were discovered cut in their edges and extending to depths of 12,000 feet or more. Laboratory experiments showed that it was possible for muddy flows to travel on the bottom beneath clear and lighter water, but there was some reluctance to abandon ideas of a still and silent sea bottom for one in which underwater flows cut canyons mightier than those of the Indus or Colorado rivers.

The matter was settled by an ingenious explanation of the events which followed the Grand Banks earthquake of November 18, 1929. On that date at 8.32 p.m. the world's seismographs recorded a severe shock which shook the coast of Newfoundland and, according to records kept by the telegraph companies, instantly broke the six cables nearest to the focus. So much was normal and easily understood, but the telegraph companies' records also showed that at intervals during the next thirteen hours six other cables progressively farther from the focus were broken. Repair crews found that the breaks were not clean, but that scores of miles of cables were missing and that the broken ends were abraded and torn.

The cause of this was a mystery until 1952, when B. C. Heezen and M. Ewing of Columbia University showed that if the shock which occurred on the continental slope had set a great slump in motion and stirred up turbid currents, these could have swept down the slopes to the deep abyssal plains on the ocean floor, breaking the cables as they reached them. The current would have reached a velocity of about 55 miles an hour soon after its start and would gradually have slowed down as it crossed the flatter ocean floor. Cores taken at the foot of the slope showed a succession of layers of sand, each grading up to finer silt and each interpreted as the deposit laid down by one turbid current. Heezen and Ewing suggested that such currents are released whenever enough mud is piled up on a slope, at intervals varying from a few years to a few hundreds of years.

Accurate charting of the floor of the north Atlantic Ocean has enabled the paths to be plotted along which these currents flow far over the ocean floors. By means of them much of the sediment carried by rivers and dumped on the continental margins is picked up again and transported to fill depressions. Much of this sediment must ultimately be washed into the deepest active trenches, there to wait metamorphism and uplift into young mountains.

The echo of seismic waves reveals that the sediments in places on the deep, abyssal plains are thousands of feet thick, but some slopes are scored bare so that coring tubes break on hard lava. In places guyots rise abruptly from the abyssal plains, partly buried and partly protruding above the swirling currents of mud. On their tops no beds of sands dropped by the currents are found, but only thick uniform layers of finest clay settling from the undisturbed body of the ocean.

Thus is an exciting story of activity on the dark floor of the ocean being unfolded. So far only a few regions have been sampled, but enough has been found to make the above account possible and reasonable.

THE GROWTH OF MOUNTAINS

It has been suggested that all the higher features on Earth have arisen directly or indirectly from volcanism occurring along one of two principal fracture systems. The mid-ocean system is the less active; it has not moved about because the ridges produced by it must have taken most of the Earth's history to grow. In contrast, the continental system produces lava so much more quickly that it takes only a few hundred million years to build high mountains. When it has built a great range like the Cordillera or the Andes, the evidence shows that eventually the range is abandoned by movement of a segment of the fracture system to some fresh location. Once active growth has ceased even great ranges fall prey to erosion by the weather, and are reduced to stumps like the Caledonian or Appalachian mountains, and finally to low lying provinces of Precambrian shields such as those of Finland and Canada.

Thus the continental blocks are the scars left in places formerly occupied by the continental fracture system. This occasional migration of segments of the continental fracture system does not destroy the continuity of the system. A section at a time moves, like a meander in a river or like a by-pass introduced into a highway, without destroying the continuity of the belts about the Earth. Because of these piecemeal movements, the fracture system which is active at present is made up of sections of many different ages, and an evolutionary sequence can be pieced together from present day examples illustrating stages in its growth. The continental fracture system consists of linked elements, most of which are arcs, and it is in terms of the evolution of arcs that the growth of mountains and continents can best be discussed (Table 2).

TABLE 2

Stages in mountain building

Stage	Example	Initial Event in Stage
1 Island arc	Aleutian Islands	Formation of arcuate fracture
2 Active mountain arc	Coast Mountains of British Columbia	Uplift and metamorphism of former island arc
3 Inactive mountain arc	Appalachian Mountains of New England	Migration of active fracture system to another location
4 Province of a shield	Grenville province of Canadian shield (contains several arcs)	Gradual erosion

The first stage in the formation of a new part of the continental fracture system is the fresh fracture of one or several new arcs. It is usual for them to form on the ocean floor not far from existing continental margins. Indeed, the centres of the arcs—not the arcs themselves—lie commonly on the contemporary position of the edge of the continent, as can be seen for the island arcs along the eastern coast of Asia from the Aleutian Islands to the Philippines.

The structure of all these arcs is similar (Fig. 2). Conical fracture zones indicated by earthquakes rise from depths as great as 450 miles, at first at angles of about 60° but at flatter angles near the surface. Where the fracture zones meet the surface they form ocean trenches. These include all the greatest deeps in the oceans.

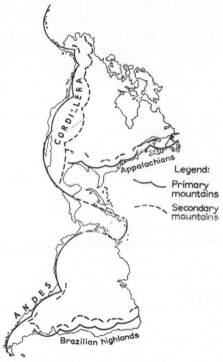

FIG. 5. Cordilleran, Andean and two Palaeozoic Mountain systems of the Americas.

The Aleutian trench and the Japan deep are examples. The occurrence of the shallowest earthquakes beneath trenches shows that they are kept open by active movement in spite of the tendency of turbid currents and other deposition to fill them. In the case of arcs close to land, activity may not be enough to keep the trenches open, so that they may become filled with sediments which are literally squeezed to the surface to form an outer chain of sedimentary islands in the place of the trench. Such islands include Kodiak Island which replaces the Aleutian trench near Alaska, Trinidad, Tobago and Barbados islands off the West Indies, and Timor Island opposite Australia.

At a fairly uniform distance of about 100 miles inside the trenches or the sedimentary islands, the main arc of volcanoes forms. Here, fed by a branch system of faults, the andesitic magma rises and accumulates, forming chains of small volcanic islands which grow to larger ones. Thus while the islands in the youngest arcs such as the Aleutian and Mariana Islands are the smallest, the islands in arcs of intermediate age are of larger size, like Okinawa which is two hundred million years old, and the oldest known arcs—Japan, New Guinea and New Zealand, all at least four or five hundred million years old—have the largest islands.

As the volcanic islands grow in size, their lavas are rapidly eroded and deposited around the islands in great eugeosynclines which mingle with the sediments brought by rivers from the old continents to fill in the seas behind the arcs. The East China Sea, for example, is entirely shallow, for it has been filled partly by offshore volcanoes and partly by detritus removed from more ancient mountain ranges on the continent and poured into the sea by the Yangtze and the Hwang-Ho Rivers.

For a few hundred million years, the growth of an island arc is gradual, but the transition from island arc to primary mountain range is marked by a profound change of a fairly rapid nature. What had been a great eugeosyncline and arc system is quickly transformed into metamorphic gneisses and granitic rocks, and at the same time raised high above sea level into great primary mountain chains like the western parts of the Cordillera or Andes (Fig. 5). These chains preserve the double nature of the old island arcs, for what had been the arc of andesitic volcanoes is lifted high to become a range of granodiorite of the same composition, like the Sierra Nevada of California, while the part that had been an outer arc of islands of deep sea sediments is less uplifted to become such a range as the Coast Range of California, or in some cases remains as a trench like the deep one along the Pacific coast of the Andes.

The cause of this transformation is still a mystery, but V. Saull of McGill University has made a most promising suggestion. He has proposed that the creation of sedimentary rocks is a process in which energy is absorbed from the Sun, and that a great pile of sediments under suitable conditions can revert to igneous minerals, giving out heat in the process. This heat may cause the upper parts of young mountains to become mobile and to form intrusive rocks. Igneous and metamorphic minerals, especially feldspars, may be less dense than the sedimentary ones from which they are made. This could explain expansion and the uplift of the mountains. After uplift, the primary ranges remain active for a time. Earthquakes continue and volcanoes again break through along the line of the old arc, as in the Cascade Mountains of northwestern United States.

Gradually the activity becomes less, and after a period which usually does not exceed two hundred million years, the ranges

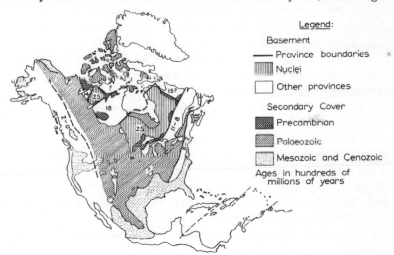

Legend:

Basement
—— Province boundaries
▦ Nuclei
☐ Other provinces

Secondary Cover
▨ Precambrian
▧ Palaeozoic
⬚ Mesozoic and Cenozoic

Ages in hundreds of millions of years

FIG. 6. North America showing basement provinces, their ages and the distribution of secondary cover.

cease to be active, fresh fractures form elsewhere, the third stage is reached and the old mountains are slowly eroded away. The primary arcs of the Appalachians are in this stage. They now form low hills across central Newfoundland, the Maritime Provinces, New England and south through the Carolinas. Other parts of them are buried by coastal deposits. These hills are gneissic and metamorphic, with remnants of ancient volcanoes in places, as in New Hampshire, marking the line of the volcanic arcs.

The final stage is reached when the mountains are reduced by gradual erosion to parts of the basement in shields. By then the primary arcs have lost much of their character, and those of different ages become hard to distinguish from one another. They were formerly all lumped together as Archaean rocks, but now age determinations are revealing ranges of different ages, and faulted boundaries are being found between old systems.

When analysed in this manner, shields are found to have been built up in zones, with progressively younger provinces towards the margins (Fig. 6). In the central parts of each continent are one or several *continental nuclei*. All of these nuclei were formed between two and three thousand million years ago. They have quite different structures from later provinces and a high proportion of volcanic rocks, but the details of these areas are difficult to decipher and are inadequately known. Everything about them suggests greater activity, more volcanoes and conditions different from those of later times, but during the last two thousand million years mountain building processes seem to have resembled those active today. Before three thousand million years ago we have little record. It may be that the Earth was melting in places and was too disturbed for any record of the earliest parts of the crust to have been preserved for us to see.

In addition to this sequence of primary mountains, there is another important group which arise as a secondary consequence of the first (Table 2). These ranges are scarcely represented during the island arc stage but with the uplift of the primary arcs, the outer part of the miogeosyncline (that wedge of sediments formed where the sedimentary rocks of the platform meet the borderland), is also uplifted. As a result the rocks of the miogeosyncline slump inwards on to the continent and are crumpled and thrust into mountains of sedimentary rocks, which always lie on the continental side of the primary arcs. The Rocky Mountains, the Carpathians and the eastern part of the Andes are examples. In all cases the volcanism and seismicity are minor in secondary mountains but the folding in them can be very intense, as in the Alps, formed where the primary arcs of the Apennine and Dinaric Mountains meet at a sharp angle.

In older stages of evolution the secondary ranges are preserved in thick folded basins of little altered sedimentary rocks, which contrast with the plutonic rocks of the older primary ranges. The Valley and Ridge province of New York and Pennsylvania is a classic example which is secondary to the primary mountains of

New England. In the oldest stage the secondary ranges are preserved as basins of sedimentary rocks called Proterozoic, which habitually lie along the continental side of the primary province of the Archaean to which they are related.

Until age determinations were made, all the older zones were lumped together, all the primary mountains in one category (Archaean), all the secondary parts in another (Proterozoic). We now have enough age determinations to show that both categories contain rocks of many different ages, but we have not yet enough to trace all the boundaries which outline the different provinces. The matter is complicated by the widespread cover of platform rocks that hides the true continental structure over great stretches of most continents. For example, the basement is exposed over much of Canada, but largely hidden in the United States (Fig. 6).

This is as far as we have space to take our interpretation of the history of the Earth's crust. It will be apparent that new discoveries in geophysics are demanding a reconsideration of much geological dogma handed down from the last century when no means existed for investigating the ocean floors, the Earth's interior, its age and the rates of geological processes, but it should be emphasized that to abandon some conventional geological interpretations does no violence to geological observations, which are usually sound and give us our most detailed knowledge of the Earth.

In selecting conclusions from many which are still under debate, the desire to tell a connected story has been used as a guide, for the Earth's history cannot be a collection of disconnected facts. Its behaviour must have been governed by constant physical laws. In the immediate future advances will be rapid, and it is not unreasonable to hope that better understanding will lead to practical assistance in prospecting for ores. To interpret the new results more scientists are needed who are equipped to understand both geology and physics. Geology and geophysics are but two aspects of the same search. They would never have been separated if geological methods of observing the visible part of the Earth had not been developed so much sooner than the physical methods required to study the rest of it.

Acknowledgement—In preparing this chapter the author has been much helped by the advice and assistance of Elizabeth Morrison and Michael Dence, whose aid is hereby acknowledged.

F

CHAPTER FIVE

The Oceans

G. E. R. DEACON

It is common knowledge that the oceans occupy 70·8 per cent of the Earth's surface and that the mean depth is nearly 2½ miles; but the active part the oceans play in regulating climate and rainfall is not fully appreciated. They are not merely reservoirs containing 97 per cent of the world's stock of water but an essential part of the machine which circulates air, water and heat all over the world and makes it habitable.

SOURCES OF ENERGY

About half the energy which reaches the Earth from the Sun is reflected back from the clouds, sea, and land surfaces and the remainder is absorbed; but the Earth does not get noticeably warmer, so on the average it loses as much energy as it gains. Much of the loss is by radiation and since the outgoing radiation, starting from a relatively cool source, is of long wavelength, some of it is absorbed in the atmosphere, mainly by the water vapour, carbon dioxide and ozone which are present there. Heat is also transferred to the atmosphere from the sea and land surfaces by direct conduction, and to a greater extent by the processes of evaporation and condensation.

The mean temperatures of the land, sea and air do not change very much, and although there may be slow trends, the Earth must as a whole radiate as much heat to space as it receives from the Sun, and the upper atmosphere must radiate as much to space as the lower atmosphere gains from the sea and land. However there are regional and seasonal differences: the equatorial regions have a surplus of incoming radiation and the polar regions have a surplus of outgoing radiation; the temperate regions gain more than they lose in summer and give up more than they absorb in winter.

These regional and seasonal differences are moderated by the circulation of heat from one part of the Earth to another; they give rise to the winds and ocean currents that temper the heat of the tropics and the frigidity of the poles, and mitigate the cold of a continental winter with heat from a warmer ocean.

The movements in the oceans seem to depend to a large extent on those of the atmosphere. The oceans are heated and cooled at the same level, the surface, and this is not such an efficient arrangement for turning heat into movement as that found in the atmosphere, which is heated at the bottom and cooled at the top. It has been estimated that the kinetic energy (the energy of movement) in the sea is not more than 2 per cent of the kinetic energy of the atmosphere, and that most of this 2 per cent is derived from the atmosphere through the drag of the winds on the water. Some of the consequences of the wind such as waves and currents are fairly obvious, but the winds can also set the deep water in motion by piling surface water against a coast or by dragging it away. The relative importance of the effects of winds, differences in atmospheric pressure and differences in the density of the sea water, in driving the ocean circulation, has still to be settled. The part played by ocean currents in determining where most heat is going to be fed to the atmosphere to help to generate the prevailing winds is also a subject of active research. When the complex sequence of events is better understood meteorologists should be able to improve their forecasting, oceanographers should be able to give navigators some indication of how the currents are likely to vary and fishery scientists should be able to appreciate and possibly predict changes that affect the fishing grounds.

There are other, smaller, sources of energy. The heat conducted through the sea floor is probably about a thousandth part of what is absorbed at the surface, and it seems to have no measurable effect on the water circulation. The heat produced by oxidation of organic matter and by other chemical reactions in the sea is also too small to be important.

THE TIDES

Another cause of movement in the oceans is the work done on them by the varying attractive forces as the Earth, Moon and Sun move relative to one another. The effect of an upward pull by the Moon or Sun perpendicular to the Earth's surface is negligible because of the much greater downward pull of the Earth's own attractive force, but the differences between the horizontal pull on the water and solid crust at all points that are nearer or farther than the Earth's centre from the Moon and Sun produce effective forces towards the nearest and farthest points. As the Earth rotates, these forces, waxing and waning as the attracting body rises and falls overhead, sweep across the Earth's surface, and set up tidal oscillations. The variations of the attractive forces are rather complex since they depend on a large number of cycles in the orbital movements of the Earth-Moon-Sun system, but they are thoroughly understood and can be predicted with great accuracy. The real difficulty in tidal prediction is introduced when attempts are made to calculate the response of water in oceans of different size and shape to the variations of the attractive forces, and progress in this theoretical work is very slow. Fortunately for most practical purposes the difficulty can be avoided by studying one part at a time. Tide records are analysed to find the effects of the varying attractive forces during one or two years, and it can then be assumed that there will be similar responses to the variations which will take place in the year for which predictions are required, and these can easily be calculated. In spite of this practical success there is much theoretical work to be done before our understanding of the tides is adequate to meet the increasing demands of navigation and coastal and harbour engineering. The Liverpool Tidal Institute is one of the world's leading centres on the theory and practice of tides.

WAVES

Although sailors have always been able to make reliable estimates of the height of the most prominent waves, systematic study of the relations between wind and waves had to wait till continuous records could be made, and the wavebands from different generating areas sorted out in much the same way as the radio wavebands from different broadcasting stations can be sorted out. The recording and analysing apparatus is primarily electronic. One of the most remarkable recorders is that devised for use in a ship at sea; it measures the wave pressures through two small holes below the water line on opposite sides of the ship, and makes allowance for the up and down movement of the holes by automatic electronic circuits using the output of accelerometers mounted near the holes. The results show that the waves we see are a complex combination of many underlying wave trains. The products of every storm can usefully be considered as the sum of a continuous range of wave trains from the shortest ripples up to long waves with half a mile or so between successive crests. Each wave train appears to travel independently with a speed proportional to the square root of its wavelength, so that the long waves travel fastest, leading an ever lengthening procession in which the predominant wavelength decreases from head to tail. The alternation of groups of high and low waves always observed in swell from a distant storm, is explained by waves travelling at different speeds getting in and out of step. The first waves to arrive from a distant storm are so long and low that they are visible only where they are retarded and steepened as they run over shallow ground. This ground swell is followed by the shorter higher swell that carries most of the energy and then by the shorter lower swell which brings up the rear in the procession.

Now that the swell from one storm can be distinguished from that of another, and from the waves made by winds near the recording station, rules for predicting the height and rate of travel of waves from wind charts and forecasts can be improved; but there is still much to do before they can take account of all the factors involved and give reliable results in all places. One of the most remarkable findings is that waves travel very great distances: when the waves in the North Atlantic Ocean are so small that wave recorders can be operated at full sensitivity the analysis of records reveals the presence of swell which has travelled from storms in the 'Roaring Forties', far south of the equator.

Long Waves

Intermediate between the tides, which are the longest oscillations, and ordinary waves and swell which reach down to the shortest, there are many other oscillations which have periods between a few minutes and a few hours. Some harbours experience backward and forward water movements known as range action which can be sufficiently active to snap mooring ropes unless special precautions are taken. The periods of the oscillations, most commonly two to three minutes, agree with the natural period of the water in the harbour—the time it takes for a complete swing if disturbed by a powerful force and left to rock like water in a dish. The force might be due to the movement of water towards or away from the coast under the action of wind, or the oscillations might be energized by long waves shown to be associated with the occurrence of high and low groups of waves and known as surf beats. The harbours most affected seem to lie on surf beaten coasts facing large oceans. Evidence of the natural oscillations of almost any estuary, bay, gulf, channel or shelf, can be seen from time to time in tide records. When they are most active the smooth rise and fall of the tidal curve takes on a saw-tooth appearance.

We know little about the existence of long waves, other than the tides, in deep water, but there is evidence that some of the energy transferred to the sea by winds or moving pressure disturbances in storms, is sent out from the storm areas in the form of long waves that are capable of exciting local resonances when they reach the coast. The speed at which a long wave travels is determined by the depth of water; it falls to about 60 knots in soundings of 50 fathoms, and disastrous long waves are sometimes caused when a storm or pressure difference travels over an extensive area of shallow water at just the same speed as a long wave. Even in the English Channel, minor surges, sufficient to result in some confusion among moored boats and holidaymakers on the beach, have been caused by such coincidence. The change of wind and pressure may be too small to attract attention, but if it travels at the same speed as a wave, adding energy all the time, the effect can be considerable.

The giant surges which produce coastal flooding like that experienced in East Anglia in 1953, can usually be shown to be due to surges from the open ocean intensified by the effect of wind and atmospheric pressure gradients over shallow water. They can have peaks which last two or three hours and look like the tides themselves, and it is most fortunate that interaction with the tide lessens the possibility of a high surge added on to a high tide.

Although much of the recent interest lies in the effect of meteorological disturbances, certain areas, such as Japan and some of the Pacific Islands, are almost equally threatened by waves resulting from seismic disturbances of the sea bed. These are usually called *tsunamis*, the Japanese word for tidal wave. They are scarcely noticeable in deep water but they become much higher and steeper as they slow down in shallow water approaching a coast, and do much damage. In the North Pacific Ocean there is a warning system rather like that for issuing North Sea flood warnings.

As far as we know, the long waves travel from one side of the ocean to another with little decrease in height, and it has been noted that a major seismic disturbance in the Pacific Ocean is followed by 5 days' enhanced long-wave activity on the coast of California. This may prove to be due to types of waves called edge waves which, in effect, trap the incoming long-wave energy at different points and send it moving relatively slowly up and down the coast, or it may be due largely to the multiple reflection of the waves at the boundaries of the ocean and scattering from islands and shoals.

The further investigation of long waves is a project typical of the aims of the International Geophysical Year since it can be notably advanced by simultaneous observations over wide stretches of ocean. During the IGY continuous records will be made at thirty or more stations on islands and round the continental margins of the Atlantic and Pacific Oceans and at a few stations in the Indian Ocean. It will not be possible to work Special World Intervals, since we know too little about long waves to predict the effects of meteorological disturbances and receive too little warning of seismic activity. The research should benefit considerably from the intensified network of meteorological and seismological observations during the IGY.

The long-wave recorder measures the difference in pressure between a small inner chamber and a large outer space open to the atmosphere, each communicating with the sea through a narrow capillary. The capillaries are too narrow to transmit enough water to show the effect of ordinary waves, and the apparatus is not sensitive to tides, since they allow time for the pressure to be nearly equalized in the outer and inner spaces. It is a better measure of waves of 5 to 60 minutes period because the flow to the outer space does not have time to back off the pressure in the smaller chamber. The work will increase our knowledge of meteorological disturbances of normal tide level as well as having useful applications to the study of harbour oscillations and coastal floods, and it will be directly useful to navigation.

OCEAN CURRENTS

Thanks to the painstaking work of marine observers, especially since the middle of last century when the marine meteorological offices of the principal nations organized the systematic collection of data, we have excellent charts showing the *average* current experienced in all parts of the world regularly traversed by ships. To gain a more detailed understanding in the hope of showing how the current is likely to vary with the wind and other factors, is proving a more difficult task than the charting done so far. The new observations clearly demonstrate the variability of even the strongest currents, such as the Gulf Stream. Instead of picturing a broad river-like flow, it is more realistic to think of an unsteady, shifting flow, with eddies ranging in width from several miles to two or three hundred, and with narrow streaks of rapid movement, all adding up to make general forward progress. The broad oceanic picture of the surface currents in the Atlantic Ocean has been so well explained by approximate calculations based on justifiable assumptions about the drag of the wind, friction and the effect of the Earth's rotation, that there can be little doubt that the prevailing winds are the main cause of the surface movements. It is interesting to note that the effect of the Earth's rotation alone requires that they should be stronger and narrower on the western side of the ocean than on the eastern side, as they are seen to be in the current charts.

The Gulf Stream along the coast of Florida, and up to the point where it leaves the coast near Cape Hatteras, may be due more to a shoreward transport of water caused by winds far from the land, than by the drag of the wind over the current itself; but after Newfoundland there seems to be little doubt that the general slow drift towards northern Europe follows the prevailing winds. In the present state of our knowledge we can only speculate about the parts played by wind and water in bringing warmth to our shores and raising the mean temperature of north-west Europe well above that of north-east Canada. The wind drives the water, but the heat carried by the water must have an important effect on the activity of the atmospheric circulation; and it is not easy to decide to what extent the wind makes the current or the current makes the wind. To solve such problems the circulation of the atmosphere and ocean must be treated as a joint problem as done in Chapter 8.

Deep-water Circulation

The existence of movements of water in the deep and bottom layers of the ocean has been inferred since the early nineteenth century, when the first deep temperature measurements in the tropical Atlantic Ocean showed the bottom water to be so cold that it could only come from the polar regions. Since then there has been built up a fairly good picture of the deep-water circulation all over the world. Slow movements of water with distinctive properties have been traced from one end of each ocean to the other. In the Atlantic Ocean cold water, with a rather high salt content, which sinks from the surface in the region between Labrador, Greenland and Iceland, spreads southwards some two miles down. It can be distinguished as far as the continental slopes of Antarctica between still colder and slightly less saline water, which spreads northwards below it and warmer water of lower salinity flowing northwards in the layer above. The North Atlantic water joins the general eastward movement round the Southern Ocean, and its influence can still be detected in the composition of the bottom water of the South Pacific Ocean. The Antarctic water spreading northwards below the North Atlantic deep current can be identified as far north as the Bay of Biscay, and the less saline water above it as far as 25°N. Seen on a true scale the depth of the oceans is so small in relation to their width that it appears remarkable that the movements in different layers can retain their identities over such great distances; and it is clear that the disturbing forces likely to cause vertical mixing are generally not strong enough to overcome the weak density gradients.

There is still much of this type of oceanic exploration to be done, and during the IGY simultaneous observations will be made all over the oceans by a large number of ships. When the observations are compared with those made some twenty-five years ago, a very active era of oceanic exploration, they will show whether significant changes have taken place in the main characteristics of the water masses; they will also provide a sound basis for similar comparisons in years to come.

Very little is known of the speed of the deep-water movements, and in this respect oceanography shows an interesting contrast with meteorology. The water masses are so well labelled by temperature and salt content that they can be followed half round the world, but we have little idea how fast they go. In meteorology the surface and upper air winds can be measured very easily but the air masses are not sufficiently well identified by temperature or by composition to give a clear picture of the general circulation. Meteorologists are developing these techniques while oceanographers are attempting to simulate the upper-air wind measurements.

The Bathyscaphe (a steel sphere with a very small window in which men can go to the sea floor) opens up new possibilities, but most of the exploration of the depths of the ocean has to be done by lowering apparatus on long wires or by using sound waves. The distance through which we can photograph or see by direct methods and by television is very small. This lack of transparency makes distant observation indirect and difficult, and the oceanographic counterpart of the meteorological balloon has to be followed by acoustic methods.

The most promising technique developed so far uses an acoustic transmitter which will work for four or five days. This transmitter is operated by batteries which are enclosed with the necessary electronic components in an aluminium tube sealed at both ends. The tube is less compressible than sea water and it can be loaded to sink to a predetermined depth where it follows the current and can be tracked by a ship fitted with hydrophones. It must be followed for at least 25 hours so that the tidal movements can be distinguished from the general drift. The speeds of the currents measured so far range from about half a mile a day at a depth of 2 miles to as much as 7 or 8 miles a day at two or three hundred fathoms. At present the situation is rather like the plight meteorologists would be in if they had only one radiosonde and wanted to use it to the best advantage, but a number of laboratories are developing acoustic transmitters and during the IGY there will be multiple ship operations, with a number of ships working close together to study the deep-water movements over small, interesting areas of ocean. The first intentions are to prove the technique and to see how consistent the deep-water movements are in time and space over small areas. The areas will be chosen to give as much useful information as possible, and the R.R.S. *Discovery II* will work with American and Norwegian ships near 52°N, 30°W.

Ever since the cold water at the bottom of the tropical ocean was discovered, many scientists have argued whether the water movements in the ocean are due to wind, or due to convection caused by the heavier water formed near the poles, or in a region of high evaporation, replacing lighter water formed near the equator or in regions of high precipitation. There was never much doubt that the surface currents are generated by the wind, though one or two extremists have taken the other view. However while those who favoured convection were ready to admit the power of the wind at the surface they could not see how it could influence the deep layers. The difficulty would be real if the oceans were of infinite extent, but since water can in fact be piled against long coast lines there can be pressure gradients at great depths as well as near the surface. One of the main features of the controversy has been that most of those taking part, although eminent in their own subjects, did not know enough about fluid mechanics to take precise account of the effect of the Earth's rotation and considerations of continuity and momentum, which are important when water moves from one part of the Earth to another; indeed they did not know enough to recognize that such factors are involved. Many of the advances are now being made by young men trained in schools of dynamic meteorology.

MIXING IN THE OCEANS

Although the deep currents appear to be very slow they are important because they carry large volumes of water and large amounts of heat; they must also have an important effect on the circulation near the surface and on the currents that are of interest to navigation. The whole circulation is active enough to ensure that the water in one part of the ocean is eventually mixed with water from any other part, because sea salt is the same all the world over. The major constituents are always present in the same proportions, except in very brackish water where a large river has just added more of one and less of another. But in spite of this ultimate mixing, accomplished over centuries perhaps, one part of the ocean can be very different from another. The water is warmest in the tropics where there is most incoming radiation, and coldest in the polar regions where the radiation is predominantly outwards, but the lines of equal temperature do not usually run east to west, being sometimes bent towards the poles by warm currents and towards the equator by cold currents. Cloudiness and evaporation also influence the surface temperature, and continental winds have a marked effect. The difference between winter and summer temperatures is not very large in the open ocean, but it can be as much as 25 degrees Centigrade in the Yellow Sea, 20 degrees off the coast of Nova Scotia and 20 degrees in the Black

Sea where the water is surrounded by land masses. In the open ocean the highest temperature is about 30 degrees Centigrade in the tropics and —1·9 degrees in the Arctic and Antarctic regions. The differences between the surface and the bottom are nearly as great. Below the warmest surface water bottom temperatures of 1 or 2 degrees Centigrade indicate a flow of cold water from the Antarctic, but in some basins which are shut off from this current by submarine ridges the bottom temperatures are much higher. In an enclosed basin like the Mediterranean Sea, the bottom temperature is an approximate measure of the lowest temperature at the surface of the northern part of the sea in the previous winter.

The variations in salt content from region to region and season to season depend mainly on the balance between precipitation and evaporation. The most saline water occurs in land-locked seas in dry areas, such as the Mediterranean Sea where it rises to 39 parts per thousand, and the Red Sea where it is as much as 40 parts per thousand. At the other end of the scale are land-locked seas in areas of high precipitation like the Baltic Sea where the salinity is 7 or less. In the open ocean it ranges from about 37 parts per thousand in the Sargasso Sea to less than 33 over extensive rainy areas west of Panama and in the East Indies. It also falls to 33 to 34 in Antarctic and Arctic waters. Near melting ice it is less; and in winter, when fresh water is removed as ice, and salt is left behind, it goes well above 34 parts per thousand. The changes with depth depend on the origins of the deep currents. A region of low surface salinity usually has more saline water in the deep and bottom currents; and in the subtropical regions of high surface salinity there is usually a minimum, about half a mile down, where the nucleus of the current sinks from the surface in Antarctic or Arctic regions.

Since warm water is less dense than cold, the decrease in temperature with depth which occurs everywhere outside the Antarctic and Arctic, produces a stable arrangement of layers in which the density increases with depth. The increase is usually fairly sharp between an upper layer in which the first 50 to 200 fathoms are well mixed by winds and currents, and a lower region in which there are only weak density gradients. This stable arrangement prevents the surface water from mixing readily with the deep water. Consequently the phosphates, nitrates and other materials which tend to become used up near the surface, where the presence of sunlight enables photosynthesis to take place, are not easily replenished from the large reservoir in the deep water where much of the decomposition of sinking organic material occurs. Where the physical conditions favour intense vertical mixing, or upwelling from the lower layers, into plenty of sunlight, the sea is very productive and there are rich fisheries. The fertility of the coastal waters off South West Africa and Peru are striking examples. The surface water is also cooled and enriched near most islands and shoals in warm water regions and near current boundaries and in localities where the currents undergo sharp changes in speed and direction. Oceanographic surveys planned with some knowledge of the physical processes have already proved effective guides to productive areas and have been used by Japanese and U.S.A. investigators in the development of mid-ocean fisheries.

BIOLOGY OF THE OCEANS

It is still possible by fishing or dredging in deep water to discover new marine animals, but the emphasis in marine biology is moving towards the studies of populations— towards learning more about the distributions of the known species in relation to their physical and biological environments, and towards learning more about the factors which make some parts of the oceans more productive than others. It is a long task, even for the smaller, slow moving organisms which are easily caught. There are usually many stages between the eggs and the adults and when these have been discovered a large number of net hauls made over a full range of seasons, places and depths have to be sorted and the different stages counted and measured. Only then can provisional hypotheses be sought to explain the distributions in relation to spawning and feeding habits, depth of water, temperature, water movements and other relevant factors. The more active animals which escape large towed nets present greater difficulties, and ideas as to their size and distribution seem to depend to a large extent on the type of gear used and the speed at which it can be towed.

The studies of productivity are making active progress with the help of more precise measurements of the dependence of the rate of photosynthesis on the intensity of the daylight, availability of nutrients and other factors. The photosynthetic activity is being measured with the help of radioactive tracer material. Samples hauled from a range of depths have a small amount of radioactive carbonate added before being suspended at their original depths in glass bottles. After 12 hours or so, they are taken up, filtered, and the radioactivity of the phytoplankton (microscopic plants) is used as a measure of the amount of carbon dioxide assimilated.

Studies of water movements have considerable importance to the biological studies. Knowledge of turbulent exchanges and diffusion near the surface will give some idea of the circulation of the phytoplankton in and out of the well illuminated zone, and how the time they spend there is affected by changes in the density, stratification and disturbance of the surface by wind and waves. It would also be useful to be able to form a precise idea of how the movements of the water may facilitate dispersion of eggs or larval stages from successful breeding grounds and the subsequent replenishment of the stock. There seems to be growing evidence that such considerations may be more important than the effect of a simple temperature difference, and it is often suspected that changes observed on fishing grounds are influenced by changes in the currents and general water circulation. Fishery scientists in north-west Europe are particularly interested in the balance between Arctic and temperate influences in the North Atlantic Ocean and during the IGY many of the ships engaged in fishery research in this area are making a special effort to plan and concentrate their observations to afford synoptic surveys of the boundary regions in summer and winter.

MEAN SEA-LEVEL

When the hourly heights of the tides are averaged over every month, with allowance for uncompleted cycles, it is found that there are considerable variations, and further averaging from year to year shows that there are also measurable annual variations. Recent studies of the seasonal variations show that in most parts of the world the fluctuations are about what would be expected from the changes in volume of the water due to seasonal changes in temperature and salinity. There are larger differences in the monsoon regions, and the annual range varies from perhaps about an inch near some tropical islands to about 5 feet in the Bay of Bengal. The mean level of the oceans obtained by averaging all the figures and taking the northern and southern hemispheres together seems to be about an inch lower in the northern spring than in the northern autumn. The variations of mean level from year to year are usually not more than an inch or two, but in many places the level of the water appears to be rising relative to the land at the rate of about 6 inches in 100 years; at others it is smaller and in some places the level is falling. Both seasonal and annual changes depend on varying balances between meteorological and climatic influences, but the long-term trends may also depend on the rising or sinking of the land owing to changes in the Earth's crust as well as variations in water level. Much has been written on this problem and it is often maintained that the sea level is rising as the volume of water in the oceans is increased by melting of glaciers and the polar icecaps (Chapter 10), but precise study is difficult without longer and more exact measurements of all the factors involved. The subject is important to engineers because of the need to provide adequate coastal defences, and it is of great interest to scientists who can make good use of a better understanding of the world-wide circulation and exchange of water between the oceans, atmosphere and continents.

This is another problem well adapted to the aims of the IGY, and tide-gauges will be installed in sixty or more new stations, many of them on oceanic islands where the information is needed for the theoretical study of the tides as well as changes in sea level.

ANTARCTIC OCEANOGRAPHY

One of the outstanding features of the IGY is the exceptionally large effort devoted to scientific study of the south polar regions and it seems remarkable that more is not being done in the Antarctic Ocean. It is, however, a very expensive task, which cannot usually be combined with the landing of men and stores, as special ships are required, and plenty of time is needed. U.S.S.R. is undertaking much oceanographic work and France, Argentina and Chile will also make observations. Apart from long-wave and sea-level recording, U.K. oceanographers have taken the view that the ocean was so well covered by temperature, salinity and other chemical measurements by the ships of the Discovery investigations, that more measurements of the same kind are not likely to add much to what is known, unless they can be made on a much more intensive scale, which seems unlikely, or until the new techniques which are now being developed for measuring sub-surface and deep currents can be widely used.

CHAPTER SIX

Geomagnetic Field

E. H. VESTINE

THE EARTH'S magnetic field is familiar to all because it exerts the force directing a compass needle. In general, a compass needle so directed does not point true North, nor does it point to the North magnetic pole—it seeks to sets itself parallel to the lines of force of the geomagnetic field. These lines of force direct the compass at an angle to true North known by scientists as the magnetic *declination* (and by seamen as the magnetic *variation*). The declination is indicated upon charts primarily for the use of navigators. The earliest world chart of this kind was constructed by the British astronomer Edmund Halley, for the year 1700. A world chart giving the declination for 1945 is shown in Fig. 1. The compass points true North only on the lines on which the declination is zero.

The ordinary compass is weighted so as to swing in a horizontal plane. A perfectly balanced and freely pivoted magnetic needle in general takes up an inclined orientation. The angle of inclination is called the magnetic *dip* (which is reckoned *positive* if the North seeking end is *below* the horizontal). The dip is a maximum at the magnetic poles of the Earth, where a freely pivoted magnetic needle would be directed vertically downwards. At or near these locations the controlling action of the geomagnetic field would be zero, or ineffective, so that a compass would be useless for purposes of navigation.

William Gilbert appears to have been the first to realize the general character of the field. Whereas his contemporaries believed that compass needles were directed by the Pole Star, he realized that the magnetic influence proceeds from within the Earth. He described the experiments which guided him in his famous treatise *De Magnete* published in 1600.

Measurements by instruments aboard a satellite would show

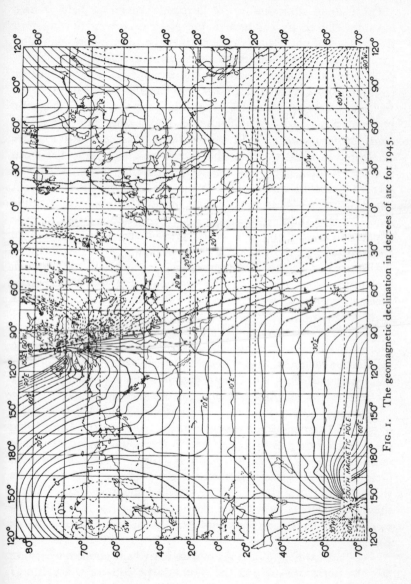

FIG. 1. The geomagnetic declination in degrees of arc for 1945.

that the geomagnetic field becomes smoother and less intense with increasing distance from the Earth.

Quite small additions to the horizontal magnetic field at high latitudes caused by changes in the electric current flowing near the surface of the Earth's central metallic core below, will alter the positions of the magnetic poles considerably. The magnetic poles being the points where the horizontal field is zero, must be continuously moving if the horizontal magnetic field in the polar regions is varying. A series of positions of the North magnetic pole noted by Roald Amundsen and other explorers or estimated from changes with time in the results of magnetic surveys, are available. It is found that the North magnetic pole has been drifting slowly (about 3 or 4 miles per annum) to the Northwest from a point in the Boothia peninsula near latitude 70·5° N, longitude 96·5° W in 1904 to an island location near latitude 73·0° N, longitude 100·0° W in 1948. The South magnetic pole appears to be drifting at a rather greater speed, since it moved from latitude 72·2° S, longitude 150·7° E in 1912, to a calculated position close to the Antarctic coast at about latitude 68·2° S, longitude 145·4° E, in 1945. It is understood that this general motion is compatible with results obtained by a recent French expedition.

Magnetic rocks near the North and South magnetic poles may cause pairs of secondary magnetic poles, or local points at which the Earth's magnetic field is vertical. It is hence helpful in locating the (principal) North or South magnetic pole to have available the results of a magnetic survey over the surrounding area.

The geomagnetic field may be represented closely by the field of a short bar magnet or dipole at the Earth's centre, lying along the straight line joining the centre to the point on the surface at latitude 78·6° N, longitude 70·1° W, (near Thule, in northern Greenland). This line is termed the geomagnetic axis: the points where it intersects the surface are termed the *geomagnetic poles*— these do not coincide with the magnetic poles since the field of the so-called *equivalent dipole* is not exactly the same as that of the Earth.

The vertical field at the geomagnetic poles is about 0·63 gauss, and the horizontal field at the geomagnetic equator is about 0·31 gauss. During the past hundred years, the strength of the equivalent dipole has been decreasing approximately uniformly at a rate such that it would fall to about one-third in 1800 years. Since 1940 the rate of decrease has been less, and some have suggested that the strength may now be actually increasing.

SECULAR CHANGE

Historical Period

Because there are large varying electric currents flowing within the Earth, the compass direction gradually changes with time. The rate of change depends on the geographical position. Table 1 gives the approximate directions of the compass at London since 1600, measured in degrees East or West of true North at intervals of 50 years. The slow temporal variation in the Earth's field, discovered in 1634 by Henry Gellibrand, is known as the *secular change*.

TABLE 1

Direction of compass at London

Year	1600	1650	1700	1750	1800	1850	1900	1950
Declination	8°E	1°E	7°W	18°W	24°W	22°W	16°W	8°W

Until quite recently, magnets were made by heating pieces of impure iron to a red heat, and then allowing them to cool. The tiny magnetic elements or particles of the iron aligned themselves parallel to the lines of force of the geomagnetic field, so that the direction of magnetization within the iron was essentially *frozen* in by the cooling process. Effects of this nature enable information to be obtained on the past geomagnetic field.

It has been found that an approximate indication of the direction of magnetization may have been preserved in fired pottery and brick. In pottery for instance, indications of the orientation of the field relative to the horizontal plane may be preserved, so that the dip below the horizon of the North seeking end of a magnetized needle can be deduced. On this basis the magnetic dip in Europe can be traced roughly for the past 3000 years, with some evidence of consistency of results obtained using different materials. The magnetism of certain Etruscan and Grecian vases has been interpreted as indicating that the dip has reversed between 700 or 600 B.C. and the present, but the known time constants for growth and decay of the field and the observations since the 13th century, leave little doubt that this interpretation is false.

Pre-historical Period

Magnetic particles called magnetite are weathered from rocks, carried in streams to the ocean, where they are aligned along the geomagnetic field as they settle to the ocean bottom. The magnetic particles included within the bottom layers may thus be indicative of the geomagnetic field of the past. After many years the layer in question becomes overlain by deep strata providing pressures tending to convert it into sedimentary rock. Sometimes annual layers or varves were formed, at the bottom of a glacial lake, from debris carried and deposited by the water resulting from the summer melting of the ice. Hence the rocks may record vestigal directions of magnetization from year to year, as well as over very long geological epochs of time. Under favourable and special circumstances the ancient directions of magnetization at various epochs may then be inferred from present day laboratory measurements, though not without some grave uncertainties yet to be elucidated.

The freezing mechanism mentioned in the previous section must also have operated under natural conditions when hot lava beds cooled, because lava includes some feruginous material. Thus after cooling, tangible indication of the direction of the geomagnetic field millions of years ago is expected to be preserved by the feruginous material, provided the lava bed remains undisturbed and unheated subsequently. By measuring the direction of magnetization of this lava in the laboratory it is possible to infer the difference in direction of this ancient field from that of today.

One trouble with the method is that it is not very exact, and changes in this *fossil* magnetism and its direction may arise due to various causes such as local heating during its history,* by the application of stresses, and by the shift in the level or tilt of the magnetized rocks. Averages must be taken over numerous samples, preferably of various kinds of rocks.

The results from fossil magnetism show that the geomagnetic field has suffered extensive changes in earlier epochs. One of the most interesting of the unchecked inferences from rock magnetism is that the field may reverse itself after long intervals. Another interesting inference, as yet unchecked by independent means, is that the continents drift, so that they undergo both rotation and

---

* T. Nagata has shown in the laboratory that certain specimens of rock from Japan *reverse* their magnetism on being heated.

translation. P. M. S. Blackett and his co-workers have considered that the measurements of J. A. Clegg, M. Almond, and P. H. S. Stubbs upon Triassic Sandstones in England may provide evidence for both the reversal of field with time, as well as for continental drift. Some of these rocks were magnetized from South-West to North-East and downwards, and others in about the opposite direction. Since both directions are different from that of the present geomagnetic field, it is reasonable to argue that the magnetizations of these sedimentary rocks acquired at deposition are likely to be retained. The departure in the direction of field in Triassic times (180 million years ago), from that of today is explained by supposing that England has rotated some $34°$ since the rocks acquired their magnetization. Further, the $180°$ change is explained by supposing the geomagnetic field is sometimes reversed. Directions in magnetization opposite to that for the present field have also been found among dykes in South Africa, America and England, among the strongly magnetized lavas in Iceland and Oregon and elsewhere. It has been claimed that reversals occurred in Pre-Cambrian rocks, but none have been noted for the long interval from the Cambrian period, 500 million years ago through to the end of the Devonian period somewhat under 300 million years ago. After this interval reversals sometimes occur every half million years or so, as judged from the study of the rocks giving at least some good evidence that they possess enduring capacity to retain a magnetization acquired at a very remote time. The reversal itself is supposed to take place relatively quickly, perhaps in 10,000 to 20,000 years.

These exciting conclusions are of course highly tentative, and fossil magnetism as an effect must be interpreted cautiously. . W. Graham has pointed out the importance of grain size upon the magnetic properties of rocks. Rock samples also are known in which there are both long lived and short lived components of magnetization, usually called *hard* and *soft* components. It is not always clear that measurements made by different workers at different times and places can be said to be based upon the hard or presumably enduring component of magnetization. Compression can impart to rock samples a new magnetic moment comparable to the natural moment of a rock sample. This magnetostrictive effect is proportional to the applied compression, and varies from one sample to another. Perhaps some of the interesting magnetizations of rocks stem from the effect of geologic stresses, rather than from changes in the geomagnetic field.

It would be reassuring if demonstrable consequences could be predicted from the conclusions based on rock magnetism. Successes of this kind are thus far lacking. A consistent magnetic field for the whole world has not yet been determined from rock magnetism using a stratum of given geological age.

SUGGESTED CAUSES OF THE MAIN FIELD

The manner in which the Earth's main field and its secular change is produced is not yet established, but there is a promising dynamo theory, mainly due to W. M. Elsasser and Sir Edward Bullard, and in addition a less fully developed thermoelectric theory. Though both theories are very complicated, the fundamental principles involved are simple.

According to the dynamo theory, the Earth's molten core rotating across a small primordial magnetic field generated electric currents which amplified and strengthened the original field. In the thermoelectric theory, small irregularities between the temperature of the equator and poles, at the junction of mantle and core, are assumed to have provided a thermocouple, driving electric currents. Attempts, as yet not too successful, have been made to imagine an effective amplifier for strengthening an initial field with which these currents can interact.

The theories may be either incomplete or incorrect because they ignore or regard as accidental two major features of the geomagnetic field—the non-coincidence by about 12° of the geomagnetic and geographic axes, and the relationship of the residual or secular change field to oceanic and land distributions. If, as seems likely, exceedingly strong electric currents flow in the core, the observed relationship to land and ocean areas suggests that additional currents may flow closer to the surface, and within the mantle. Another possibility in, for instance, the Pacific region, is that there may be a screening of fields from the core which penetrate the mantle from below.

Core motions, on a regional scale, may alter the geomagnetic field locally to produce the secular changes in the Earth's surface magnetic field.

There are observable surface irregularities in field, in areas from 5 to 100 miles or more across, which may have a strength of the order two or three per cent or so of the normal magnetic field of the Earth. These patterns of high or low field intensity which are called *magnetic anomalies* are usually neglected in drawing world charts for navigation. Their neglect affects navigation only slightly, because in travelling along, the effects tend to cancel. The anomalies arise almost entirely from patchwise irregularities in the distributions of the magnetic materials in surface rocks. They are sometimes measured using magnetic instruments aboard an aircraft, in order to help locate iron and nickel ores, and geologic structure useful in the search for oil and minerals.

Mathematical analysis of the Earth's surface magnetic field shows that any permanent external part of the Earth's main field arising from electric currents flowing within or beyond the atmosphere, cannot contribute more than about one per cent to the whole. Cosmic rays (Chapter 16) do not arrive at the Earth in the pattern expected if the geomagnetic field were entirely of internal origin. Important deflecting influences of enduring character therefore exist, probably at distances of many Earth radii. Since these influences react strongly upon the very high speed cosmic rays, the effects may be profound upon the much slower particles producing aurorae.

OTHER GEOMAGNETIC VARIATIONS

A number of distinct temporal variations of the geomagnetic field occur in addition to its secular change. These are most readily understood if studied in relation to other phenomena with which they may be associated, such as solar, auroral or ionospheric features.

Of these temporal variations the most regular are those depending upon the position of the Sun and the Moon relative to the Earth, and hence upon local solar and lunar time. In low latitudes the part directly related to solar time is prominent among the variations present every day. This solar daily magnetic variation (which is minute compared with the main field), is thought to be caused by winds in the electrically conducting ionosphere. The moving masses of ionized air produce electric current-systems as in a dynamo (Chapter 12). The winds are driven by the heating action of the Sun and arise also from tidal forces acting upon the upper atmosphere. The lunar daily magnetic variation repeats itself about every lunar day, or at intervals of about 23 solar hours, but with progressive changes in form throughout the lunar month. The gravitational influence of the Sun, though much weaker than that of the Moon, builds up much larger tides due to resonance. In consequence the equatorial amplitude of the solar daily magnetic variation is about twenty times that of the lunar. Measurements of upper air winds by radio and other means will be likely to prove of great value in explaining the daily variations.

Violent changes in magnetic field known as *magnetic storms* occasionally arise together with related solar, auroral, cosmic-ray and ionospheric phenomena. In the polar regions many storm-like effects, on a reduced scale from that of world wide storms are found almost every day. Finally, there is a considerable amount of irregular and small aperiodic and periodic disturbances of frequencies up to a few cycles per second which are at present unexplained.

The sources of these varying magnetic fields, including those of magnetic storms, is mainly within the atmosphere, with an undetermined part arising from the region beyond.

CHAPTER SEVEN

Composition and Structure of the Atmosphere

D. R. BATES

THE ATMOSPHERE is very massive by ordinary standards: thus the portion directly above one square foot of the Earth's surface weighs almost a ton; and the whole weighs about five thousand million million tons—enough to provide each of the world's inhabitants with two million tons of air. The amount of matter contained may perhaps best be appreciated by noting that if the atmosphere were compressed until it became as dense as water, its thickness would be over 30 feet. To pass through so much matter is not easy. Hence the atmosphere acts as a powerful shield. It protects us from meteors and primary cosmic-ray particles. Towards the Sun's electromagnetic radiation it is admirably selective, stopping harmful ultra-violet and X-radiation, but transmitting vital visible radiation.

AIR

Near the end of the eighteenth century, C. W. Scheele, A. L. Lavoisier, Joseph Priestly and others established that air consists of two gases, 'fire air' which supports combustion, and 'foul air' which does not. Agreement that it is a *physical mixture*, like gunpowder, rather than a *chemical compound*, like sodium chloride, was not reached until the following century. Curiously enough one of the most cogent arguments invoked was based on incorrect measurements which led many scientists to believe that the composition varies markedly from place to place and from time to time and in particular to believe that the relative amount of 'fire air' or oxygen, as it is now called, is higher in the country than in a city, and is dependent on meteorological conditions. As techniques improved, the apparent variability diminished, and in 1912 F. G. Benedict carried out a series of very precise analyses from which he concluded that: 'Air is a physical mixture with the definiteness of composition of a chemical compound'. The wording used is rather too strong since, for example, the balance between oxygen and carbon dioxide may be upset by processes such as respiration, and photosynthesis. However, it may be said that the relative amount of nitrogen, the main constituent of 'foul air', is essentially a geophysical constant.

The *fractional volume abundance* of a constituent of a gas mixture is defined to be the volume the constituent would occupy if isolated, divided by the volume of the gas mixture, the two volumes being measured at the same temperature and pressure. Clearly the sum of the fractional volume abundances of all the constituents is unity. Special significance is attached to the fractional volume abundance since it equals the fraction of the molecules in the gas mixture which belong to the constituent.

TABLE 1

Dry ground-level air

Constituent	Fractional volume abundance	
	Hundredths	Millionths
Nitrogen	78·08	
Oxygen	20·95	
Argon	0·93	
Carbon dioxide	0·03	
Neon		18·2
Helium		5·2
Methane		1·5
Krypton		1·1
Nitrous oxide		0·5
Carbon monoxide (variable)		0·1 to 0·2
Xenon		0·1

Table 1 gives the fractional volume abundances of the constituents of *dry* ground level air. In general, air is moist. The fractional volume abundance of water vapour is of course extremely variable—it may rise to about one fiftieth or even rather higher.

For many purposes it is sufficient to regard air as composed of only nitrogen and oxygen with the molecules of nitrogen four times as numerous as those of oxygen.

Nitrogen occurs in organic matter, usually as a constituent of proteins, and undergoes a complicated cycle through the biosphere. A general scheme for this cycle was first presented in 1841 by J. B. A. Dumas. Fig. 1 shows the essential features. G. E. Hutchinson has estimated the *turn-over period* (that is, the time needed for the nitrogen to pass once through the cycle), to be of the order of 100 million years.

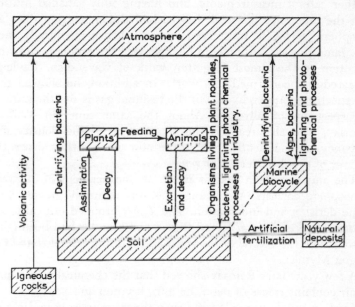

FIG. 1. Nitrogen cycle.

Oxygen takes part in the carbon dioxide cycle to be described later and has a turn-over period of only a few thousand years. Marine phytoplankton is perhaps the plant of most importance in the oxygen economy.

Inert Gases

After nitrogen and oxygen, the most abundant constituent is argon. This constituent (like the much rarer constituents neon, helium, krypton and xenon), has the remarkable property of being *chemically inert*, that is, of not combining with other substances. Its discovery was foreshadowed as early as 1785 by Henry Cavendish, who found that a small amount of gas always remained when he subjected a mixture of oxygen and air to electrical sparking and to the action of chemicals which would have removed the expected products. In 1892 Lord Rayleigh, while carrying out a systematic investigation on the densities of gases, noticed that the density of seemingly pure nitrogen prepared from air was slightly greater than the density of nitrogen prepared by ordinary chemical methods. During the next two years he made further careful measurements, and having fully satisfied himself that the difference was real, he reached the conclusion that 'atmospheric nitrogen' must contain some heavy chemically inert gas. James Dewar, with whom he discussed the problem, drew his attention to the almost forgotten work of Cavendish. Rayleigh repeated and confirmed this work. In addition, he showed that the spectrum (Appendix VI) of the residual gas is not the same as the spectrum of nitrogen. About the same time Sir William Ramsay, who also realized the significance of the density discrepancy, independently isolated the new gas. He thus shares the honour of the discovery of *argon*.

The announcement that as much as one per cent of our own atmosphere consists of a strange gas was naturally greeted with some derision and indignation. *The Times* brooded critically, the *British Medical Journal* feared that 'a sad blunder had been committed', and the *Electrical Review* made scathing reference to 'The Argon Myth'.

A few years later Ramsay showed that the chemically inert part of air contains traces of neon, helium, krypton and xenon.

Argon is much more plentiful than the other inert gases because its isotope of mass 40 units is a decay product of the potassium isotope of the same mass. Though helium is continually being released from radio-active rocks, it remains a very rare constituent, since it can escape from the atmosphere (page 107). Only an exceedingly minute fraction of the helium released is the isotope of mass 3 units and there is difficulty in understanding why the amount of this isotope present is as much as one millionth of that of the normal isotope of mass 4 units. Cosmic rays produce some, but seemingly not enough. K. I. Mayne has suggested that the main source may be the extra-terrestrial dust that is collected by the Earth.

Carbon Dioxide

The value of the fractional volume abundance of carbon dioxide quoted in Table 1 is an average. Systematic departures from the average occur.

The most striking geographical effect is that the air over the polar seas is relatively poor in carbon dioxide: for example, a fractional volume abundance of only about half the average has been recorded by K. Buch on the south-western coast of Spitzbergen. It is likely that the effect is a direct manifestation of oceanic control. The possibility of such control arises because seawater can take up and give out carbon dioxide, and the equilibrium pressure of the gas is less over a cold region than over a warm region.

There is some evidence for a very slight seasonal variation, the fractional volume abundance in winter being perhaps 2 per cent more than in summer. If real, the variation is probably biological in origin.

Life processes cause an important cycling. Carbon dioxide is removed from the atmosphere by the photosynthetic action of plants. It is returned in several ways—by the respiration of plants, by their decay and by their being used as food by animals. According to Hutchinson, approximately 70 thousand million tons of carbon dioxide are removed and returned each year. Since the amount in the atmosphere is 2400 thousand million tons the turn-over period is of the order of 35 years.

A cycle similar to that described, but vaster, takes place within the oceans. However, in spite of the deficiency over the polar seas, Hutchinson considers that the transport of carbon dioxide across the water-air boundary is slow* and the amount in the atmosphere is the equilibrium value for the land cycle. This equilibrium value depends on the total mass of carbon dioxide that could be formed from the carbon of the organic matter in and on the ground, which mass is estimated by W. W. Rubey to be some 2600 thousand million tons. Leakage of carbon into and out of the land cycle occurs and affects its scale. The leakage is partly due to the oceans and, as H. C. Urey has pointed out, is partly due to chemical reactions between carbon dioxide and the silicate rocks.

Between 1900 and 1935 the fractional volume abundance of

* He considers the corresponding transport of the less soluble oxygen may be quite rapid.

carbon dioxide rose by almost 9 per cent, corresponding to a global mass increase of 200 thousand million tons. G. S. Callender suggested that industrial fuel consumption, which in the same period caused the release of approximately 150 thousand million tons of carbon dioxide, is directly responsible for the change. This suggestion has been challenged by Hutchinson, who argues that about half the total released must accumulate in organic matter, and some may also leave the land cycle, so that industrial fuel consumption causes a smaller nett increase in the amount of carbon dioxide in the atmosphere than would at first be supposed. If this is correct, some additional factor must be invoked to explain the observational data. In Hutchinson's view the additional factor is the change that has taken place during the twentieth century in the ratio of agricultural to forest land.

Minor Constituents

In 1938 A. Adel with the aid of an infra-red spectroscope detected nitrous oxide in the atmosphere; and in 1948 and 1949 M. V. Migeotte similarly detected methane and carbon monoxide. Each of these gases takes part in a cycle.

Nitrous oxide is destroyed rapidly by the action of sunlight. Its continued presence therefore necessitates that it is also produced rapidly. The source has not yet been identified. One theory is that nitrous oxide is formed by certain chemical reactions in the lower atmosphere. Another is that it is formed by soil microorganisms. If valid, this last theory may have implications of interest to agricultural scientists, for the required yield is such that nitrous oxide would have to be the principal end-product of denitrification.

As is well-known, methane is produced by decaying vegetation in marshes. In addition, some may originate in ordinary soil and some may seep out of natural fuel beds. The amount entering the atmosphere annually from these three sources is difficult to determine, but may perhaps be of the order of 100 million tons. Calculations by Hutchinson give the surprising result that the annual contribution from enteric fermentation in domestic cattle and similar large animals is comparable, being about 45 million tons. Little can be said about the loss processes which must be occurring to keep the amount in the atmosphere at the observed 4300 million tons.

Carbon monoxide is a major by-product of modern civilization, some 200 million tons being vented into the atmosphere annually by internal combustion engines and solid fuel furnaces. The total amount present is provided within a few years. Soil micro-organisms destroy carbon monoxide and preserve an equilibrium.

EXPLORATION IN ALTITUDE

Pressure, Density, and Temperature

Since the pressure at every level must be just sufficient to sup-port the weight of the air above, it is obvious that the pressure decreases as the altitude increases. A more detailed examination of the equilibrium shows that the rate of the decrease is proportional to the local density of the air; and the gas laws of Boyle, Avagadro and Charles show that the density is proportional to the pressure multiplied by the mean weight of the gas-particles (atoms and molecules), divided by the temperature on Kelvin's scale.* Thus the *three* basic parameters, pressure, density and temperature, are connected by *two* mathematical relations. The first of these relations enables the pressure-altitude graph to be deduced from the density-altitude graph or *vice versa*; and if the constitution, and therefore the mean gas-particle weight, is known the second enables the temperature-altitude graph to be determined from either of the other graphs, or again, *vice versa*. Hence only one of the three graphs need be given. We shall concentrate our attention on the temperature-altitude graph as it is the most revealing. However, before considering the actual atmosphere, it is useful to consider the pressure-altitude and density-altitude graphs in a hypothetical *isothermal* atmosphere† of uniform composition.

In the hypothetical atmosphere specified, the pressure and density fall off at the same rate. Moreover, the factor by which they fall off between any two levels does not depend on the altitude, it depends simply on the separation between the levels. The separation corresponding to a fall-off by a factor of 10 is called the *decimal scale height* of the atmosphere.

An atmosphere at a temperature of 285 degrees Kelvin (12 degrees Centigrade) with a mean gas-particle weight of 29 units

---

* The temperature in degrees Kelvin equals the temperature in degrees Centigrade plus 273 degrees. Thus 0 degrees Kelvin corresponds to minus 273 degrees Centigrade, which is the lowest temperature theoretically possible.

† An isothermal atmosphere is one in which the temperature is everywhere the same.

(the approximate values for ground level air), would have a decimal scale height of about 12 miles: at an altitude equal to this the pressure and density would therefore be one tenth the ground level values, at 24 miles they would be one hundredth, at 36 miles they would be one thousandth, and so on.

The decimal scale height is proportional to the temperature on Kelvin's scale, divided by the mean gas-particle weight. It follows immediately that the rate at which the pressure and density decrease with increase in altitude is faster in an atmosphere which is cold than in one which is hot and also is faster in an atmosphere composed of heavy gases than in one composed of light gases. Any atmosphere may be imagined as made up of a number of approximately isothermal and uniform layers to each of which a decimal scale height may be assigned.

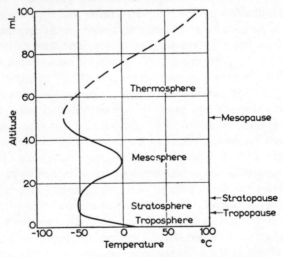

FIG. 2.   Temperature-altitude graph for atmosphere.

Turning now to the actual atmosphere, the mean temperature-altitude graph up to the 100 mile level is shown in Fig. 2 which is believed to be accurate below the 50 mile level, but may be significantly in error above. As one ascends, the temperature first decreases sharply, then, after remaining almost constant for an interval, rises to a maximum at an altitude of about 30 miles, decreases, passes through a minimum at an altitude of about 50 miles, and finally increases again, probably levelling out at a high value (*perhaps* as high as 2,000 degrees Centigrade), some-where in the region beyond the 100 mile level—which region is not included in Fig. 2 since the information relating to it is meagre and unreliable.

A convenient classification of the atmosphere into subspheres is based on the temperature variation. The first region of falling temperature is termed the *troposphere*, the approximately iso-thermal region above is termed the *stratosphere*, the region from this to the temperature minimum near the 50 mile level is termed the *mesosphere*, and the hot region between the minimum and the *exosphere* or fringe of the atmosphere is termed the *thermosphere*. Replacing the suffix *sphere* by the suffix *pause* gives the name used for the top boundary of a region. It is customary to refer to the part of the atmosphere below the stratopause as the *lower atmos-phere* and the part above as the *upper atmosphere*.

Most of the probing of the troposphere and stratosphere has been done with the aid of balloons. Ascents with observers, such as the notable ascent of rather more than 13 miles which was made in 1938 by the helium-filled Explorer II, have yielded important results; but they have gone out of favour since the necessity of carrying a heavy load (including a pressurized cabin if the region above the 5 mile level is to be entered) prevents the peak altitude attainable from being great enough to justify the danger and expense. A limit to what can be achieved is set by the fall-off in the buoyancy of the air (which is of course proportional to the density). It may be noted that the buoyancy lift force arising from the displacement of one thousand cubic feet of air is about 80 pounds at ground level, 11 pounds at 10 miles, less than a pound at 20 miles and only an ounce or so at 30 miles. In spite of this fall-off modern neoprene-latex unmanned balloons are easily able to take heavy equipment to above the 20 mile level. The measure-ments made are transmitted by radio or recorded on film.

In the past much effort was devoted to obtaining information on conditions in the then inaccessible mesosphere and thermosphere by various indirect methods. These methods have become of secondary importance. Rockets are now the main source of precise data. Results are usually telemetered back to the ground. However, if necessary material recovery may be effected by arranging that during the downward part of the flight, the rocket breaks into sections of poor aerodynamic shape which, being retarded by high

H

air-drag, do not strike the Earth's surface at speeds sufficient to cause undue damage.

TABLE 2

Rocket	Peak Altitude (for pay-load indicated in brackets)
Wac Corporal	40 miles (25 pounds)
Aerobee	60 miles (150 pounds)
Deacon (launched from Skyhook balloon)	65 miles (30 pounds)
Viking (Mark 7)	135 miles (400 pounds)

Table 2 gives an indication of the performances of some of the American rockets. The new British rocket, the Skylark, should be able to lift 150 pounds rather over 100 miles.

The existence of these remarkable vehicles does not mean that the properties of the mesosphere and thermosphere are easy to determine. Much ingenuity is in fact required. A fundamental difficulty is that the air at great altitudes is extremely tenuous and the time available for a measurement is brief: for instance, the density at the 60 mile level is only of the order of a millionth of the density at the Earth's surface, and only about 6 minutes would be spent above this level, even if the summit of the trajectory were as high as 150 miles. Trouble also arises from the tendency of rockets to exude gases continually.

As already mentioned, little is known concerning the region above the 100 mile level. Very few studies have been carried out by the rocket scientists and those that have refer solely to the density. The greatest altitude at which a measurement has been made is 134 miles—according to R. J. Havens and his associates the density at this altitude is about one ten-thousandth of the value at 60 miles.

Much remains to be done but it is expected that the artificial satellites will lead to rapid progress being made, for accurate tracking of them will provide data which will enable the air-drag suffered, and hence the densities at extreme altitudes, to be calculated. When the density becomes known it will be possible to estimate the temperatures though some uncertainty will be caused by the lack of information on the mean gas-particle weight (which is a function of the altitude).

Reference has been made to the suggestion that the temperature rises to a very high value. This suggestion originates from theoretical investigations on the exosphere.

As has been stated, the exosphere is the fringe of the atmosphere. More precisely, it is defined to be the region lying above the critical level where the average distance a horizontally moving gas-particle travels before colliding with another gas-particle equals a certain specified fraction (approximately one half), of the local decimal scale height. The density at the critical level may be shown to be of the order of a million-millionth of that at ground level. Such a density is thought to be encountered at an altitude of several hundred miles.

Between the infrequent collisions the gas-particles in the exosphere behave as would heavy projectiles shot up from the thermosphere.

Some may rise far above the critical level and then drop back again; others may have sufficient speed to overcome the Earth's gravitational attraction and escape into outer space as was first realised by G. J. Stoney. Light species tend to move faster than heavy species and therefore are more likely to escape. The rate of escape is a rapidly increasing function of the temperature at the critical level.

H. Petersen, F. A. Lindemann and others have shown that the amount of helium released from radio-active rocks during the geological life of the Earth exceeds the amount now in the atmosphere (cf. Table 1). Assuming Stoney's mechanism to be responsible for the loss of helium that must have occurred, L. Spitzer deduced that the temperature at the critical level is either about 1800 degrees Centigrade or, though usually less, is occasionally more—perhaps for 2 per cent of the time is 2300 degrees Centigrade; and even greater values may be required, for Mayne has recently concluded that the amount of helium released and lost is far greater than has been supposed. Some theorists find the high temperature mentioned difficult to accept.

The preceding account ignores the dependence of the properties of the atmosphere on the time of day, the season, the sunspot number and the geographical position. No attempt will be made to describe what is known of the general pattern. A false impression might, however, be left if attention were not drawn to the fact that some of the variations are considerable: for example, the altitude and temperature of the tropopause are about 10 miles and minus 80 degrees Centigrade in the tropics, and about 7 miles and minus 50 degrees Centigrade in the temperate zones.

Constitution

Because of the tendency of heavy gases to sink and light gases to rise, pronounced changes in the composition of the air were at one time confidently expected to be found on ascending even short distances above sea level. In 1826, in apparent confirmation of this expectation, Joseph Dalton reported the ratio of oxygen to nitrogen to be less at the tops of mountains than in Manchester. His erroneous conclusion was due to his failure to realize that samples of air must not be kept in damp bottles in contact with cork before being analysed.

Diffusive separation, as the separation of heavy and light gases by gravity is termed, proceeds extremely slowly except at great altitudes where the air is very tenuous. Winds have an opposing mixing action; and they are not confined to the region near the Earth's surface, they also blow in the upper atmosphere as is evident, for example, from the violent motions of meteor trains (Chapter 15). Seriously underestimating their influence, and making other misjudgments, scientists inferred that hydrogen becomes the most plentiful atmospheric constituent at altitudes above 50 miles. This is now known to be incorrect: thus measurements with rocket-borne instruments have established that diffusive separation is unimportant up to at least the 85 mile level, and furthermore, spectroscopic observations on aurorae strongly suggest that nitrogen and oxygen remain the principal constituents throughout the atmosphere. The altitude above which diffusive separation is too rapid to be prevented by winds, has not yet been determined with certainty, but it is probably about 100 miles.

From what has been said it must not be supposed that no changes of composition occur. Measurements made from aircraft and balloons show that an important change in fact sets in only a few miles above sea-level. The air becomes exceedingly dry.* This is probably due to the extreme coldness of the air near the tropopause (especially over the tropics): in effect the tropopause acts as a water vapour trap, the region beyond corresponding to a desert on the leeward side of a range of high mountains.

Changes also take place as a result of chemical reactions initiated by the incident solar ultra-violet and X-radiation. The

* The Meteorological Office report that experiments carried out from Canberra aircraft over southern England showed the fractional volume abundance of water vapour at the 9 mile level to be only several millionths.

atmosphere absorbs this radiation. In being absorbed, some of the radiation splits oxygen molecules (O_2) into oxygen atoms (O). These oxygen atoms may re-unite or they may join to oxygen molecules to form ozone (O_3) which may be broken down again into oxygen atoms and molecules; and many other reactions take place. Though the task of calculating how the composition of the atmosphere is affected is far from easy, considerable progress has been made.

S. Chapman predicted that as one passes upwards through the region near the 60 mile level the oxygen changes from being mainly molecular to being mainly atomic. This prediction, made in 1931, has been verified recently by a group of rocket scientists led by H. Friedman. The reason for the change in the form of the oxygen may readily be understood. In equilibrium the splitting of molecules and the uniting of atoms balance. Now as the altitude is increased, the time that elapses before a fixed number of molecules are split into atoms *shortens* since the disrupting radiation becomes more intense; and further, the time that elapses before a fixed number of atoms unite to form molecules *lengthens* since the fall in the pressure reduces the frequency with which the necessary collisions occur. It follows at once that the equilibrium ratio of the number of oxygen molecules to the number of oxygen atoms is a decreasing function of the altitude. Detailed calculations show that this ratio drops sharply from very large values at altitudes of 55 miles and less to very small values at altitudes of 65 miles and more.

However, as M. Nicolet has pointed out, winds and diffusive separation prevent photo-chemical equilibrium from being established and in consequence, the transition from a molecular to an atomic region is neither as abrupt nor as complete as originally supposed: for example, it is now estimated that oxygen molecules are far from rare, even at the 100 mile level, but instead are there at least about one twenty-fifth as numerous as oxygen atoms.

In the case of ozone, the efficiency of the formation processes relative to that of the destruction processes diminishes rapidly both as one goes towards very low altitudes and as one goes towards very high altitudes; at these extremes the equilibrium ozone content of the air therefore tends rapidly towards zero, and at an intermediate altitude (about 15 miles) it passes through a maximum. Actually below this maximum photo-chemical equilibrium is approached much too slowly to be reached, and the local concentration of ozone varies irregularly, being controlled mainly by the rate of vertical transport of air masses by currents. Ozone is nowhere a major atmospheric constituent—at the maximum of the diffuse layer to which it is confined its fractional volume abundance is only four millionth. Nevertheless it is a very important constituent: it is, for instance, responsible for the opaqueness of the atmosphere to radiation of wavelength shorter than 2900Å.

The theoretical studies were preceded and stimulated by observational studies which have continued since 1880 when W. N. Hartley established the existence of ozone in the atmosphere by the identification of absorption bands appearing in the solar spectrum near the 2900Å transparency limit.

The amount of ozone present may be determined by measuring the extent to which solar or stellar ultra-violet radiation is absorbed in passing through the atmosphere. It is not constant. During the past quarter of a century, G. M. B. Dobson, A. R. Meetham and others have carried out extensive researches to elucidate the pattern of the changes. There are systematic variations with season and with latitude which we shall not describe. In addition, interesting correlations with the weather have been found. For example, the passage of a warm front is generally accompanied by a fall in the amount of ozone and the passage of a cold front by a rise; again in a cyclone or an anti-cyclone, the contours showing equal pressures and those showing equal amounts of ozone are closely similar and are inversely related in the sense that high pressures are associated with low amounts of ozone and low pressures with high amounts.

Investigations on the altitude distribution of ozone were begun in 1934 by E. and V. H. Regener and by F. W. P. Götz. The Regeners used an ultra-violet spectrometer which could be lifted 20 miles by two balloons. By taking spectra of the Sun at intervals during an ascent, they were able to deduce the amount of ozone above each of a succession of levels, and hence were able to find the altitude distribution. Götz devised and exploited an ingenious method (rather too complicated to be described here), which requires only ground level measurements. To obtain data for the region well above the maximum of ozone layer it is necessary

to resort to rockets. With their aid R. Tousey and his associates succeeded in 1952 in determining the distribution up to an
altitude of 40 miles. There is in general excellent agreement with
the predictions that had been made from consideration of the
photo-chemical equilibrium.

Nitrogen molecules (N_2) are exceptionally stable and though
some are split into nitrogen atoms (N) in the upper atmosphere
the effect is probably less pronounced than for oxygen. Proper
quantitative studies have not yet been made. The splitting gives
rise to numerous chemical reactions. Several of these yield nitric
oxide (NO) the ionization of which by solar ultra-violet radiation
is believed to be one of the processes yielding free electrons in the
ionosphere (Chapter 12).

In the breakdown of water vapour (H_2O) and methane (CH_4),
hydrogen atoms (H) are freed. Their presence in the 40 to 50 mile
region is of importance in connection with the nightglow (Chapter 13).

Heat Balance

Most of the incident solar energy is contained in the visible
radiation which can penetrate right through the atmosphere. The
Earth re-emits the energy it receives from the Sun, but being a
much cooler body it does so mainly in the infra-red region of the
spectrum. Infra-red radiation is strongly absorbed by water
vapour, carbon-dioxide and ozone. These constituents therefore
act like the glass of a greenhouse—they trap the out-going energy.
The effect is of the utmost importance for without it the mean
surface temperature would be lower by almost 40 degrees Centigrade and life could not exist.

Following the pioneer work of E. Gold in 1909, many theoretical
studies have been carried out on the temperature distribution
through the troposphere and stratosphere. R. Emden examined
what would happen if the atmosphere were in *radiative equilibrium** under the combined influence of the solar and terrestrial

* In radiative equilibrium each packet of air emits exactly as much energy as
it absorbs. This balance can be achieved by a suitable adjustment of the temperature for the emission rate is a rapidly increasing function of the temperature,
whereas the absorption rate is almost independent of the temperature: thus if a
packet initially emitted less than it absorbed its temperature would rise until the
two rates became equal, while if it initially emitted more, its temperature would
similarly fall.

radiation. He showed that there would be a bottom layer in which the fall-off with altitude of the temperature would be so steep that it would cause convective instability—the cold air at the top of the layer would be too dense relative to the warm air at the base and violent vertical motions would ensue reducing the temperature gradient. This convective layer is to be identified with the troposphere. A layer just above, to be identified with the stratosphere, is found to be almost isothermal in radiative equilibrium. An elaborate treatment by R. M. Goody has confirmed that the troposphere is a convective layer, and has established that the general properties of the lower atmosphere can be explained by taking account of this, of the solar and terrestrial radiation and of the altitude distribution of the three absorbing and emitting constituents.

Conditions of radiative equilibrium extend into the mesosphere. The observed rise in temperature (cf. Fig. 2), is due to the absorption of solar ultra-violet radiation by ozone. It should be noted that even the very small amount of ozone in the region of the temperature maximum is sufficient to absorb much of this radiation.

Several absorption processes (including that leading to the disruption of oxygen molecules), contribute to the heating of the thermosphere. Owing to the scarcity of efficiently emitting molecules, the upper part of the region is not in radiative equilibrium. Thermal conduction* is important and severely limits the temperature gradient. This limitation is what causes some theorists to doubt if the temperature can reach the very high value claimed at the base of the exosphere.

---

* Conduction is the heat transfer mechanism which makes ill-designed saucepan handles get uncomfortably hot. The conductivity of a gas is independent of its density.

CHAPTER EIGHT

Climate

E. T. EADY

CLIMATOLOGY, the study of climate, is one aspect of the study of the Earth's atmosphere, which itself is part of the study of the physics of the Earth. Not only is climatology causally related to several other branches of geophysics, but it is a science of the same kind. It is necessary to stress this because for a number of reasons climatology seems to occupy a special position. We are all directly aware of climate and it is not necessary to explain all the basic concepts. Because the part of the atmosphere with which we are concerned is so accessible it is relatively easy to accumulate vast quantities of data and these may be studied empirically, that is to say, we may look for patterns and relationships without necessarily having any idea *why* they exist. Empiricism is an important part of scientific method and is usually dominant in the early stages of development of a science. Climatology is peculiar only to the extent that methods in general use are still almost entirely empirical. It is usually taught as part of geography (not physics), with emphasis on the descriptive side. The scientific principles involved are barely mentioned and they are used only to provide qualitative, superficial explanations. Whether they are right or wrong does not seem to be of much moment, because they are never used to *calculate* anything.

EMPIRICISM

One may well ask, as some climatologists do: 'What is wrong with empiricism?' It may be very interesting to know just why the climate is what it is but we study climatic data because we want the answer to practical problems of life, agriculture, water supply and so on. If we can answer these problems simply by systematic arrangement of the data, are we not right to concentrate on this task and leave the explanations (which promise to be complicated), until later? We cannot reach a decision until we have studied the problems which need to be answered for the crux of the matter is the success, actual or promised, of methods which ignore physical relationships.

Meanwhile it is desirable to remind ourselves just why purely empirical methods have been found wanting in other sciences. Empiricism treats each separate problem on its merits regardless of what is known of problems which are in fact closely related. There must therefore be as many empirical rules as there are problems. Moreover, if the answer to the problem depends on several factors, an empirical formula will usually be complicated and it will take a long time to discover even a very rough answer, because so many possibilities have to be tested. In fact if we are *completely* ignorant of any theory we must test everything that might be involved which is not a practical proposition; and it may well be that the data we really need are not there to be analysed, because we had no idea that they should have been obtained. Of course, every empiricist makes what use he can of theory: he may call it intuition—but intuition is merely unformulated (or not clearly formulated) and untested (and therefore unreliable) theory. The reason why theory plays an important role, particularly in the more fundamental sciences, is that there exist certain simple rules (called 'laws of nature') which are of very wide application, so that a host of apparently different problems are seen, once these laws are understood, to be particular cases of the same problem. Moreover, these laws are often very accurately true, so that rules derived from them simply by calculation may be far superior to any derived empirically. A classical example comes from astronomy. Empirical and very complicated rules for predicting the positions of the planets were derived before the time of Copernicus and Newton. Newton's discovery of the law of gravitation made the rules simpler as well as more accurate. No one today would dream of constructing the Nautical Almanac by the use of empirical rules. Now if climatology is a branch of physics we start with the advantage that many of the basic laws of physics are already known. The difficulty, as we shall see, lies in the application of them.

This argument suggests, on very general grounds, a philosophy of approach and a working hypothesis, but to clinch it we need to see what it involves in terms of particular practical problems.

STATISTICAL APPROACH
It is both logical and convenient to begin with a critical examination of what climate is and what use we would like to make of our knowledge of it. Climate is made up of weather (rain and snow, temperature, humidity, wind, etc.) and any information regarding these elements and the processes affecting them is relevant. What distinguishes climatology from meteorology is merely our point of view. We may define climate as the *statistical aspect* of weather. In other words we try to describe and understand the broad features as distinct from the peculiar features: for example the rainfall at a given place as distinct from the individual storms of varying intensity, duration and frequency.

Averages
The simplest property we can extract from a set of observations which are numerically expressed is their *average*. Since most elements (e.g. temperature) depend not only on time and place but also on height above the ground, we can form many different averages depending on the way we group the observations. The choice of grouping depends on the use to which we intend to put the statistics. Thus we may form *time-averages* at a given place (observing station) with the idea of specifying, to a certain extent, the climate of this particular place. This is such a common procedure that there is a risk of regarding it as a method of *defining* climate, but we shall see later that there are serious disadvantages in regarding climate *simply* as 'average weather'. Alternatively we may form *space-averages* at a given time. For example, we may calculate the average temperature reported by all observing stations within a fairly large area. This is not, like the time average, an immediately intelligible quantity because although we may live in the same place for a long time we cannot live in many places at once. Nevertheless the variation with time of this space-average can indicate that climate *changes* and one of the major problems in climatology is to understand why it does so.

The average is not the only property we can extract from a set of observations. We can in fact form an indefinite number, each with its own significance, but we shall confine our attention to the second simplest property, the *mean deviation*. This is a measure of the extent to which individual observations fluctuate about their average value. Let us compare two places which have the same (annual) average temperature and rainfall. In one of these places temperature and rainfall vary little, in the other they vary widely. According to a simple-minded definition of climate as 'average weather' the climates are similar but the places would be very different to live and work in: for example vegetation and agricultural possibilities and problems would be quite different. Of course the mean deviation is itself a kind of average so that we could attempt to re-define climate in terms of *two* averages but even this, as we shall see, is not satisfactory.

Up till now we have talked about observations in a very abstract manner—simply as a set of numbers. Let us now be specific and consider a typical sample, say a long record of temperature measured at close intervals of time. If we plot the points and join them to form a graph (or better still, consider the continuous record given by a thermograph), we see that there are large fluctuations, but the record has nevertheless a very marked pattern. Although one day differs from every other in detail almost all have this in common, that it is warmer by day than by night. Now let us group together all parts of the record corresponding to a particular day of the year, say January 1st. Let us compute, for all firsts of January over a number of years, the average temperature at midnight, at one a.m., and so on. If we plot the points we obtain a graph of the average diurnal variation of temperature at that time of year. We may do the same for all other days of the year. The curves of diurnal variation are rather similar for all days, though there is a gradual change in amplitude (i.e in range of temperature) through the year. We could regard the whole mean temperature curve obtained by joining up the daily curves as a measure of one aspect of the climate of the place, but this is unnecessarily precise. For most purposes we may be content to describe the *daily oscillations* by two figures only—the average diurnal range over the summer months and that over the winter months, but this is not a good description of the curve as a whole. Besides the diurnal oscillation there is evidently a trend towards generally higher temperatures in summer and lower ones in winter. We can obtain a precise picture of this variation by 'cutting-out' the diurnal oscillation. This is done very easily by averaging over all hours of the day the values given on the mean temperature curve, and plotting a new curve of mean *daily* temperature. The oscillation represented by this curve can be described rather roughly by one

figure—the *annual range* of temperature—it being understood that
the maximum occurs in summer and the minimum in winter.
Sometimes this is not a full enough description of the curve.
For example, in India the highest temperatures occur about the
end of Spring—before the rains. Hence to give even a rough idea
of the thermal aspect of climate we need *at least* three figures in
addition to the annual average.

We may treat other aspects of climate in a similar manner, sort-
ing out the diurnal and annual variations. Rainfall has a diurnal
variation. It may be marked (in low latitudes and in summer) or
barely noticeable (in high latitudes and in winter). When it is
marked the highest rainfall is, over land, usually in the afternoon.
Over the sea there is a tendency (especially near coastlines) for
rather more rain at night. Of greater practical importance is the
annual variation. In contrast to the simple and regular curve of
annual variation of temperature, that of rainfall varies very greatly
from region to region. There is no world-wide epoch of maximum
and there may be more than one maximum. The shape of the curve
(depending as it does on geography as well as latitude) is so individual that it cannot be represented by a single figure.

Irregular Fluctuations

It is clear that in order to describe the climate of a place as
expressed by annual means and diurnal and annual oscillations, it
is inconvenient to be tied down to a definite number of figures, but
supposing these have been specified to our satisfaction for the
particular use we have in mind, do we need to consider anything
else? Let us go back to our original long record of temperature and
subtract from each value that given by the mean temperature curve
for the corresponding time of day and day of the year. In this way
we cut out both the diurnal and annual variations. The resulting
curve seems to consist only of irregular fluctuations. In low latitudes
the fluctuations are much smaller than those of the original curve,
in higher latitudes less markedly smaller. If we had given the same
treatment to a rainfall curve we should have found fluctuations
very nearly as large as in the original curve. Now all these fluctuations are due to individual weather systems which never repeat
themselves. *Temporary* patterns often appear: for example patterns with a period of *about* five days are fairly common especially
in such places as Australia, but the periods and amplitudes change

and other patterns soon replace them. In any case they are not tied to a particular time of year. Now it was precisely in order to eliminate these random fluctuations that we formed averages in the first place: if there were no fluctuations the observations in

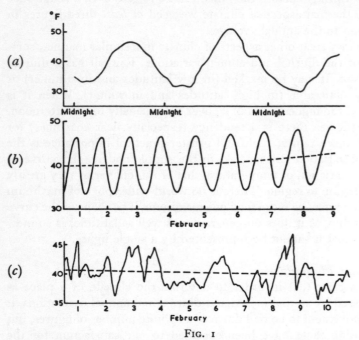

FIG. 1

(a) Actual Temperature Curve (Thermograph Record). Extends indefinitely in time. Note changes from day to day.
(b) Mean Temperature Curve. Extends over *one year*. Note relative smoothness due to averaging over many years. Mean *daily* temperature curve dashed.
(c) Fluctuations. The result of subtracting (b), repeated indefinitely, from (a). Extends indefinitely in time. Trend line dashed.

one particular year would tell us all we need to know. Can we therefore be satisfied that we have already extracted from the data the quintessence of climate? Let us recall the remark we made earlier regarding the significance of fluctuations for life and work. What we have done since then is to separate the fluctuations into regular ones (diurnal and annual) and irregular ones. The regular ones can easily be allowed for in ordering our activities because they can be forecast precisely. The irregular ones must often be considered more seriously than their mean deviation seems to warrant, because they represent a risk which cannot be accurately forecast, and we may have to insure ourselves against unusually large deviations (e.g. 'unseasonable' frosts). Hence we cannot be satisfied with a description of climate which includes only regular variations. We must include figures to represent *mean deviations of irregular fluctuations*, perhaps different at different times of year.

Let us look again at the curve of irregular fluctuations. The fluctuation which occurs at a particular time seems to be entirely a matter of accident, with the restriction that the larger the fluctuation the less frequently it occurs. This kind of behaviour is very common (in all sciences, not only physics) and statisticians have a standard technique for dealing with it. In the absence of evidence to the contrary, each fluctuation is regarded as a random selection from a particular set of numbers called the 'normal' distribution. This distribution, which is completely specified when we are given the mean deviation, has the feature that the relative number of large fluctuations decreases with increasing size according to a definite law. Now if the actual set of fluctuations is represented well enough by this schematic distribution we can easily compute how 'good' our climatic averages are. If we form the average of a set of numbers which are random samples and compare it with averages determined from other sets, we find that the averages themselves fluctuate, though to a smaller extent than the individual numbers.

This fluctuation represents an uncertainty regarding the 'true value' of the average. As the number of members of the set increases so the fluctuation of the averages usually decreases. In other words, if we construct our mean temperature curve from the data over a hundred years, we expect to obtain a more reliable estimate than if we average over ten years. If the fluctuations were in fact well represented by the 'normal' distribution we could calculate the 'probable error', that is, the amount of uncertainty regarding the 'true value' of the average, and this decreases towards zero as the averaging period increases indefinitely. This would imply that, though our calculations would always fall short of complete accuracy, there nevertheless exists a quantity which we could define, unambiguously, as *the* (long-term) average temperature (or rainfall) curve.

Is this the true state of affairs? Unfortunately, it would be rather difficult to make a direct test from the records because existing records are of limited length. However, there is some indication from the records themselves and conclusive evidence from a different source. If we look closely at the record obtained by cutting out the diurnal and annual variations we see that there is distinctly more 'pattern' in it (albeit of a transient nature) than we would expect if the individual values were like those drawn from a hat. We have already referred to one kind of pattern with a 'period' of oscillation of roughly five days, but there is evidence also of less well-defined patterns of much longer period. The temperature may remain *on the whole* distinctly below the average of the record for long periods—months or years—to a much greater extent than is to be expected simply by accidental coincidence of cold fluctuations. Experience is not misleading in suggesting to us that certain years, or periods of years are distinctly colder (or warmer) than others. In a long record we may even notice a general trend towards higher or lower values. There is good evidence that in most parts of the world there has been a general upward trend in temperature over the past century to the total extent of about 1° F.—this does not sound very much, but years we distinctly remember as 'warm' do not differ from average by so very much more than this amount. It is evident therefore that we *cannot* consider the curve from which diurnal and annual variations have been removed simply as a horizontal line (*the* average value), on which are superposed random variations due to particular spells of 'weather'. A better description would be a slowly varying 'trend' curve on which are superposed random and relatively rapid fluctuations, the trend representing the *change* of climate with time. There is, however, a difficulty. How are we to distinguish the trend from the fluctuation? It seems that we cannot, after all, give an unambiguous and generally acceptable definition of climate. We have to discriminate *arbitrarily* between the fluctuations which we are going to smooth out, and the details in the trend we are going to retain. Thus we may represent thermal climate by average values over individual years, over decades, or over longer periods. In any case climate is not represented (for each element, apart from diurnal and annual variations and the size of rapid random fluctuations) by a single number but by a *time-series* of numbers.

Climate in the Past

Although the *slow* fluctuations represented by the trend are of sufficient importance for us to be dissatisfied with the simple idea of a climate fixed once and for all, it is a little disconcerting to lose the value, representing a supposed long-term average, with which other values, such as decadal means, may be compared. Is it possible that there really is such a value but that the atmosphere takes much longer to settle down than our schematic model of random fluctuations suggests it ought? This would be the case for example if the trend curve were made up of a number of different regular oscillations of different periods, the size of the oscillation decreasing gradually as the period lengthened. The length of existing records of temperature or rainfall is too short to answer the question, so we must use indirect evidence. Though none of this evidence is sufficient to tell us precisely what the climate of a region was at some time in the past, it is good enough to suggest, and in some cases to *prove*, that the climate was very different from what it is now. It comes from our knowledge of the *effects* of climate on the land, on its vegetation and on the people who lived on it.

The source of our knowledge of past civilisations is archaeological exploration together with written or traditional history. For a civilisation to develop several conditions are necessary, one of the most important being that it must not be too difficult or take too long to acquire enough food. There must be time to spare (for the population as a whole) for 'non-productive' work of a military or priestly kind, for craftsmen's work such as armoury and jewellery, for building houses, palaces and pyramids. Now the ease or otherwise with which food may be obtained, depends on the natural vegetation or the artificial vegetation with which it may be replaced and this in turn depends on the climate. A rainy climate, as in the Congo, is not suitable because too much time and effort must be expended in keeping the natural forest at bay. Too dry a climate, as in the Sahara, is not suitable because nothing can be induced to grow. It is not an accident that so many of the earliest civilisations grew up in certain fertile regions from Egypt to North-west India where the climates (and natural resources such as large, permanent rivers for additional water supply, as well as for communication), have much in common. Nor is it an accident that 'rainmaking' continued, as in more primitive societies, to be

I

one of the most important priestly functions. The climate was favourable, but for it to swing too far away from the norm could mean disaster. Could it be that the decay of some civilisations, particularly those that were never re-established, was due primarily to a change in climate making its basis insecure so that the final blow from without fell on a society already doomed? The problem is so complex that we may never be certain, yet a strong suspicion remains that the 'long-period oscillations' of climate, far from being very small may be at least as large as the changes over decades. The seven lean years may have become seven hundred or more.

We might hope for more definite information from a study of the history of the land rather than the people because less complex problems are involved. The source of our information in this case is geological exploration in its widest sense. It includes direct evidence of plant life in the more recent past, such as is afforded by a study of pollen grains embedded in mud dredged from the bottoms of lakes. The limits within which a given species of plant grows easily and abundantly are not fixed *precisely* by the distribution of temperature and rainfall; but there is a distinct climate which is 'optimum' for the species, taking into account both its natural requirements and competition with other plants. If we have a number of species including some which (now) grow easily in low latitudes, and others which flourish in high latitudes, we may, in spite of some overlapping, arrange them in a hierarchy corresponding to their optimum temperatures for growth. If now, as is evidenced by the relative frequency of pollen grains, which are the seeds of these species, we find a marked and persistent tendency for high-latitude species to replace low latitude species during the course of time (which is measured by the depth from which the mud has been dredged, the most recent being of course at the top) it is reasonable to infer that the climate has got colder. We may even make a rough estimate of the amount of temperature change. But although we may feel that we are right we cannot be quite sure. Plants can adapt themselves to their surroundings by evolutionary development, some species may have been stricken with disease, the changed distribution may be due to some environmental factor other than temperature. It is only when independent lines of evidence point to the same conclusion that we can have real confidence. As we go further back into the past, evidence from fossil animal and plant life becomes rather more indefinite because we *know* evolutionary changes have occurred. However, we may infer something of the probable mode of life of the animals and hence about the probable climate .We may speculate on the connection between change of climate and bursts of evolutionary development, and (at other times) the sudden extinction of many species, but real knowledge is less than in the case of human civilisations. It may be that in this case we should reverse our procedure. Instead of attempting to obtain evidence of climatic change from evolution we should perhaps try to find out what kinds of climatic change are possible or probable, thereby perhaps throwing some light on evolution.

The geological evidence regarding past climate is not limited to fossils, because the rocks and soil are themselves affected by weather, but before considering this other evidence we should remember the large (and useful) collections of fossils which constitute the coal measures. We may think of these now not as particular fossil plants but as evidence that large forests existed for a long time in the area which may not now be afforested. There is little doubt that we can infer the climate at that time was relatively wet. We can also infer that it was not very cold, but we cannot be *certain* that the heat was tropical, however rich the seams. Temperate as well as tropical forests could, it appears, have been sources of coal. Nevertheless, if coal were to be found in Greenland or Antarctica, this would be a proof that the climate had once been much warmer than at present. The final product of the weathering of rock to form soil depends not only on the chemical nature of the rock, but also on the conditions in which weathering takes place, that is, on the climate. The buried soils of past ages tell us something about the climate, but the information is rather indefinite if only because it is difficult to separate out the effects of rainfall and temperature. If only we knew one of these we could make a rough estimate of the other. With all this uncertainty whichever approach we make, it is gratifying that there exists one kind of evidence which is both unambiguous and precise. This is evidence of the action of *ice* on rocks, of past glaciation. It enables us to answer quite definitely the question we posed earlier. The long-term 'oscillations' in the climate trend are not necessarily smaller than the short-term ones. Some of them are *much larger*.

This is not the place to discuss in detail the evidence for past ice action since, in view of its importance, a separate chapter is devoted to this (Chapter 10). We should however note the salient features which relate to climatology. In the first place the evidence is so detailed that there is small risk of misinterpretation. Secondly, the existence of ice-sheets implies a fairly definite restriction on climate, the period of averaging being thousands or hundreds of thousands of years: a few very exceptional years are insufficient to explain the facts. To maintain a thick, extensive and persistent sheet of ice, we need an average (annual) temperature not far from freezing-point. In particular the summers must be cool and relatively damp. An adequate supply of snow or cold rain is needed to maintain the ice-sheet because various processes (evaporation, melting and wind action) immediately or ultimately remove the top layer while the whole sheet is gradually subsiding and flowing outwards to disappear finally in warmer regions or in the sea. Now even in low latitudes we observe ice-action if we go high enough up: there is plenty of it on the Himalayas. This is related to the fact that temperature *in general* decreases with elevation. Hence although the existence of pre-historic ice flows in areas which are now warm (such as South Africa or India south of the Himalayas) implies a very considerable change in climate, this might be due *merely* to a change in elevation. We know from other lines of evidence that, although its time-scale is very long, the surface of the Earth is as restless as the atmosphere. If this were the only cause of climatic change then this change would be a local and, in a sense, 'accidental' effect. There would be no reason to expect systematic changes of climate elsewhere. However, there are reasons to doubt this explanation. The elevation needed to account for the South African (Permo-Carboniferous) ice-sheet would be very unusually large and extensive, comparable with the presently existing Tibetan plateau. We should expect other evidence that the land was very high and this seems to be lacking. If we consider the very much more recent ice-sheet which covered almost the whole of the British Isles and much of Western Europe as well as other places, we have the added difficulty that the supposed great elevation must have disappeared very rapidly. There is no evidence for this. In fact Scandinavia seems to have risen slightly after the weight of the ice was removed (Chapter 10). We must conclude that in this case at least the change of climate had nothing to do with local geography. It was almost certainly just one aspect of a change which was *world-wide* and *large*.

If we accept the idea that evidence of past ice action is not simply evidence of past geography (which does not of course imply that geography plays no part in determining climate) we are led to take a greater interest in the details. The most recent (Quaternary) ice age seems to have had a 'structure' with relatively warm interludes, followed by a return of icy conditions. Very large changes in climate have probably taken place in periods as short as a hundred thousand years. If this seems long compared with periods of practical interest this is partly due to the low 'resolving power' of our investigations. The main consideration however is the principle involved. If general weather can change significantly over short periods, as we well know, and also over very long periods, as we have discovered, then it is not unreasonable to suspect that significant changes are possible *whatever* our period of averaging. Should this be the case we must finally abandon the idea of a climatic norm which makes sense only if we can regard the fluctuations as accidental. Large persistent trends cannot be the results of accidents: they must have a cause and we ought to be able to discover what it is. This leads us back to the argument with which we began. If climate is now to be defined not in terms of a set of numbers fixed for all time, but in terms of a *time-series*, then if climatology is to be of any use at all we must discover some rules for predicting future members of the series. The empirical method is to write down all the members to date and look for regularities. If we regard the members as means over individual years we have, for many observing stations, quite long sets to play with, but no one has yet discovered any evident regular features. Supposed regular variation of fixed period have all been shown to be false as new data have been accumulated. If we are interested in the behaviour of means over decades or centuries we have not even enough figures to suggest ideas. In fact it looks as if the problem is too complicated for empiricism to have much chance of success. We might do better, at least in the long run, if we tried to find out what kind of behaviour the laws of nature would lead us to expect.

PRACTICAL PROBLEMS

Before getting involved in physical ideas applied to the atmosphere let us consider in rather more detail the practical problems we wish to be able to solve. These problems in applied climatology

do not all need to be answered to the same degree of accuracy.
For example, we might have some choice on the siting of the house
we are going to live in for the next ten years. In comparing the
records we should do well enough if we used means over the last
decade (or over a longer period). Any fluctuation during the next
ten years is likely to be too small to worry us unduly and in any
case may well affect all possible sites in the same way. It is fairly
certain that, if a choice on grounds of climate is worth making at
all, the differences in climate between the sites will be due primarily to difference in local geography. In fact if we possess some
knowledge of the way these geographical differences act, we may
be able to decide without bothering to look at the records at all
(e.g. valleys for frosts, hill-tops for wind). In this case *either* theory
or empiricism is good enough. On the other hand we might have
some choice regarding the period to take for our next summer
holidays. Statistics are of some use if we are willing to take the
rough with the smooth over many years but they are not at all
satisfying when used to estimate the weather in a given period of a
particular year. Our problem is one of long-range weather forecasting, i.e., our main concern is to forecast a *particular* fluctuation.

Let us now consider the more important problems of agriculture
and water supply. Everyone knows that in some regions the success of crops depends critically on rainfall. Famine and plenty may
alternate according to the vagaries of the monsoon. These fluctuations from year to year are most serious in places where rainfall
is marginally sufficient but no country is completely safe—we have
droughts (and floods) even in England. In principle the main
problem is rather like forecasting the weather for summer holidays.
We would like to know in advance what the particular fluctuation
is going to be so that we can take precautions. Quite a number of
variations from routine (even to the extent of sowing different
crops or different varieties) might be useful and practicable if we
were reasonably confident about what is in store. There are,
however, some extra complications. We have hitherto barely
mentioned the third dimension. It is general knowledge that we
get colder if we go a long way up—to a mountain top or in an
aeroplane—but not everyone realises how much weather and climate can vary within a few feet of the ground. On a clear windless
night when there is a frost recorded at four feet (the standard

height for records) there is often a much more severe frost on the ground surface. Not only sunshine but also temperature and humidity can be different under the leaves of a growing crop from measurements made just outside. It should be remembered that we have to think not only of the crop but of the insects which feed on it and carry diseases: they live in a different climate from ours. Of course there are some close relations between crop-climate and the climate measured by near-by well-exposed instruments, but unless we have studied both for some time we cannot be sure that we have extracted the relations that matter. It would be too much to expect us to keep long records for each kind of crop in every locality. Such whole-hogging empiricism would be quite impracticable. We have to learn how to *calculate* the practically important features of the climate to be expected in and around a specified crop in terms of the general climate.* This is going to involve a thorough knowledge of the physical processes which cause these specific modifications.

We may look at the problems of water supply from the point of view of the civil engineer. The drainage area is given. How big should the dams and reservoirs be to utilise the rainfall safely and efficiently? Like the problem about where to live this is a relatively long-term problem. If, as is often the case, the undertaking is a large one it may not be economical to plan for less than, say, fifty years ahead. It differs from our earlier problem however to the extent that we need to know the answer much more accurately. The run-off which we are aiming to utilise is the difference between the rainfall (or snowfall) and the evaporation of water back into the air. The evaporation is not usually very much smaller than rainfall; both fluctuate considerably and we may expect their difference to fluctuate even more. The reservoir has to be designed so that it will never (or almost never) fail. Since cost is proportional to size it is clear that the penalties, financial and otherwise, of making the reservoir too large or too small are severe. We need the greatest possible accuracy in forecasting not merely the mean run-off during the fifty years but the largest fluctuations which will actually occur during the period. Of course if records for the particular area for the last fifty years are available these will be of considerable use but they do not usually answer our questions

* Well-exposed instruments are used precisely because their readings depend *least* on local peculiarities.

accurately. Rainfall is affected by local geography so that even to determine it correctly for the past fifty years we need a large number of measurements properly distributed over the area. Evaporation is very difficult to measure directly and usually is estimated by means of a formula in which we have no reason to have confidence. It will of course be different in the next fifty years if the land utilisation changes, quite apart from fluctuations. We might do better if we included data from similar areas, but what is a similar area? A general theory of the size of relatively short-period fluctuations (which may be easier than that of the long period ones and is certainly going to be easier than forecasting *particular* fluctuations) would go a long way towards enabling us to make much better use of the records.

The above examples suffice to indicate the kind of problem we have to solve. Let us now consider another example because it illustrates an unfamiliar aspect of climate. Aircraft pilots make great use of weather forecasts but they are not interested solely in the weather we experience on the ground. Much of the information (winds, cloud thickness, icing conditions) refers to the air several miles above the ground. If this weather is averaged we obtain the climate of the upper air. For example, the winds may be averaged and from the charts so obtained air-lines can determine the most economical routes from one place to another. Fewer people are, of course, interested directly in this kind of climate but there is a very good reason why we ought to include it in our survey. As we shall see in the next chapter, climate is indivisible. Once we start thinking in terms of physical causes we find that we have to think in terms of the atmosphere as a whole. What goes on at high levels is as much a cause of weather and climate as what goes on near the ground. In fact what we experience as weather is simply one aspect of the process of mutual adjustment between different parts of the atmosphere which is taking place continuously. Over short periods this interaction, up to heights of at least ten miles, is evident on the charts plotted by weather forecasters. Over the longer periods, when we can speak of climate, there may be significant interaction up to higher levels. In fact, if we use the word in its most general sense we can speak of climate at all levels in the atmosphere, though we may have to modify the elements of which it is composed. Even the ionosphere (Chapter 12) has climate. There are for example long-term average winds, even if the air moving there is not in quite the condition we are familiar with, and our interest is transferred from clouds to electrical conditions. No one has yet however discovered any important relation between the climates of the extremes of our atmosphere.

THE OCEANS AND THEIR IMPORTANCE

We have so far avoided mention of conditions over the major part of the Earth's surface, the oceans, because climate there is no different in kind from climate over land. Diurnal variations are small and annual variations rather less (on the whole) than over land but otherwise there are no very striking differences. Although mariners' problems (particularly with regard to winds) played a large part in stimulating interest (and seamen themselves contributed greatly in the early stages of development of modern meteorology) the same methods are appropriate in dealing with these as with problems of weather and climate over land. The most important difference in practice is that much more money and effort must be expended to obtain data over the sea (and particularly in the upper air above the sea) so that we have in fact much less information.

This point of view is reasonable if we are concerned only to examine and arrange the new data, but once we are led to think in terms of mechanism and causes we are forced to take a much deeper interest in *the oceans themselves*. As we shall see in the next chapter, the oceans supply not only the excess of rainfall over evaporation which yields our water supply, but they are vast reservoirs of heat which *drive* the atmosphere and cause weather and climate. They are more important in this respect than the land not merely because they are larger reservoirs but because they are *in motion*. A change in the circulation of water in the oceans could be and almost certainly is associated with changes in climate. Since this circulation of water in the seas is itself caused mainly by atmospheric winds, we get into a vicious circle unless we consider the atmosphere and oceans *together*. It is fortunate that in spite of the much more sluggish behaviour of the oceans their motions are governed by the same kind of laws which apply to the atmosphere. Many of the processes occurring in the atmosphere have their analogue in internal motions in the oceans.

CHAPTER NINE

The General Circulation of the Atmosphere and Oceans

E. T. EADY

IN THE previous chapter the point was made that in order to make full use of climatic data we have to know how the atmosphere *works*. We shall now consider what is as yet known about the mechanism, for although the general circulation is only one aspect we find that we cannot understand it without knowing much about other, more detailed, aspects. It will be best to begin with a definition. The general circulation is the global aspect of the motion of the atmosphere. We concentrate our attention on broad air-current systems, ignoring for the moment all the complicated and rapidly varying details. Though the emphasis is on wind systems in the first instance, we do not ignore the aspects of weather with which we are usually more directly concerned. It is merely that winds are a convenient basis for discussing associated changes of cloudiness, rain and temperature. We have noted earlier that from the point of view of their *dynamics*, the oceans and the atmosphere must be considered together as components of a single system. Nevertheless, it will be convenient to begin by concentrating our attention on the atmosphere.

THE ATMOSPHERE

The term 'general circulation' is to some extent misleading, in that it suggests a *steady* flow of air. Now, when we were attempting to define climate we found that, no matter what period we averaged over in order to eliminate rapid fluctuations, we still found slow temporal variations of the smoothed elements. Similarly, when we average over *space* in order to smooth out local fluctuations and make clear the broad pattern of the flow, we find that this varies with time, no matter how large the area over which we smooth, and there is still variation if we average over a period as well. At any one instant we may think of the air motion as composed of superposed flow patterns of different 'scales'. Since the motion often appears to be rather like the circular motion in an eddy, we may rather loosely refer to the patterns, or parts of patterns, as 'eddies'. The scale is then defined as the average horizontal size of the eddies.

For present purposes we shall ignore the very little eddies and even those some ten miles across associated with local showers and thunderstorms. The largest eddies, which we shall later have to study in detail, are the weather systems, showing near the ground as depressions or anticyclones some one thousand miles across. The general circulation is disclosed by smoothing out all eddy-motion up to and including the scale of weather systems. Since the depressions, and their opposites the anticyclones, move about, we may smooth them out by averaging over space or time or both. Usually time averaging, over five days or more, is preferred since it gives a more sharply defined picture. The resulting pattern changes with time more slowly than even the largest eddies which have been smoothed out, and in quite a different way. Though the currents vary in shape and intensity they have some features which seem to be always, or almost always present. Not surprisingly there are systematic changes with the seasons but there are also changes, some comparatively slow, which are not simply seasonal. They are evidently related to differences in weather between one year and the next and, on a longer time-scale, to changes in climate.

Let us first consider those features of the general circulation which are always, or nearly always, present. Because they are permanent they show up strongly when we average over a long period—say fifty years. The flow pattern near the ground is familiar to most of us and is shown in many atlases. What concerns us at the moment is not the detail, which is complicated, but the broad features. We may note:

(i) A broad belt of easterly winds between latitudes 30°N and 30°S. The flow is weaker near the boundaries and near the equator.

(ii) A broad belt of *generally* westerly winds between 30°N and 60°N and a corresponding belt between 30°S and 60°S.

There is some seasonal variation, the whole pattern moving a few degrees of latitude towards the summer hemisphere, but this motion is much less than the apparent motion of the Sun ($23\frac{1}{2}°$ lat.). There is also a seasonal change which is evidently related to geography, particularly to the large land mass of Asia. In winter there is an anticyclonic flow (i.e. the winds correspond, in the northern hemisphere, to clockwise rotation of air) over Asia as a whole, while in summer there is a generally cyclonic (anticlockwise) flow over southern Asia and the north Indian Ocean. These flow patterns are called *monsoons*. The broad belts of easterly (*trade*) and westerly winds which otherwise dominate are called *zonal* because they blow along lines of latitude. It is true that the trade winds are north-easterly and south-easterly in the northern and southern hemispheres respectively but we must remember that we are concerned with the flow pattern through the *whole* of the atmosphere. At a height of one mile above the ground the *average* flow is much more nearly zonal. Similarly the westerlies, which are, on the average, south-westerly near the ground in the northern hemisphere (north-westerly in the southern hemisphere) become almost westerly as we rise in the atmosphere. For a reason we shall speak of later, all winds become, on the average, more strongly westerly as we continue to rise, so that at a height of 7 miles the zonal winds are westerly almost everywhere. Somewhat above this level at about latitude 30° (N or S) we encounter the strongest average winds in the lower atmosphere. The maximum *average* wind there is about 100 miles per hour. These two strong wind belts are called *jet-streams*. At higher levels (in what is called the *stratosphere*) the winds decrease before beginning to increase again.

We can understand much about what happens in the lower atmosphere (called the *troposphere*) without knowing much about what happens above it, so we shall postpone a discussion of stratospheric currents.

It is instructive to see how associated features of the general circulation, pressure and temperature, fit into the pattern we have described. We know that the Earth is an oblate spheroid because the centrifugal force associated with its spinning motion acts most powerfully at the equator, tending to force it away from the axis of rotation. Now a westerly wind is air rotating more rapidly than the Earth and the *extra* centrifugal force would push it towards the equator were there not an equal and opposite force acting to keep it in position at its original latitude. This additional force is supplied by a difference in the pressure of the air, the pressure being greater in the equatorward direction. Similarly, an easterly wind can persist only if pressure increases towards the poles. Our description of the zonal winds is therefore *consistent* with the observation that there exist two belts of high pressure, at latitudes 30°N and 30°S respectively. We have *not*, of course, explained *why* the pressure belts and zonal winds exist. Near each of the poles the pressure rises again, implying the existence of generally easterly winds at about latitude 70° (N or S). Rather careful averaging is needed to verify, from the wind data, that these rather feeble *polar easterlies* actually exist. A wind, *calculated* from the distribution of pressure, is called a *geostrophic* wind. It is a fairly good approximation to the true wind only if the wind is a large-scale average and it is not changing too rapidly. There are rather subtle reasons, which it would take too long to discuss, why the formula used is somewhat inaccurate (especially in low latitudes) when applied to *time-averaged* charts. We may apply similar ideas to winds which are not zonal. An immediate deduction from the geostrophic formula is that cyclonic winds blow round regions of low pressure and anticyclonic winds round regions of high pressure in *both* hemispheres. We may check this against the monsoon circulations we have described. It is worth remembering that cyclonically rotating air is spinning in the same direction as, and therefore faster than, the Earth, whereas anticyclonic rotation is in the opposite direction and is therefore slower than the Earth. The rotation of the Earth we are referring to is its *vertical component*, that is the rate at which the ground beneath us is *spinning* about the *local* vertical. Except at the poles this is *less* than the rate of spinning of the Earth as a whole and depends on latitude. It is zero at the equator: there the ground is turning about a *horizontal* axis.

Temperature and Other Elements

The temperature pattern, like the pressure pattern, is closely related to the wind pattern. In discussing the most obvious general characteristic, the decrease of temperature from the equator to the poles, we start with the advantage that we can account for it quite simply. The poles are colder because sunshine comes in at a lower angle and is therefore, for unit area, less intense.* The pressure decreases more rapidly with height when the air is cold than when it is warm (Chapter 7). Considering the effects of temperature alone (i.e. assuming uniform pressure at the ground) the pressure at a given height (say 7 miles) will be greater above the equator than above the poles. This corresponds to a geostrophic westerly wind at 7 miles in both hemispheres. Such a wind change (due to horizontal variation in temperature) is called a *thermal wind*. The true wind is obtained by adding (algebraically in this case, more generally, for winds in any direction, vectorially) the winds near the ground, which in this case are comparatively small. Hence the winds consistent with the temperature pattern agree broadly with the observed winds. To the extent therefore that we have explained the *temperature* pattern we have therefore explained the zonal westerly winds aloft. We have tacitly assumed that the temperature difference persists as we go up and this is found to be true throughout the troposphere. The second generalization we can make about the temperature pattern is that, in the troposphere, temperature decreases with height. The division between troposphere and stratosphere is *defined* in terms of the way temperature varies with height: in the lower stratosphere it varies little with altitude. Consistent with the dividing point (called the *tropopause*) being lower in high latitudes we find the lower polar stratosphere (except in winter) to be a little *warmer* than the equatorial stratosphere. This agrees with the westerlies decreasing with height in the lower stratosphere.

As we should expect from the change with latitude of the annual variation in the length of the sunlit period, the annual variation of temperature is much larger in high latitudes than in low latitudes. A consequence is that the westerly winds aloft are much stronger in winter than in summer. We cannot however be satisfied with this as a complete explanation, because if we were concerned only with direct solar heating, then during, and especially towards the end of the polar night, the polar regions should become very much colder than they are observed to be. Their comparatively mild climates arise from warm winds bringing heat from lower latitudes. We are immediately confronted with an important characteristic of the general circulation. Narrowly interpreted as a

---

* When we try to calculate *how much* colder we find that this problem is just as complicated as, and closely related to, all the other problems we shall discuss.

system of long-term average currents it is an incomplete mechanism. For zonal winds cannot transfer heat between latitudes*, and this heat transfer is not only one of the most important things we want to calculate, but it affects, through the thermal wind relationship, the zonal winds themselves.

Leaving this problem on one side, let us glance at the nonzonal annual temperature change. This is much larger over land than over sea and we may relate it to the changes in monsoon winds. In *this* case high summer temperature is fairly distinctly related to low surface pressure and low winter temperature to high surface pressure. From the thermal wind relationship it may be seen that the monsoon flow patterns die out as we ascend and become quite different in the upper troposphere. This does not explain the *existence* of monsoon patterns nor has the relation found between surface pressure and temperature any *general* validity.

Finally let us examine the patterns of cloud, rainfall and evaporation. To a considerable extent these vary in the same way. We may note a marked correlation with the pressure at the ground (strictly, the pressure 'reduced' to mean sea-level), heavy rainfall in particular being associated usually with low pressure, and, therefore, cyclonic mean winds. Thus there is a belt of heavy rainfall near the equator, a comparatively dry region including many deserts in the sub-tropical high pressure belt near latitude 30°, and another rainy belt near and on the equatorial side of the low pressure belt near latitude 60°. Since cold air cannot take up so much water vapour as warm air the annual rainfall and the annual evaporation decrease *on the whole* with increasing latitude, but cloudiness is not affected in the same way.

The effect of geography is even more marked than in the case of temperature so that the above picture is very crude indeed. Nevertheless, though crude, it is of value, for it indicates a relation between rainfall and the more mechanical aspects of the general circulation we considered earlier. Further evidence is the North-South annual motion of the rain belts with the pressure and wind patterns (though to a slightly greater extent). The relationship is actually much closer than has so far appeared because cloud and rainfall are directly related to *vertical* motion of the air.

* The actual deviation of mean currents from latitude circles complicates but does not basically affect the conclusion.

Clouds, from which rainfall descends if they are sufficiently thick, are formed when the air expands and cools as a *consequence* of the vertical motion of the air. Unfortunately it is not possible to measure the upward drift over a large area because it is both irregular and very small—less than one hundredth, on the average, of the horizontal flow. It is possible to *calculate* it however, though calculations are not yet sufficiently detailed or accurate to enable us to present a complete picture. We can make these calculations from a knowledge of the horizontal wind alone, so that to this extent rainfall appears as a by-product of the general circulation. However, the production of cloud and rain entails a release of latent heat which alters the temperature of the air so that we cannot obtain an accurate idea of the mechanism of the general circulation, without including rainfall and evaporation as an integral part. Evaporation affects the mechanism mainly through the absorption of latent heat associated with it. In so far as it is dependent on wind and temperature, evaporation, in turn, depends on the general circulation.

THE OCEANS

We are concerned here only with those aspects of the motion and thermal effects of the oceans which are intimately connected with the atmosphere. Waves are raised by the wind, but we shall not discuss them as they are dealt with elsewhere (Chapter 5). The tides are not appreciably connected with weather but there are large-scale currents and drifts which we must consider in some detail.

Not only are they caused by wind, cooling by the air or evaporation into the air, but they react back on the atmosphere by moving large quantities of heat, which ultimately enter the air at a place determined partly by the strength of the ocean currents. These currents constitute the general circulation of the oceans.

Though the details are different, the circulations of the oceans and atmosphere are processes of the *same kind* and much of what we have said about the atmosphere applies equally well to the oceans. In particular, the relationship between ocean currents and pressure and temperature at different depths in the sea is exactly similar to the corresponding relationships (geostrophic wind and thermal wind) in the atmosphere. The only difference is that density of sea water depends not only on temperature but also on the quantity of salts dissolved in it—that is on its *salinity*. Hence the thermal wind corresponds to the *thermohaline* ocean current, the decrease of current with depth associated with horizontal variation of density. It may also be noted that the long-term average currents in the oceans are no more a satisfactorily complete description of long-term behaviour than are the average winds in the atmosphere. Heat, salt and other things are transported *across* the mean currents by eddies which smooth out in the long-period mean, just as heat, water vapour, etc., are transported by large atmospheric eddies (weather systems) across the climatic-average winds. We can in fact assume ocean current behaviour to be *similar* to that of air currents unless there are definite reasons why behaviour should be different.

The most important factors, which cause the ocean circulation to be different from that of the atmosphere are as follows:

(i)   Neglecting the very small heat supply from radio-activity in the Earth, the oceans are heated, by sunshine and by exchange of heat with the atmosphere (evaporation, 'convection'—to be explained later) at the *top*. The atmosphere, as we shall see, is heated mainly at the *bottom*.

(ii) Friction, associated with the setting up of surface gravity waves on the sea, acts as a *brake* on the atmospheric circulation. It is the primary *driving force* of ocean currents.

(iii) The oceans are bounded, right up to the top, by continents. Mountain ranges are more limited and extend only part of the way up in the atmosphere.

(iv) There is no significant analogue of cloud formation and consequent release of latent heat inside the oceans. In fact, all the processes which affect the density of sea water (including rainfall, run-off and the melting of ice which dilute the salt-content and evaporation and freezing which concentrate it) occur at the top.

Other factors, such as the much greater density and heat capacity of water as compared with air, and its much smaller motion and compressibility are merely quantitative. It is curious and significant that the relative magnitudes of many quantities (such as horizontal and vertical variations of density), which are determined by mutual adjustment as the mechanism operates, attain values

K

such that corresponding processes in the ocean and in the atmosphere are often of equal importance.

Let us now look at the observations, concentrating our attention on the broad features. Most obvious are the surface currents which consist mainly of *gyrals*, the water circulating anti-cyclonically about centres situated in the sub-tropical atmospheric high-pressure belts. (Fig. 1). Typical is the North Atlantic gyral consisting of the North Atlantic drift, towards the East, most

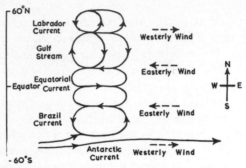

FIG. 1.   Surface gyrals in Atlantic and Antarctic current in relation to wind stress.

clearly indicated near latitude 40°N on the western side, and a general drift towards the West below latitude 30°N. The circulation is completed by a very narrow and strong current towards the North, called the Gulf Stream, just off the American coast (at the edge of the continental shelf) and a general slow drift towards the South in other longitudes. There are similar circulations in other oceans, that in the North Pacific being particularly strong. They are evidently caused by the 'twist' of the wind stress, which acts towards the East poleward of the sub-tropical (Azores) anticyclone and towards the West in the trade wind belt. A calculation shows that currents should be produced in roughly the regions where they are observed and it also accounts for the strong concentration on the West side of the oceans (east coast of continents). Poleward of the latitude of strongest westerly winds (about 50°N) there are, in the northern hemisphere, cyclonic gyrals. That in the North Atlantic includes the Greenland currents and the Labrador current. The trade wind stress piles up water on east continental coasts. This yields not only the 'head' of water which drives the Gulf Stream and similar currents but it also forces

water back towards the East near the equator (the equatorial
currents) where the trade wind stress is weakest. The southern
hemisphere is peculiar in that in a range of latitudes, between the
tip of South America and the tip of Graham Land (Antarctica),
there is no land against which the westerly wind stress can pile
up water. No gyral is set up, the wind stress accelerating the water
until an equal and opposite stress is set up, due to the motion of
water over the bottom of the ocean. This Antarctic current flows,
roughly along lines of latitude right round the Antarctic continent,
though at a considerable distance from it. All the currents we
have described decrease as we go down. In *most* places the motion
of water near the bottom of the ocean is probably very
sluggish.

Less well known, and less well understood, is a different kind of
drift called the 'vertical circulation' which is most marked in the
Atlantic Ocean. Although the most evident motions are the gyrals,
there is superposed on these in the Atlantic a general drift near the
top, from South to North and a compensating drift at greater
depths from North to South (Fig. 2). The circulation is completed
by water sinking in the northern part of the North Atlantic
(somewhere near Iceland), and rising in the Antarctic, somewhere
near the Antarctic current. Because the drift is very slow*, compared with other motions it has not been measured directly.
Sections in vertical planes along parallels of latitude (the planes in
which the water particles move) indicate quite clearly, however,
the existence of this circulation. At lower depths temperature and
salinity act as 'markers' indicating the origin of the water mass and
there is a well marked bulge of *comparatively* warm saline water at
great depths—greater than a mile—pointing towards the South.
At the surface there is displacement of the region of maximum
salinity, caused by evaporation in the sub-tropics, towards the
North. A circulation of this type, corresponding to rotation about
an E-W axis, is called *meridional*.

There exist meridional circulations in the atmosphere, the most
marked being the Hadley *cells* in which air rises near the equator
and comes down on either side near latitudes 30°N or S (Fig. 3).
Near the ground there is a general drift towards the equator consistent with the very marked equatorward component of the trade

* A water particle would probably take hundreds of years to complete the cir-
cuit.

winds. Between 30° and 60° latitude in either hemisphere there are
other meridional atmospheric circulations, sometimes called the
Ferrel cells, which are reversed in direction as compared with the
Hadley cell of the same hemisphere.

We may note two ways in which the oceanic meridional circulation differs from the atmospheric ones. Firstly, the atmospheric
circulations are nearly symmetrical about the equator, whereas
the Atlantic circulation is not—perhaps connected with the fact

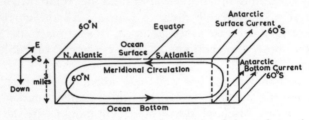

FIG. 2.   Meridional circulation in Atlantic ocean in relation to Antarctic current.
The figure is not to scale and Earth's curvature is neglected.

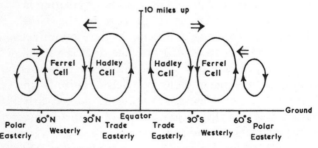

FIG. 3.   Meridional circulations in the troposphere. Broad arrows indicate eddy
transport of angular momentum. Surface zonal winds indicated below figure.

that the Antarctic current has no analogue in the northern hemisphere. Secondly, the atmospheric drifts cannot be geostrophic
since there are no boundaries against which a pressure difference
could be built up. The Atlantic circulation (north of the tip of
South America) *could* be geostrophic, so that the thermo-haline
current, yielding the *difference* between the upper northward
current and the lower southward current, may be used, together
with the fact that the *total* northward flow is small (and can be
estimated), to estimate the strength of the circulation. The results
are not very reliable because of complications near coast lines

but they are in general agreement with estimates obtained by other means. The interesting conclusion emerges that the meridional oceanic circulation may, because the large temperature contrast between top and bottom compensates for the smallness of the current, transfer as much heat to the northern end of the Atlantic as does the Gulf Stream.

To some extent the distribution of temperature and salinity in the oceans is implicit in our description of the currents. Surface temperature decreases from the equator towards the poles for the same reason as it does in the atmosphere. Since sea and air are in contact their surface temperatures cannot remain very different for long. Surface salinity is greatest in the dry belts of the atmosphere, where evaporation minus rainfall is a maximum, and least in the wet regions. At great depths the oceans are everywhere very cold being indeed only slightly above freezing point. Although a decrease in temperature is in many regions partly compensated by a decrease in salinity we find everywhere the heaviest water at the bottom.

Variations due to all causes are largest near the top; at great depths the oceans are more nearly uniform. Surface actions, (solar heating, evaporation, wind stress) affect *directly* only a comparatively thin top layer. Elsewhere the distribution of temperature, salinity etc., is determined in a process of mutual adjustment in which water movements are involved. Some of these movements are the direct consequence of surface actions. For example, as equilibrium is approached, a surface stress sets up circulations in the water beneath which are in planes *at right angles* to the stress. The effect of the stress is thereby communicated to great depths, setting up currents there *in the direction of* the stress.

The mechanism can be understood by considering the particular case when the circulations are meridional. For motions of *this* kind there is a theorem which tells us that the angular momentum (mass times velocity of rotation about the Earth's axis times distance from the axis) does not change with time. Now when a particle moves North or South its distance from the Earth's axis changes. If it moves to a lower latitude the final result is that its velocity *relative to the Earth* must decrease if we regard motion towards the East as positive. Hence with a stress towards the East (due to a westerly wind) we can have a steady state if the increase in speed due to the stress is just balanced by the decrease due to equatorward motion. Now in the lower portion of the meridional circulation the water is moving poleward, and this necessitates an increase in the current towards the East, i.e. the effect is as if the stress acted at this lower level. Admittedly this merely shows how the effect of a surface stress *could* be transmitted to great depths. A detailed calculation shows that such a circulation *must* be set up. It also shows that a similar effect is obtained whatever the direction of the stress. An immediate consequence is that the anticyclonic stress which produces for example the Gulf Stream gyral, sets up circulations in which warm saline surface water is *forced* down thousands of feet in the middle of the gyral. The exact shape of the circulation and the currents set up at great depths is determined by the fact that at each stage the thermo-haline current relationship must be satisfied. Warm saline water at great depths in the region mentioned is in fact observed. It could not have got there by any other process than the one we have described.

The forcing down of light surface water as a result of the wind stress increases the potential energy of the oceans, i.e. it generates energy of position which could be transformed into energy of motion (currents) by a suitable displacement of the particles. Actually this transformation takes place automatically. By trial and error, as it were, the ocean finds motions which enable eddy-currents to grow at the expense of the potential energy. Once started, no matter how small they may be initially, the eddies continue to grow until they attain a definite maximum size. Another way of describing the state of affairs is to say that the initial state is *unstable*. The condition for this kind of instability in a rotating fluid is that there should exist a *horizontal* variation of density and the associated thermo-haline current or thermal wind. A fluid in this state is called *baroclinic*. Now the atmosphere is, as we have seen, made baroclinic *directly* as the result of unequal solar heating at different latitudes. Hence the same kind of eddy ought to exist in the atmosphere. It does: the eddies are in fact the weather systems we have referred to before. We shall have more to say about the atmospheric eddies later. A general property of these eddies which can be proved theoretically is that they transport heat (or whatever else is the factor causing low density such as *defect* of salinity) horizontally towards the high density region and upwards against gravity. The result therefore of oceanic eddies developing on the sides of the masses of light water forced down by the wind stress is that, in the steady state, the base of the light water is 'eaten away' as fast as it is forced down.

While we are on the subject of oceanic circulations we may, in the light of what has been said, recall the meridional circulation in the Atlantic. It is clear that the westerly wind stress in the Southern hemisphere due to the Roaring Forties and Fifties must set up a meridional circulation reaching right down to the bottom where the increase in bottom velocity due to poleward motion is cancelled by friction on the ocean floor.* Now at the equatorward edge of the Antarctic current the meridional flow is towards the North at the top and towards the South at the bottom, i.e. in the same direction as the Atlantic meridional circulation. Instead of descending at the edge of the Antarctic current, it appears that the water moves right across the equator to high northern latitudes before sinking. It is possible that the water chooses this path because it is the one of least resistance. Surface water forced down near latitude 40°S would tend to spring back because it is lighter than the water below. On the other hand near Iceland the water is nearly uniform right to the bottom and the water can sink without resistance. The question remains: "Why is the circulation concentrated in the Atlantic and not observed (with certainty) in other oceans?" It is conceivable that the answer has something to do with the Atlantic being situated immediately to the lee of the constriction of the Antarctic current between South America and Antarctica. Some distance downstream from the constriction there is a submarine ridge, of which the South Sandwich islands are peaks, extending right across the Antarctic current. The bottom stresses in this region, and consequently the meridional circulation, must be much greater than average. The whole problem needs further investigation.

The factors we have considered in this brief study of the ocean currents are purely mechanical. From this point of view special substances dissolved in the sea such as phosphates and oxygen, though they are essentials of life, are of direct interest only to the extent that they affect density, or as 'markers' for following water masses. Nevertheless a precise understanding of the mechanical

---

* This 'friction' is not of the ordinary type. Water flowing over submarine hills and mountains sets up internal waves which carry away energy and very effectively brake the main current.

factors would enable us to predict the concentration of all factors affecting suitability of the sea to particular forms of life—a matter which may be of some interest to fishermen.

HEATING

Let us now return to the problems of the atmospheric circulation. The general nature of the mechanism is clear. Unequal heating makes the air baroclinic and therefore unstable. The large eddies, which develop as a result, transport heat upwards and in the direction towards the poles. The heat carried by the eddies reduces the temperature in low latitudes somewhat below that which would be observed if only direct solar heating were involved and increases the temperature in polar regions. This eddy-transport of heat explains the fact that polar temperatures do not fall very low indeed during the polar night. To understand the process more accurately we must study the solar heating process in more detail. Part of the heat from the Sun is reflected back from the tops of clouds and never reaches the Earth. A small part of what remains is absorbed by the air but most of it reaches the surface. Some of this is reflected back (especially in high latitudes from snow or sea) into space. The remainder is absorbed in the top layers of ground or ocean. Thus most of the heat which comes into the atmosphere does so through the land or sea surface.

It is not however enough to consider only the incident heat. This by itself would cause a steady rise in temperature of the Earth as a whole and we know that the surface temperature of the Earth has not changed very greatly over many hundreds of millions of years. Hence on an average the Earth must lose heat at almost exactly the same rate as it gains heat. It does so in the same way as the Sun does, by radiation, the only difference being that Earth-radiation is long-wave (infra-red) and therefore invisible. Because the atmosphere is partly opaque to long-wave radiation (primarily because it contains water vapour) the effective cooling surface, that is the surface from which radiation can escape into space without being re-absorbed, is not on the ground but some distance up in the air, at an average height of about 4 miles. The exact position of the cooling surface is the level above which the total opacity of the air has a definite value, and this is closely related to the temperature at the cooling level itself, because the amount of water vapour the air can contain depends only on its temperature.

It follows that the cooling level is rather higher in low latitudes and also, since heat radiated by a given substance depends on temperature alone, that the outgoing Earth-radiation varies much less with latitude than does the incoming solar radiation. Hence although the *total* incoming and outgoing radiations balance they do not do so at every latitude: in low latitudes there is a net gain, in high latitudes a net loss, the change-over occuring at about 35° latitude (N or S). There must be a long term balance everywhere, so that the excess heat in low latitudes must in some way find its way to high latitudes.

The only mechanism which can carry the heat fast enough is transport by a moving fluid. In fact the larger part of the heat is carried in large atmospheric eddies—the weather systems (Fig. 4).

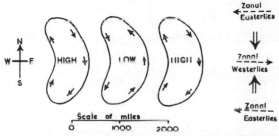

FIG. 4.   Flow pattern in train of weather-system eddies (schematic). Full lines denote isobars (or stream lines). Small arrows denote winds. Actual eddies are more complicated and variable, both in space and time. The pattern drifts, irregularly, towards the East. Broad arrows indicate transport of angular momentum due to flow pattern.

The eddies operate a shuttle-service, the air in one part of the eddy being warmed, moving to high latitudes and there radiating away some of its heat. The other part brings back cold air to be warmed in its turn. The inequality in the heat-balance at different latitudes is all the time tending to increase the temperature contrast, the eddy transport to smooth it out. Neither process is quite steady: the heat balance, for example, depends on cloud amount which depends on eddy activity, which depends on temperature contrast, which depends on heat balance at an earlier time, and so on. Hence there exists a fluctuating balance between these two processes. Any semi-permanent change in the equilibrium between them corresponds to a change in world climate.

The smaller part of the heat transport is by ocean currents. Since these are driven primarily by wind-stress, which depends on the atmospheric circulation, we must expect these also to fluctuate. Ocean currents have much more inertia both mechanical and thermal—the density and heat capacity of the oceans is much greater than that of the atmosphere. There is therefore a greater preponderence of slow variations in the sea than in the air. Hence the effect of ocean currents on changes of climate is probably much greater than their effect on short-period changes.

Let us consider now the dependence of heat-balance on height above the ground. We have seen that the radiative cooling occurs *effectively* at about the middle of the troposphere. In fact, due to the complexity of the long-wave radiation spectrum of water-vapour, this cooling is spread over the whole of the troposphere. Even after allowing for the heating due to direct absorption of solar radiation, there is net cooling of the whole of the troposphere at an average rate of about 2°F per day. Most of the solar heat is, as we have seen, absorbed in the top layers of sea and land. For long-term balance this heat must find its way into the upper air, some of it as far as the tropopause. Once again eddy-transport is the only mechanism fast enough. Some of the heat is taken up by large eddies of the weather system type but these can take heat up only if they take it also a much greater distance sideways (polewards).

To distribute the heat correctly the assistance of smaller eddies of a rather different type is needed. Near the ground suitable eddies are produced by the flow of air over rough ground or over ocean waves. Elsewhere, or alternatively, heat is taken up by eddies—up to ten miles across— of *convection*. Convective eddies are like weather systems in that they arise from density differences, this time in the vertical. Convection occurs in a nearly incompressible fluid like sea water when, due to cooling or evaporation, the upper part becomes denser than the lower part. The fluid is then unstable (top-heavy), and eddies of convection grow automatically because the fluid is never *exactly* balanced. In air there is a complication due to its compressibility. It is the distribution of *potential* density that matters i.e., we must compare air only when compressed at the same pressure. If *potential* density increases with height* which is the case if temperature falls with height at more than a certain rate (called the adiabatic lapse-rate) the air is unstable and convection develops. As in the case of weather systems, heat is transported by growing eddies towards the region

* The *actual* density always decreases with height.

of greater potential density, that is, upwards. If now the upper troposphere cools until there is a slight increase of potential density upwards throughout the troposphere a state of balance can be set up between eddy transport and radiative heating and cooling. Actually we observe *on the average* a decrease in potential density upwards. The weather system eddies can grow in these conditions, when convective eddies cannot, and they are continually taking heat up to reduce the effectiveness of radiative cooling. Nevertheless, conditions are not uniform so that in the equatorward-moving parts of weather-system eddies, where the air aloft is cold but the air below is heated by contact with the ground, they are usually convectively unstable. Convection through deep layers produces a characteristic type of weather (cumulus clouds, local showers or thunderstorms, with clear bright intervals).

Convection can and does occur in the oceans, for the reasons we have mentioned, at certain places and times.* In the top layers it is particularly important in late autumn and winter when the air is usually colder than the sea and cools the surface. This convection extracts heat from considerable depths so that the sea surface temperature is only slightly reduced. It is because eddy motions in the sea spread heating and cooling over great masses of water that the annual variation of surface temperature over the sea is much less than over land. The temperature of the air in contact with it is also stabilized so that annual temperature variation near coasts, especially those with prevailing onshore winds, is less than in the middle of continents.

We have noticed some similarities in mode of origin and in behaviour between convective eddies and weather-systems. We may in fact regard the weather-system eddies as convective-type eddies greatly modified by the rotation of the Earth. Convective eddies feed on energy of position which is reduced when (potentially) heavy fluid moves down in the growing eddy and light fluid moves up to take its place. Weather-system eddies do the same but the exchange takes place along *sloping* surfaces. The most effective exchange direction is at an angle to the horizontal of just one half

* Not all the movements in the seas are wind-driven or of eddy type. Increase of density at the top can sometimes result in more or less steady currents. The flow through the Straits of Gibraltar, light water in at the top, heavy saline water of smaller amount out at the bottom, is due simply to evaporation exceeding rainfall and run-off from rivers in the Mediterranean. Drifts due to similar causes also exist in the oceans.

that of the surfaces of constant (potential) density existing prior to eddy development. In the atmosphere and oceans the slopes involved are very small, corresponding to displacements of one unit or less in the vertical for one hundred units horizontally. The slope is usually upward in the poleward direction. Eddies of this kind can and do grow even when, as is normally the case, potential density decreases upwards, because this is consistent with an upward *increase* along the gently sloping exchange-surface. The mechanism by which eddy-patterns sort themselves out is of some interest. It is rather like natural selection in the theory of evolution. Patterns corresponding to most efficient transformation

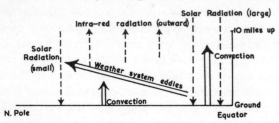

FIG. 5.   Transfer of heat by radiation and eddy-transport in northern hemisphere. Eddy-transport by convection and weather systems shown by broad arrows. Solar and terrestrial radiation shown by dashed lines with arrow. Meridional circulations (especially Hadley cells) also transfer some heat.

of energy of position into energy of motion grow fastest and biggest and these dominant eddies are the ones we observe. The transfer of heat is the same for the two classes of eddy, i.e. in the exchange-direction towards the (potentially) cold fluid. This heat transfer is in fact only another way of describing the reduction in energy of position. The eddies can grow only *because* they transfer heat. Another way of looking at the process is to regard it as an irregularly functioning and inefficient natural *engine*. For the weather-system eddies the warm 'source' of heat is at low levels in low latitudes, the cold 'sink' at high levels in high latitudes. The 'sources' and 'sinks' are not *given* however—it is a case of *solvitur ambulando*.

Besides their primary property of transporting heat the weather-system eddies have a secondary (in a sense accidental) property of transporting angular momentum. The cause of this is rather subtle, though the fact is evident enough from the meteorologists' charts. In some latitudes southerly components of wind are more often associated with westerly components than they are with easterly components: there is a distinct preference for either south-westerly or north-easterly winds as compared with other directions. This means that air with more than average angular momentum is moving North, air with less than average angular momentum is moving South. The effect is that angular momentum is transported towards the North. To the North the zonal winds are accelerated, to the South they are retarded. In other latitudes, where the preference is for south-easterly or north-westerly winds, there is transfer of angular momentum towards the South. Now we *observe* that the weather-system eddies are not symmetrical about North-South lines. The flow patterns are swept back at the edges towards the West so that the high and low pressure areas look somewhat like fat boomerangs. Application of the geostrophic wind formula then shows that these eddies must be transporting angular momentum from the edges towards the middle i.e. towards the latitude at which eddies are most intense. Since eddies develop most easily in middle latitudes this means that the zonal winds are accelerated there. The acceleration continues until the surface winds become westerly and of sufficient strength for frictional forces to balance the acceleration. At the same time easterly winds are generated at both edges—the trade winds and the polar easterlies. A rather complicated theoretical analysis shows that large eddies *ought* to behave in this manner.

The transport of angular momentum by the weather-system eddies is concentrated where the winds are strongest, near the top of the troposphere. Now when we were discussing the Antarctic circumpolar current in the oceans we discovered what must happen when a zonal stress is applied at a level where it cannot be destroyed by friction. A meridional circulation is set up which effectively transfers the action of the stress to the bottom layer. Now transport of angular momentum *from the sides* at the top of the troposphere has exactly the same effect as a zonal stress acting at the same level. Consequently meridional circulations are set up in the troposphere. Below the region where the angular momentum at the top is being increased we have the Ferrel cell. Below the region in low latitude where it is being decreased we have the Hadley cell. Because the effective stresses are opposite the meridional circulations are in opposite senses. There should also be a very feeble meridional circulation near the poles in the same sense as the Hadley cell of the same hemisphere. There are some indications that the convective eddies also transport angular momentum, though they can do so effectively only in the vertical because of their small *horizontal* size compared with weather systems. They probably transport angular momentum downwards. Because convection is more intense in low latitudes the effect should be most noticeable there. If this is so, then for equilibrium the Hadley cell must rotate faster, the Ferrel cell a little slower.

Though not much energy is expended in generating the surface zonal currents they are of vital importance in climatology. As the air is forced to flow over large mountain ranges and plateaux, over surfaces of different roughness, over surfaces heated at different rates, it sets up flow-patterns on a scale slightly larger than that of the travelling weather-system eddies. These are nearly stationary for long periods.* They govern the place of development and movement of the weather-system eddies, thereby affecting the average weather. The difference in weather between one year and another is associated with differences in large-scale flow pattern. Nevertheless there are some regularities in these flow-patterns which show up in the long period averages. Particularly striking are the upper-troposphere flow-patterns over North America and eastern Asia: they are attributable mainly to the effects of large elevated regions. It is easy to 'explain' the monsoon patterns in a very general way. For example heating in summer is most effective over land in low latitudes. If we apply the thermal wind relation and also use the fact that the amount of air sucked in at the bottom as the heated air rises is roughly equal to that forced out at the top, we obtain something like the observed solution—a depression at the ground and an anticyclone at some higher level. But to obtain the true flow pattern and also to understand why the monsoon is different in different years (the practially important problem) we need to ask what keeps the flow pattern nearly stationary and enables it to fit in with patterns due to other causes.

THE STRATOSPHERE

We must deal very briefly with conditions in the stratosphere. This does not matter too much because as far up as the base of the ionosphere the *principles* involved are exactly the same. Some new

* The setting-up of these patterns constitutes part of the friction which brakes the zonal winds. (Compare the remarks on bottom-friction below the Antarctic current.)

features appear, however. Of considerable interest is the presence
of ozone (especially at a height of 20-25 miles) in small but very
important quantities. (cf. Chapter 7). The amount above a given
place varies from day to day, the variation being closely related to
the tropospheric weather systems. The upward extension of large
weather-system eddies into the stratosphere, predicted on theoretical grounds, accounts broadly for these changes, though more
detailed calculations are desirable. The most striking feature is,
however, the distribution with latitude. Although more ozone is
formed in low latitudes, because sunshine is more intense, the
greatest concentration is in high latitudes. This effect could not be
produced simply by 'mixing'. Nor is ozone the only 'marker'
substance affected in this way. The 'rain' of very small radioactive
dust particles, originally thrown up into the stratosphere by
hydrogen bomb explosions in rather low latitudes, is concentrated
apparently in rather high latitudes. Resisting the temptation to
regard this simply as divine retribution we may be inclined to
suspect that this and the ozone distribution result from a peculiar
feature of the general circulation in the stratosphere. As in earlier
attempts to explain the trade winds, meridional circulations have
been invoked, but, warned by our experience with the zonal wind
problem, we may be chary of accepting this as the whole story—
or even the main part of the story. It is possible that the true explanation is quite complicated, involving, perhaps, not only eddy-
transport of angular momentum with associated meridional circulations but also yet another accidental eddy transport phenomenon
associated with the increase in relative concentration with height of
both ozone and radioactive dust. The subtleties of eddy-transport
phenomena are not yet fully understood.

If, from this incomplete survey, the reader has gained the impression that general circulation problems are complicated, this is
as it should be. The point is that mere complication does not prevent their being solved. Much of the complication shows itself
when we attempt to give precise answers instead of vague ones.
Precision is important, not only because for practical reasons we
need numerical answers, but because it is the surest way of distinguishing the true from the seemingly plausible. To answer
problems in any branch of geophysics we need vast quantities of
observations but we also need precise, consistent, mathematical
theory to make proper use of them.

CHAPTER TEN

Ice Ages

E. J. ÖPIK

THE FACTUAL data upon which our knowledge of the ice ages is based belong chiefly to the realm of geology; important supplementary material is provided by geographical exploration. However, as regards interpretation, the problem is found to be on the crossroads of many sciences. The multifarious nature of the study of the ice ages also forcibly invades the observational side, simply because the data are often so incomplete that their factual meaning remains obscure without the illuminating help of a working hypothesis.

As a consequence of the interlocking of theory and observation, it is often difficult to disentangle fact from fancy. An example is offered by the *astronomical* chronology of the ice ages, based on calculated variations in the eccentricity and obliquity of the Earth's orbit, which in their turn influence the amount of solar heat received in different latitudes and seasons and thus cause fluctuations of climate. Although the calculations of the orbital elements are quite reliable, their climatic consequences have been unduly exaggerated. The chronology, derived from the coincidence of the computed highs and lows of solar heat with the retreats and advances of glaciation, must be stamped as illusory; there is no cause-and-effect relationship between the two sets of phenomena.

This does not mean that the astronomical chronology has been devised in vain. Although incorrect, it helped in systematizing the observational data and in giving direction and purpose to research; its unifying role could be compared to a banner in battle or a dogma of faith, a symbol of no material value, yet of considerable influence on material events.

It would take several pages to list all the theories of the ice ages. However, many of them are without sufficient foundation and need not be considered. Only a few remain which do not contra-

dict physical laws or observational facts. It stands without doubt
that the climatic fluctuations, including the ice ages, are primarily
caused by the variation of solar radiation. The variation may be
only apparent and due to changes in the reflecting power of the
Earth arising from cloudiness or volcanic dust; or more probably,
it may be due to a true variation in solar heat output.

THE CLIMATES OF THE PAST

Palaeoclimatology, or the science of past climates, makes use of
various geological criteria. The most important indicators are the
fossil remains, or prints in sediments, of living organisms, animals
and plants. The requirements of ancient organisms as to temperature and moisture can be inferred from a comparison with similar
living organisms, which enables us to reconstruct the climatic
environment; plants and cold-blooded animals are more at the
mercy of the weather and are better indicators of climate than
warm-blooded animals who can adapt themselves to a wider
range of temperature. This method works best for recent epochs,
the organisms of which were more similar to those of the present.
The farther we go into the past, the less familiar are the plants and
animals, and the greater the uncertainty in the climatic deductions.
Nevertheless, the mere presence of vegetation would indicate the
absence of glaciation; a deciduous forest would require a moderate
climate with sufficient moisture; reptiles would be a sign of summer warmth and their abundance would suggest mild winters.

Criteria next in importance are furnished by inorganic sediments indicative of the type of erosion—whether by wind, water,
or ice. Especially important are the traces left by glaciation and the
melting of glaciers: *moraines*, consisting of boulder clays; or their
fossilized equivalents, the *tillites*; scratches on bedrock, produced
by ice-driven rock fragments and indicating the direction of the
ice flow.

These criteria describe the *local* climate at the time of deposition
of the fossils or sediments.

Great differences as compared with the present climate in the
same locality have come to light. Over vast periods of geologic
time tropical or subtropical vegetation covered the present temperate zones of Europe and North America, with animals corresponding to the concept of a warm climate; Greenland and the
Antarctic, without any trace of ice, were warmer than Europe is

L

now; coral reefs, at present confined to tropical seas, abounded in the waters that temporarily covered parts of northern Europe and North America, and at the more remote epochs of the Palaeozoic era (250 to 500 million years ago), reached into Greenland and Spitzbergen. On the other hand, for certain short periods, the warm climate was interrupted by glaciation, ice sheets similar to those now covering Greenland and the Antarctic invading the former seats of luxurious life.

The interpretation of these changes was for long bedevilled by the possibilities of polar wandering and continental drift. If the poles were not fixed with respect to the Earth's crust, or if the continents were a kind of floating islands in the pitch-like viscous ocean of the underlying magma, apt to change their position with respect to each other and the axis of rotation, great variations in the climate of a given locality could be brought about by changes in the geographical latitude. Alfred Wegener and his followers actually tried to explain in such a purely mechanical manner all palaeoclimatic changes; the succession of warm and cold periods was ascribed to the transplantation of the same locality from the tropics to beyond the arctic circle, and back again. Among other things, Wegener believed that Greenland was at present travelling westwards at a speed of some 60 feet a year; this, as well as other exaggerated surmises of the theory of continental drift, have been refuted by direct astronomical observations, and by accumulated geological evidence.

It has now been proved that during the past 100 million years, the relative positions of the poles and the continents were essentially the same as at present. To be sure, some low-lying continental plains were temporarily submerged, yielding marine fossils in places where there is now dry land; but the geographical latitude of a locality was practically constant. The changes in climate were in the same direction all over the Earth's surface. During the warm period even the poles were free from ice and enjoyed a moderate climate. The subsequent Quaternary glacial epoch* which started

* Ordinarily the expression *ice age* applies to an individual advance of glaciation, whence for the entire Quaternary period of repeated glaciations the plural, or the term *ice ages*, is used. With the discovery of ancient pre-Quaternary glaciations (such as the Carbo-Permian), this term has become somewhat ambiguous. We propose here to use for the whole complex of repeated glaciations, like those of the Quaternary, the phrase *glacial epoch* (*alias major ice age*), as distinct from single advances or *glaciations*.

300,000 to 1,000,000 years ago, was accompanied by a cooling of the entire surface simultaneously in both hemispheres; the incessant major and minor fluctuations, reflected by the advance and retreat of glaciation, were parallel in North America and Europe.

All this indicates that the cause of the climatic changes during the past 100 million years was of a general, probably extraterrestrial nature.

More difficult is the interpretation of climatic changes for the earlier geologic epochs. The approximate permanence of the poles and continents since the Cambrian period 500 million years ago, appears to be a plausible working hypothesis; although the Carbo-Permian glacial epoch in the subtropical continents of the southern hemisphere (230 million years ago) seems to require some displacement in the continents and the poles, the abandonment of the hypothesis of permanence in this case would create more formidable difficulties for the interpretation of the earlier glacial epochs.

However, the uncertainty that arises in the perspective of time is unable to obliterate the traces of the major global fluctuations of climate. From the history of the last 100 million years it is known that during the warm period, ice sheets were completely absent, even from the poles; the ice caps developed only when the global climate had deteriorated considerably. This can be assumed to hold also for the less clearly understood earlier epochs; whenever continental ice sheets were recorded, a world-wide cold glacial epoch seems to be indicated; and when ice sheets were absent, a warm climate all over the surface must have prevailed. The similarity of the deposits in ancient glacial epochs with those of the Quaternary, and the typical fluctuations revealed by the repeated large-scale advance and retreat of the glaciation, apparently common to all these epochs, strengthen the view that the recent glacial epoch and those of old were caused by the same cosmic factor. The qualitative similarity of palaeoclimatic records for the recent and ancient warm epochs in various parts of the Earth would in its turn point to the approximate constancy of the cosmic influences, chiefly solar radiation, during these epochs.

The glacial epochs were of very short duration as compared with the warm periods; they occupied not more than 10 per cent of the total time, and probably much less than this. They were repeated at seemingly equal intervals of about 250 million years. Except for weak 'mountain glaciation', no clear connection with periods of mountain building (orogenesis) is apparent. The mighty Caledonian orogenesis, 340 million years ago, was clear of extended glaciation; the apparent coincidences of the Variscian (240 million year ago) and Alpine (beginning 50 million years ago) orogenes with the Carbo-Permian and Quaternary glacial epochs is hardly relevant: active mountain building preceded the ice ages in both cases by tens of millions of years. Thus, although mountain building has sometimes been suggested as the cause of the ice ages, this idea cannot be accepted. In any case, the repeated ice ages during one major period of glaciation cannot be explained by mountain building or by other changes in the geographical relief: the latter could not have changed so quickly (within 100,000 years) and so regularly, nor have major changes of relief occurred during the Quaternary glacial epoch. At present, at the foot of the Himalaya, the highest mountain range in the world, at a temperature of 68°F (68 degrees Fahrenheit) there is no ice; its glaciers descend to a height of 10,000 feet and a temperature of 36°F; the temperature does not differ much from that for other glaciers.

Yet, during the Carbo-Permian glacial epoch, continental ice accumulated at the present foot of the Himalaya. The Himalaya itself was non-existent at that time, its future rocks either resting at the bottom of the Tethys sea, or waiting to be deposited there in the 200 million years to come. There was ice-covered land to the south—the present Indian subcontinent, which is believed to have been part of hypothetical Gondwana. The flow of ice was from south to north, and the ice reached to the sea shore. We have to conclude that the temperature there was at an arctic level. How this could happen in a region which at present is within the tropics, stretching between 17° and 24° northern latitude, is one of the greatest geological puzzles we are confronted with; especially because in the northern hemisphere only few, often doubtful traces of ice have been found, whereas vast ice sheets were stretching over subtropical regions of the southern continents Africa, Australia and South America.

In summing up, we may state that two types of global climate have occurred intermittently: a normal, warm climate, prevailing most of the time, with an average global temperature of about 72°F (58°F at present), and with a reduced difference between the climatic zones; and relatively short glacial epochs, with a cool climate, the global temperature fluctuating between 36°F for the greatest extent of glaciation and 62°F for the warmer periods of retreating ice, and with an accentuated difference between the climatic zones. The presence or absence of continental ice sheets, especially around the poles, is the crucial criterion for distinguishing between the two types of climate.

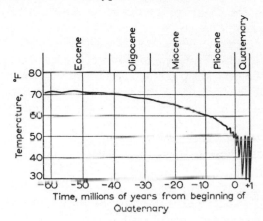

FIG. I.   Schematic variation of mean annual temperature since the beginning of the Tertiary, Middle Europe, according to P. Woldstedt. The time scale of the Quaternary is enlarged five times, as compared with the Tertiary.

Our present time falls within the Quaternary glacial epoch. Four major advances of glaciation have already taken place*, with the ice sheets reaching into moderate latitudes of Europe and North America. The last advance took place 10,700 years ago, after which the ice melted and retreated in a few thousand years. Between the glacial advances there were three prolonged *interglacials*, when the climate was sometimes even milder than at present, though never reaching the level of the preceding 100 million years. (Cf. Fig. 1.)

ICE SHEETS OF THE PRESENT

By being born in a glacial epoch, about 100 centuries after the last advance of its fourth glaciation, we enjoy the privilege of being able to study the ice sheets directly.

* The successive advances have been named Günz, Mindel, Riss and Würm, each after an Alpine valley where its moraines are to be found. (A different nomenclature is used in America—cf Fig. 4).

Perennial ice may occur in three principal forms: continental ice sheets; mountain glaciers; and surface ice on water.

Continental ice sheets are sustained by snow precipitation. Their expenditure consists of summer melting (ablation) and outflow through 'ice rivers'. The flow is caused by pressure of the overlying layers, partly also by the slope of the bedrock, and is explained by the plastic properties of ice which in this respect is similar to pitch. The ice rivers break up into icebergs at the sea shore; the floating icebergs melt ultimately in warmer latitudes. When precipitation exceeds expenditure, the ice sheet grows, and *vice versa*. The thickness of the sheets may be 3000 to 6000 feet and more. The elevation of their surface favours a low temperature. Therefore, even when formed over lowlands, the surface of the ice sheet acquires the climate of a mountain plateau; melting is inhibited and snow accumulation favoured. The ice is formed out of the snow by compression under its own weight; because of the mode of formation, bubbles of air are included and its density is lower than that of compact ice. The ice sheets are indicative of glacial epochs and may be formed in lowlands only when the summer temperature is low enough.

Mountain glaciers are in many respects similar to the ice sheets, except that, as the name implies, they may originate all over the world in mountains of a sufficient altitude. The snow line, where accumulation equals ablation, is higher in warm climates and lower in cold ones. It depends also upon the amount of snow precipitation, but in a much lesser degree than assumed by the proponents of 'precipitation theories' of the ice ages. It must be noted that the flow of mountain glaciers is caused by their slope and is faster than that of continental ice; with a large supply of snow they are more likely to reach into lower warmer regions than the continental ice sheets.

Surface ice in the oceans occurs at present chiefly in the form of pack-ice, broken into floes which under some circumstances may overlie each other. In winter the pack-ice may become continuous, and so it may have been persistently in polar waters during the great glaciations. The first-year ice, 2 to 6 feet thick, if surviving summer melting, may attain 10 feet the next winter; further growth is prevented by melting at the bottom through contact with sea water. As a cooling factor, reflecting sunlight from its snowy surface, pack-ice is of great climatic importance. However,

its relative amount is small, almost insignificant in the water
balance of the globe. It responds to seasonal changes, and varies
quickly with climatic factors. Thus, the amelioration of world

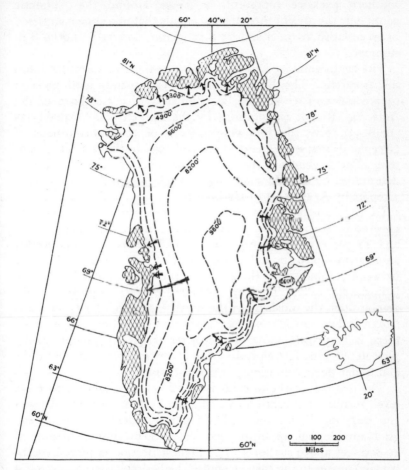

FIG. 2.   Map of glaciation of Greenland according to A. Bauer. The cross-
hatched areas are not under ice cover. Broken lines show the height above sea
level of the ice surface, in feet. The arrows indicate 'ice rivers'.

climate during recent decades has led to freeing of the shore waters
of Northern Russia and Siberia for summer navigation. In the
northern hemisphere pack-ice covers the whole Arctic Ocean,
extending in winter southwards along the coasts of Greenland

and Labrador and through the Bering Straits; if packed symmetrically around the pole, its area would correspond to a polar cap reaching to latitude 71°N in winter, and 75°N in summer. The southern pack-ice represents a fringe around the Antarctic continent; the area of the pack-ice equals that of a zone comprised between latitudes 72°S and 65°S in winter, and 72°S and 69°S in summer.

The continental ice sheets of today are those of Greenland and the Antarctic. The best explored is Greenland, with 690,000 square miles of ice surface, as compared with 5,000,000 of the Antarctic. Recent explorations by the French polar expeditions (1948–53), give the following picture of the subcontinent of Greenland, that monument in ice and rock of the last big glaciation. The thickness of the ice and the relief of the bedrock were determined by seismic sounding. The glaciological data are from a report by A. Bauer, of Strasbourg.

Of the 840,000 square miles of Greenland, 79 per cent are covered by the ice sheet, 3½ per cent are under detached glaciers, and 18 per cent are free from ice. The ice-free regions occupy shore strips up to 100 miles wide south of 73° latitude in the west, between 70° and 78° in the east, and the whole northern shore in latitudes 80° to 82°. They are inhabited by various polar animals, among them the musk-ox in the north-east which feeds on grass, frozen and preserved fresh during the winter, or polar night, when there is very little snow. The ice-free strips are predominantly plateaux of 3300 feet elevation; the absence of ice at this altitude, and under polar conditions, is worth noting.

The bedrock of the interior is mostly at, or slightly above sea level, forming a gigantic bowl rimmed by the marginal plateaux and carrying the ice sheet. The latter represents an ice plateau gradually sloping up from 3000 feet to a maximum altitude of 10,800 feet above sea level. The highest portion is placed eccentrically, nearer to the eastern shore; the bedrock there is almost at sea level, so that the greatest thickness of the ice is 11,000 feet. The surface of the ice does not follow the relief of the bedrock underneath; evidently, it is determined by the meteorological conditions of snowfall, ablation, and the 'drainage' by plastic flow of ice along the 'ice rivers', fourteen of which have been mapped. The average thickness of the ice sheet is 4960 feet, its total volume 620,000 cubic miles, corresponding to 560,000 cubic miles of meltwater. The ice is probably below freezing point to the bottom. At an elevation of 5240 feet its temperature is decreasing inwards from 9°F at 60 feet below the surface to 2°F at a depth of 410 feet; this may reflect the warming-up of the climate in recent times, the ice at a depth of 410 feet being composed of snowfall of about 250 years ago. The seaward drift of the ice during this interval of time must have been only about 5 miles.

These figures more or less correspond to the average conditions of the Greenland ice cap. At a higher elevation of 9800 feet the temperature of the ice, 18°F below zero, varied little with depth down to 500 feet.

At such low temperatures the ice would not melt under its own pressure and thus, should remain solid throughout. From seismic soundings it appears that between the ice and the true bedrock there is a 600-foot layer of 'permafrost', that is, frozen soil or debris saturated with and cemented by ice.

The ice sheet gains yearly 107 cubic miles of water equivalent (i.e. melt-water volume), from the meagre precipitation of 12 inches. This represents the snowfall over the entire surface of the sheet.

Melting is efficient only below the 'summer' snow line which is at an altitude of 4560 feet. The area where melting takes place equals 16·5 per cent of the total; over this area ablation by melting equals 75 cubic miles annually. The balance of snowfall over melting is thus 32 cubic miles per year.

The drainage by the ice rivers is estimated to remove 57 cubic miles of ice, or 51 cubic miles water equivalent annually. This more than outdoes the excess of snowfall and leads to a net loss of 19 cubic miles water equivalent annually. The ice sheet is thus at present decreasing, which is confirmed by direct observations of the recession of glaciers. If the shrinkage continues at the present rate, the 560,000 cubic miles of ice will be spent in 30,000 years. The ice sheets of the last glaciation have disappeared from Europe and America in about one-tenth of this time. The shrinkage of the Greenland ice cap is thus comparatively slow. With the present trend, the ice sheet is almost stable; yet it is very sensitive to minor climatic fluctuations.

With 107 cubic miles of snowfall, the Greenland ice cap will be completely replaced, or 'rejuvenated', in about 5000 years. This is the effective time of circulation of ice in the sheet. It is too short for the internal heat of the Earth to cause noticeable warming.

The Antarctic sheet is little explored yet. It is probably similar to that of Greenland, differing only in size. Seismic soundings in Queen Maud Land gave an ice thickness of 8200 feet about 350 miles inland. The profiles of the Greenland ice sheet suggest that the thickness of the sheet varies but slightly with the distance to the nearest outlet, that is, the sea shore. On the other hand, from considerations of the ice flow, the thickness is expected to increase with its extent. A conservative estimate would assign to the sheet of Antarctica a thickness exceeding that of Greenland by 10 per cent. The area being 7 times greater, the volume of ice in the Antarctic is some 4,300,000 cubic miles water equivalent. The present volume of other glaciers (of Iceland, and the mountain glaciers), is less than 1 per cent, that of pack-ice less than 0·2 per cent of the volume of the two principal ice sheets. The area covered by ice sheets and glaciers equals 2·7 per cent of the Earth's surface, or 10 per cent of that of the continents; 97 per cent of the area is accounted for by Greenland and the Antarctic.

The area covered by pack-ice equals 3·6 per cent (2·7 in the northern and 0·9 in the southern hemisphere), of that of the globe in February, and 3·9 per cent in July (1·7 in the northern and 2·2 in the southern hemisphere).

SEA LEVELS AND ISOSTASY

The formation of ice caps on land leads to a withdrawal of water from the oceans and to a lowering of sea level; the melting of ice causes the sea level to rise. Should all the ice of Greenland and Antarctica melt, the 4,860,000 cubic miles of water so obtained, if spread over the surface of the oceans, would yield a layer 186 feet thick.

However, the ocean level would rise by a smaller amount. The Earth's interior at depths greater than, say, 10 miles, is not perfectly solid; although composed of apparently solid rock down to a depth of 1860 miles, its substance is viscous like pitch; under a persistent, even weak, pressure acting for thousands of years, it would flow like a liquid, but would appear stronger than steel when acted upon for a short while, for example, for days or years only. The thin hard crust, covering the plastic interior, would bend like paper if the load were great enough. The surface layers are thus floating on the plastic, quasi-liquid interior. The continents, being composed of lighter rock, have more buoyancy and float on the magma like a ship on water; the rocks of the ocean bottom are heavier and have sunk themselves deeper into the magma. Whenever load is added to a portion of the Earth's surface, this portion will subside like a ship under cargo, in accordance with the law of buoyancy: the weight of the cargo must be equal to the weight of the increased water displacement. This principle applied to the Earth's crust is called *isostasy*, and the sea-level changes ruled by it are *eustatic*. The magma just underneath the crust has a density about 3 times that of water; therefore, when extra water is poured into the ocean, the sea bottom yields by one-third of the added water layer, and the eustatic change of sea level equals only two-thirds of the extra column of water.

The eustatic rise of sea level, due to the melting of Greenland and Antarctic ice caps, is thus two-thirds of 186, or 124 feet. Should complete melting happen, submergence of vast low-lying shorelands would cause considerable loss of land area. However, the effective living space would be increased because of the freeing of Greenland and Antarctica, and because of the milder climate in the northern stretches of Canada and Siberia.

For similar isostatic reasons an ice cap, provided it exceeds a minimum size of, say, 100 miles in diameter, will increase the height of a continent by only 70 per cent of its thickness. its base subsiding by the remaining 30 per cent; and *vice versa*, the removal of the ice would cause the rock base to rise by 30 per cent of the thickness of its former ice cover. The base of the Greenland ice cap, as determined from seismic soundings by the French expeditions, is at a mean altitude of 2040 feet above sea level, only a few isolated regions (prospective lakes) in the middle of the continent reaching to depths of 800 feet below sea level. The removal of the ice would raise the bedrock level by 1490 feet, to an average height of 3530 feet, with the lowest depressions lifted up to about 700 feet above sea level. Thus, Greenland is a true continental plateau, and suggestions of its being composed of two islands are incorrect.

The uplift of continental masses after the removal of glacial sheets has been actually observed in Scandinavia. Former glacial shore lines are there at present 700 to 900 feet and more above sea level, indicating an uprising of this amount during the 9000 years since the ice melted. Owing to the imperfect elasticity, or high viscosity of the substratum (magma), the uplift is gradual, stretching over thousands of years; it still continues. Thus, the Baltic shore of Sweden still rises 4 inches per century in the south, 1½ feet per century at Stockholm, and almost 4 feet per century in the north where the ice stayed longest and was thickest. The delayed isostatic adjustment of the Earth's crust lasts 20,000 to 30,000 years; the original rise to one-half of the total took about 8000 years. This figure depends only upon the viscous properties of the magma and should be the same for all localities on the Earth's surface. The isostatic uplift of Scandinavia points to an average thickness of 5740 feet for its ice sheet during the last glaciation about 12,000 years ago.

TABLE 1

Rise in sea level since last glaciation

Time Thousands of years Before Present (B.P.)	0	1	2	3	4	5	6	7	8	9	10	12
Sea Level Feet below present	0	4	8	12	18	20	26	44	49	62	79	122

On the other hand, eustatic changes of sea level in regions not affected by isostatic uplift are a direct measure of the variation in volume of the ice caps. They are likely to overestimate changes which took place less than 10,000 years ago by about 25 per cent, because the isostatic adjustment of sea bottom lags by thousands of years behind. Also, recent slow changes may be caused by rapid melting 8000 to 12,000 years ago, on account of delayed isostasy; this could cause only a decline in recent sea levels (from the delayed subsidence of the sea bottom). Therefore, a postglacial rise in sea level must be real under all circumstances. Actually, such a rise seems to have taken place continually since the last glaciation, according to F. P. Shepard and H. E. Suess, as shown by Table 1, derived concordantly from North Holland and the Gulf Coast of North America. The continuous rise in sea level has persisted despite well-known climatic fluctuations during this period, such as the 'climatic optimum', in temperate zones 4000 to 8000 years ago, and the subsequent deterioration. Evidently the postglacial fluctuations were of minor importance, being unable to reverse the steady shrinking of the glaciers.

The sea level 12,000 years ago was 122 feet lower than now, which indicates that the volume of the ice caps was double that of the present. The volume of ice during its maximum extent must have been very much greater. The English Channel and part of the North Sea were land even during the last advance. Unfortunately, the sea level during maximum glaciation in Northern Europe cannot be a good basis for estimating the volume of the ice, because of isostatic subsidence and uplift. In the Mediterranean this difficulty does not arise; there the shore line of the second (Mindel) glaciation of the Quaternary was about 650 feet below present sea level, which indicates a volume of ice withdrawn from the ocean about 6 times the present amount, or 31 million cubic miles. Direct estimates, based on known areas of glaciation at the time of maxima, are somewhat smaller. Thus, V. Romanovsky and A. Cailleux give 19 million cubic miles for the third (Riss), and $17\frac{1}{2}$ cubic miles for the fourth (Würm) glacial. These figures do not take into account the Siberian glaciation down to about 60° latitude which seems to have been unknown until lately. The overlooked area is 2,100,000 square miles which would add 2 million cubic miles to the above estimates. It may be that the thickness of the ice sheets during glacial maxima has been underestimated; an increase of thickness by 48 per cent would lead to agreement with the estimate from sea level. After all, the difference of 48 per cent must not be regarded as too serious, for such estimates. It seems that both methods agree reasonably well in assigning a maximum volume of 20–30 million cubic miles to the Quaternary ice sheets.

There is one serious source of uncertainty in using the variation of sea level for the evaluation of the exchange of mass between the ice caps and the sea. The sea level depends not only upon the total amount of water on the surface of the globe (which appears to have remained more or less constant for the past 500 million years), but upon the relief of the Earth's surface, especially of the bottom of the ocean. This relief seems to have been subject to a kind of pulsating rhythm, causing the sea sometimes to invade the low-lying parts of the continents, and to recede at other times. These periods of *transgressions*, when the sea level was high, alternated with low-level *regressions* within time intervals of 15 to 30 million years. The changes have been so slow that, for a few hundred thousand years of the Quaternary, no important influence could have been expected from this factor. Nevertheless, F. Zeuner has shown that, for the interglacials and pre-glacial epochs, as we go back in time the sea level becomes systematically higher, reaching 200 feet above the present level in the first interglacial, 330 feet just before the first glacial, and 600 feet at an earlier epoch. The upper limit of sea level, corresponding to complete melting of the present ice caps, was found to be 124 feet. Thus, the high ancient sea levels could not have been due alone to the melting of the caps, but also to a regression which has been at work during the Quaternary.

THE QUATERNARY

The present glacial epoch amidst which we live, the Quaternary, began with the Günz glaciation whose date may be anything from 300,000 to 1,000,000 years ago. The uncertainty is due to the lack of reliable timing criteria for time intervals of from 35,000 to 10 million years. Intervals shorter than 35,000 years are determined by radiocarbon dating and partly by G. de Geer's method of 'varves', or annual depositions of clay at the bottom of lakes. Intervals over 10 million years are reliably determined by radioactive methods based on the decay of uranium and thorium into lead isotopes. For marine (deep-sea) sediments part of the gap up to 400,000 years can be filled by the radio-active ionium method which, however, has not yet been directly applied to the Quaternary.

For deep-sea cores, or long cylindrical slabs cut out of the bottom sediments, temperature determinations by the method of oxygen isotopes (developed by H. C. Urey) have yielded important results. At different temperatures, microscopic animals living near the surface of the sea use different proportions of the oxygen isotopes 18 and 16 for their calcareous shells; these shells segregate in the bottom sediment of the corresponding geologic age; the age, partly at least, can be determined by the radiocarbon method, and the ratio of the oxygen isotopes at various depths thus gives the temperature variation near the surface of the ocean with time. An independent check on the temperatures is furnished by the zoological analysis of the species of *Foraminifera*, the animalcules responsible for the calcareous shells; some of them belong to warm climates, others to cold ones, and from the relative number of different species (recognized by their shells), the degree of warmth near the water surface can be inferred. The zoologic and isotopic results are in good agreement. The application of these methods, together with radioactive carbon dating, constitutes the most important recent progress in the study of the Quaternary. The temperatures of deep-sea cores reflect the main climatic fluctuations already known from research on land, so that both sets of data can be correlated.

The chronology of deep-sea cores can be extended by using the rate of sedimentation as found for the same core for the first 30,000 years by the radio-active carbon method. This is not a very reliable procedure, because the rate of deposition of the bottom clay in the same core reveals considerable variations (sometimes in the ratio of 10 to 1, but mostly less); the greater erosion on land during a glacial stage, as compared with an interglacial, could have had its effect on the marine deposits. Nevertheless, the order of magnitude of the results can be relied upon. Absolute rates of deposition in different cores from the tropical and equatorial Atlantic have been found to vary from 0·9 to 110 inches per 1000 years; thus, different cores are hardly comparable unless they are taken from a similar geographic environment.

According to C. Emiliani and H. E. Suess, the deep-sea cores indicate that during the last maximum of glaciation 18,000 years ago the ocean temperature in the Caribbean in 15°N was 68 to 72°F, as compared with present-day 84°F; in Mid-Atlantic on the equator the corresponding figures are 62°F (glacial) and 78°F (present). The average lowering of temperature in the tropics was thus about 15°F, to be compared with a drop relative to the present of 22°F in middle Europe, as estimated from the flora. The difference between the climatic zones was thus greater during the glaciation than it is now. The glaciers reached at that time down to the Lough Derg–Carlingford line in Ireland, leaving free the southern part of it; they bridged the Irish Sea, went through the Lake District in England, covered all Scandinavia and reached into northern Germany; Holland remained free of ice. In America the glaciers reached considerably farther south than in Europe, their southern border lying about 150 miles south of Cleveland, Ohio. During their greatest extension at earlier advances, the glaciers reached even farther south, covering all Ireland, leaving free only southernmost England and covering all present Holland.

From Emiliani's palaeotemperature determinations, dated by Suess from radio-active carbon measurements until 35,000 years B. P. (Before Present), and extended from the rate of deposition until about 100,000 years B.P., the ocean surface temperatures

TABLE 2

Ocean surface temperatures

Time: Thousands of years Before Present (B.P.)	Temp. °F*	Temp. °F†	Temp. °F‡
0	85	85	78
4	85	85	76
8	73	79	68
12	68	74	67
16	69	68	63
20	70	71	63
30	71	71	66
40	72	74	69
45	72	74	68
50	72	69	68
55	71	67	69
60	73	72	69
70	78	77	69
80	80	81	73
85	83	81	75
90	81	78	78
98	81	—	74

* Lat. 16° 36′ N., long. 74° 48′ W., depth 9,700 ft.   † Lat. 14° 59′ N., long. 68° 51′ W., depth 13,600 ft.   ‡ Lat. 0° 10′ N., long. 23° 0′ W., depth 12,300 ft.

within the tropics and near the equator are found to be as given in Table 2. The figures apparently cover the whole cycle of the Würm glaciation, the fourth and most recent glaciation of the Quaternary glacial epoch, beginning with the third interglacial about 100,000 years B.P. and ending with the present time, that is, with what is to become the fourth interglacial, if a fifth glaciation should occur.* It is seen that the decrease of temperature began 85,000 years B.P., and lasted 70,000 years, the minimum of tropical ocean temperature being reached about 15,000 B.P. In contrast the rise since 12,000 years B.P. took only 8000 years to be accomplished.

The retreat of the glaciers was not steady and continuous, instead it indicates minor climatic fluctuations (cf. Fig. 3) similar to

* It may be remarked that the Carbo-Permian glacial epoch had at least five major glaciations.

those of postglacial and historical times. According to A. Penck the
stages appear to be of very different length: thus from the amount
of deposit the second interglacial is estimated to have lasted four
times longer than the third. As a guess, Penck gave 660,000 years
as the total duration of the Quaternary.

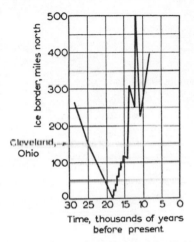

Fig. 3.   Glacier border in the Great Lakes region, North America, according to
R. F. Flint.

Work by Emiliani on the temperature fluctuations since 273,000
years B.P. suggests that the rises in temperature are more rapid
than the falls (cf. Fig. 4). This is a familiar type of asymmetry
encountered in the light curves of pulsating variable stars, and
in the sunspot cycle.

THE CAUSE OF THE ICE AGES

Theories by Sir George Simpson and others assume that glaciation is caused originally by an increased temperature of the globe.
The greater moisture content of warm air would increase the
precipitation, and thus the accumulation of snow and glaciers.
Such qualitative reasoning cannot be accepted. Snow can accumulate on the ground only when the temperature is near freezing
point; when the global temperature rises, the snow line shifts
polewards, and the area of accumulation decreases. Over this area
the degree of moisture remains practically constant, corresponding
to the constant temperature of the snow line. The decreased area

M

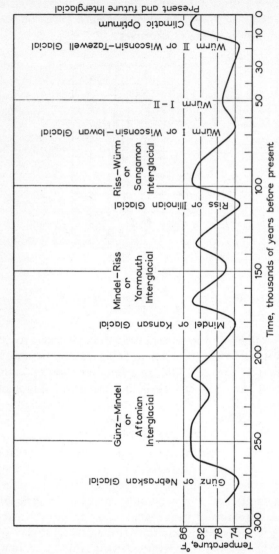

FIG. 4. Caribbean surface temperatures and chronology of the Quaternary after C. Emiliani.

means decreased accumulation of snow and less favourable conditions for the formation of ice caps.

Modern data for palaeotemperatures in the tropics indicate that glaciation develops and retreats simultaneously with the fall and rise of global temperature. The agent responsible for this can hardly be anything else but variations in the radiation of the Sun.

The smaller differences in temperature between the climatic zones and between the seasons during the warm periods of the Tertiary and earlier, as compared with glacial times, can be attributed to two main causes: the greater heat capacity of moist air, and the reflection of sunlight by the polar caps.

The heat requirements of high latitudes, especially in winter, are to a great extent covered by transport from warmer regions of the Earth. In moving polewards, the warm air gives away a definite amount of heat per cubic foot for each degree of cooling. This amount varies with the moisture content, the latter in its turn depending on temperature. The heat capacity rapidly increases with temperature so that when this is high less cooling of the air moving polewards is needed to cover the radiation to space; the temperature of warm air will decrease less than that of cold air when reaching high latitudes. Therefore, during a warm period, the temperature difference between pole and equator will be smaller than during a glacial period. The same applies to the difference between summer and winter temperatures.

In addition, when an ice cap is formed, sunlight is strongly reflected from the snow surface and thus lost to space. This loss must be covered by extra heat transport, which means that the equatorial air will have to lose more heat when reaching the polar cap: the zonal difference in temperature between the climatic zones will be accentuated during an ice age.

The three Post-Cambrian period (500 million years B.P.) glacial epochs—the Eocambrian, the Carbo-Permian and the Quaternary—followed each other within approximately equal intervals of time. There are known at least five Pre-Cambrian period glacial epochs, of which the Huronian, dated about 1000 million years B.P. seems to have been very intense. All these suggest an interval of about 250 million years for the repetition of the glacial epochs.

The succession of cold glaciations and warmer interglacials during one glacial epoch, a feature of the Quaternary, is also a feature of the Carbo-Permian. Lack of data prevents the making of definite statements in this respect for older epochs, but it is probable that this is their general feature.

The most probable cause of these large-scale climatic changes seems to be the variability of solar radiation. The variability appears to consist of two components: relatively shortlived decreases in the total radiation of the Sun, leading to the glacial epochs; and the glaciation-interglacial fluctuations during one glacial epoch. It has been shown that, in the normal course of evolution of a star like our Sun, the conversion of hydrogen into helium in its deep interior, together with gas diffusion, would create zones of instability and mixing; this in turn would lead to a temporary decrease in solar radiation and cause a glacial epoch on Earth. When equilibrium is restored, the Sun regains its former intensity of radiation, and a warm climate returns. This process is repeated after intervals of the order of several hundred million years, which explains the recurrence of the glacial epochs.

More difficult is the question of the succession of several glaciations during one glacial epoch. The phenomenon seems to be of great complexity, corresponding to a perpetual variation of solar radiation according to various cycles and amplitudes, of which perhaps the sunspot cycle is one. This continuous 'flickering' of the Sun may have been going on all the time, but in warm periods its minima may not have been sufficient to cause glaciation, and they may have therefore passed unnoticed. Or it may be a secondary effect of the main disturbance, confined to the glacial epochs only. When hydrogen from space accumulates in the Sun, the outer layers become gradually more transparent until an instability arises which causes mixing and a temporary decline in solar luminosity. The mixing is repeatedly triggered off by the main disturbance in the deep interior. Curves of variation of solar luminosity, reminiscent of what happened during the Quaternary, have been calculated. However, in this case the decline in global temperature should proceed faster than the subsequent rise, contrary to what oxygen-isotope data for the ice ages have shown.

The Sun emits so-called corpuscular radiation, chiefly ionized hydrogen atoms which cause the aurorae (Chapter 14). The loss of hydrogen, due to emission, may be greater than the gain from space. In such a case the outer layers of the Sun would gradually become poorer in hydrogen and thus heavier (because the heavier elements remain). Eventually they would collapse inwards, causing mixing. The result would be a rapid rise in solar luminosity, with a subsequent gradual decline, more similar to the observed variation of temperature during the glacials. However, no calculations have yet been made for this case.

There is no convincing proof yet that the correct model of solar variation has been found, but the explanation of the major variations—the repetition of glacial epochs after long periods of normal warm climate—appears to be quite plausible. The 'flickering', or the succession of glaciations and interglacials during one glacial epoch, presents a more difficult problem, just like the problem of sunspots and their cycles; possibly, a theory that solves one of these would also solve the other.

CHAPTER ELEVEN

Meteorology

B. J. MASON

METEOROLOGY, which is concerned with the physics and dynamics of atmospheric processes, covers such a wide field that in a short chapter one could little more than catalogue its multifarious activities and problems. Emphasis is thus placed on those topics which at present occupy the centre of the stage, and are consequently of greatest interest to the general reader. These particular aspects have also been chosen to show the scope and diversity of meteorology, in which observation, theory and experiment are all brought to bear upon the study of a wide variety of phenomena ranging in scale from the atomic to the global.

Weather forecasting takes first place, not only because of its practical importance, but because it highlights the problems and the difficulties involved in understanding the behaviour of the atmosphere. Also, the advent of high-speed electronic computers has opened up new possibilities in this field. The physics of clouds and precipitation represents one of the most vigorous and exciting aspects of meteorological research, the study of which has revealed the feasibility of producing rain artificially, foreshadowing the possibility of exerting some degree of control on the weather.

FORECASTING THE WEATHER

Weather forecasting is the main preoccupation of meteorology as a profession; further synoptic meteorology, the scientific study of the structure and evolution of weather systems as revealed by charts, poses many of the problems and provides much of the stimulus for research into the physics and dynamics of atmospheric processes. Not that meteorological research is consciously aimed solely, or even principally, at improving the art of forecasting. Its true object is to increase our understanding of the atmosphere and its ways; but one hopes, of course, that this greater knowledge will in the long run, lead to more accurate, detailed and useful prediction of the weather.

In spite of considerable advances in meteorological science, it is probably fair to say that, for reasons which will presently appear, the accuracy of forecasts for 24 hours ahead has not *substantially* improved during the last 30 or 40 years. The scope and utility of forecasting have, however, increased enormously. This has largely been the result of two world wars and rapid developments in aviation, which have both specified the requirements and made available the necessary resources for reliable and quite detailed short-period forecasts of conditions at high levels, and of surface weather at airfields. The introduction in 1939 of the radio-sounding balloon to provide contemporaneous information on pressure, temperature, humidity and winds up to great heights heralded a new era in meteorology. With regular and synchronous ascents from a fairly dense network of stations covering more than half of the northern hemisphere, we now have a reasonably good picture of the three-dimensional structure of the atmosphere up to heights well within the stratosphere.

Progress in weather forecasting has, so far, to be reckoned mainly in terms of its greater frequency, detail and usefulness to an ever increasing clientele. This progress may be attributed mainly to improved data, more efficient organization and communications. There is now some reason to hope that with our gradually increasing understanding of atmospheric behaviour, and the development of high-speed electronic computers, appreciable improvements in accuracy, reliability and range may yet be achieved. But before describing these new developments, it seems appropriate to outline the scope and limitations of the conventional forecasting techniques with the object of revealing the problems, and also the main features of the weather systems with which they are concerned.

The Principle of Synoptic Forecasting

The synoptic method is to represent the physical properties of the atmosphere on charts which will provide, within the limits of the observational data, a convenient, small-scale picture of the atmosphere.

The preparation, at suitable intervals of time (usually 3 or

6 hours), of new maps giving a two-dimensional representation of conditions at the Earth's surface and at a number of levels in the upper air, allows the evolution of the atmospheric structure to be studied, significant trends to be extrapolated into the future, and the drawing of forecast charts to represent conditions at some definite time ahead.

The Construction and General Features of Synoptic Charts

Meteorological observations, made simultaneously at a large number of stations at fixed times, provide a large number of spot values of pressure, temperature, humidity, wind etc., from which the meteorologist attempts to construct continuous distributions in space as far as this is practicable with two-dimensional charts.

The surface chart shows the mean sea-level isobars—lines which join places having the same pressure when the individual readings are corrected to the values which would obtain at sea level. The resulting isobaric pattern delineates the main areas of high pressure (anticyclones), which are usually associated with fine, settled weather, from regions of low pressure (cyclones or depressions), which are usually associated with unsettled and often stormy conditions. The surface chart also shows the positions of fronts which are zones of demarcation between air masses of different life history, usually reflected by differences of temperature and humidity. Fronts are often associated with rather characteristic patterns of disturbed weather as illustrated in Fig. 1. The remaining wealth of observational data, surface temperatures and humidities, the distribution of cloud and rain, surface winds and visibilities, are not generally suitable for continuous representation and are plotted as spot observations to be integrated mentally by the analyst.

In an attempt to obtain a three-dimensional representation of the atmosphere, a series of maps portraying near-horizontal sections of the atmosphere are constructed, on the basis of the radiosonde observations from the upper air, for the 700, 500, 300, 200 and even the 100 millibar* pressure surfaces (corresponding to heights of about 10,000, 18,000, 30,000, 38,000 and 53,000 feet). Instead of plotting the horizontal distribution of pressure at a

---

* The millibar is one thousand times the fundamental metric unit of pressure i.e. 1000 dynes per square centimetre. The pressure of the standard atmosphere taken as 760 millimetres (or very nearly 30 inches) of mercury is therefore 1013·2 millibars.

given height, it is now more usual to draw on upper air charts contours of the height in the atmosphere at which a given pressure is reached. Where the barometer is high so also is the contour height, and the chart of isobars and the contour chart look very

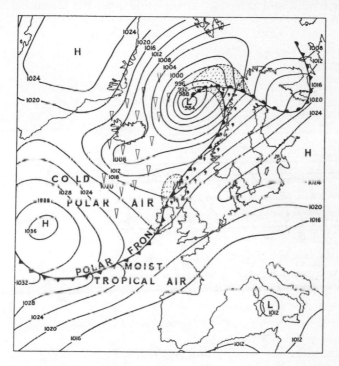

FIG. 1. A surface chart showing isobars at intervals of 4 millibars, centres of high (H) and low (L) pressure, and a well-developed depression (cyclone) formed on the polar front, which marks the boundary between the cold polar air and the moister, warmer air of tropical origin. The winds blow clockwise round the anticyclones and anticlockwise round the cyclones at angles of about 30° across the isobars. The outbreaks of scattered showers in the cold air, the rather widespread continuous rain near the centre of the depression, and the occurrence of drizzle ahead of the weak cold front are typical features of such a situation.

similar. Temperature in the free atmosphere, being less affected by local conditions than is temperature near the ground, may be represented by a system of isotherms or, as is now the practice on upper air charts, by 'thickness lines' which indicate the vertical thickness between consecutive pressure surfaces, a quantity which is proportional to the mean temperature of the layer. The observed winds are not always represented by isopleths, more often being left in the form of spot values.

The configuration of the isobars on the surface map determines the strength and direction of the wind near the ground. Except

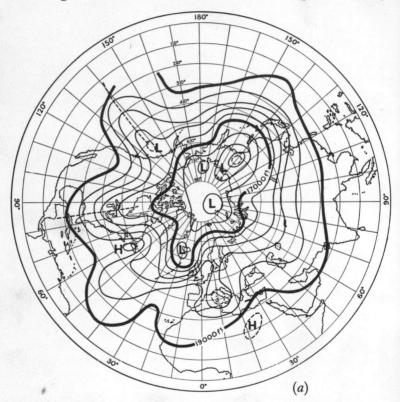

(a)

near the equator, we may, as a first approximation, regard the air as being influenced by only two forces, due respectively to the pressure gradient and the Earth's rotation. It will flow as a steady wind only when these two forces are equal and opposite; and since the excess centrifugal force due to motion over the rotating Earth always acts at right angles to the motion, it follows that when equilibrium is reached the wind must blow at right angles to the pressure gradient (i.e. along the isobars), with low pressure on the left in the northern hemisphere and low pressure on the right in the southern hemisphere. This so-called *geostrophic wind* is only an

approximation to the real flow, though for many purposes a very
good approximation. Actually, near the surface the wind blows
at an angle of about 30° to the isobars because a frictional drag on
the air introduces a third force directed against the motion. The
wind speed is proportional to the pressure gradient (i.e. the

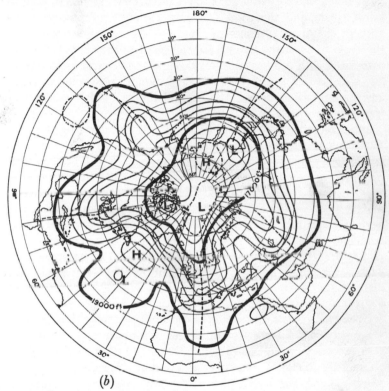

(b)

FIG. 2 a and b. Charts showing the contour pattern at 500 millibars for the northern
hemisphere. The air flows along the contour lines, the wind being strongest
where the lines are closest together. The belt of strong westerly winds occurring
in middle latitudes is known as the jet stream. The maps show the long waves in
these upper westerlies and the formation of cut-off cyclones and anticyclones.

crowding of the isobars), and in practice is determined by measuring the separation of the isobars with a transparent scale, which is
calibrated in terms of a theoretical relation between wind speed
air density, latitude and isobar separation.

On the upper air charts the air flow follows the contour lines,
with the lower contour heights to the left in the northern

hemisphere. Again the wind speed is inversely proportional to the separation of the contours, which have the advantage over an isobaric representation, that they allow the wind speed to be measured at different levels with the same scale without having to take specific account of the fact that the air density changes with height.

In many ways it is an advantage and a convenience to take the wind speed and direction as being closely represented by the pattern of isobars or contours; but it is a grave disadvantage that the departures of the wind from the geostrophic value (which are associated with convergence, divergence and vertical motion of the air, and hence the development of cyclones, anticyclones, clouds and precipitation, in fact the very elements of the weather) are left unrepresented.

Figs. 2a and 2b show two typical charts of the contours for the 500-millibar surface. They represent the flow round the hemisphere at about 18,000 feet above the ground. It will be seen that a meandering belt of westerly winds encircles the hemisphere, the wind being strongest in middle latitudes where the contours are closest together. This sinuous band of very strong winds reaching, perhaps, 150 miles per hour, which is known as the *jet stream*, coincides with a region of very sharp temperature gradient and is closely associated with the polar front, a prominent feature of the surface map marking the zone of transition between the cold polar air and the warm sub-tropical air (see Fig. 1). The north and south excursions of the upper flow, known as ridges and troughs, are referred to as the *long waves* in the upper westerlies. A single wave may span from 45 to 90 degress of longitude, i.e. from 3,000 to 6,000 miles. Long waves generally move rather slowly and may show little change of form over a period of a few days as shown in Figs. 2a and 2b, which show long-wave patterns for times 48 hours apart. Since individual depressions and the small anticyclones are often steered along the general flow at these levels, a nearly stationary long-wave pattern may determine the general character of the weather for a week or even longer. Areas beneath and in advance of the troughs are notably unsettled, and the areas beneath the ridges have the fine, settled weather typical of anticyclonic conditions.

The Development of Weather Systems

It is of interest at this stage to say something of how the main features of the weather charts—the long waves, the cyclones and the anti-cyclones—arise. The genesis, growth and decay of these systems are the central problems of dynamical meteorology. In recent years, approximate solutions of the complicated hydrodynamic equations describing the motion of the atmosphere have been obtained, which show tolerably well how disturbances resembling long waves and cyclones may start. But the theory (which has to linearize the essentially non-linear equations to make them tractable), cannot deal with their subsequent development; this is a task for the new high-speed computers, as we shall see later. The ideas which have emerged from the recent theoretical work are, very briefly, as follows.

Because in tropical and sub-tropical regions the atmosphere receives more heat from the Sun than it radiates to outer space, while the reverse is true in polar regions, a temperature gradient exists between the equator and the poles at all levels, associated with which there is a pressure gradient which increases with height. This pressure gradient (directed from poles to equator), together with the rotation of the Earth, gives rise to a global belt of westerly upper winds (particularly dominant in middle latitudes), the strength of which increases with height in the troposphere, but falls off again in the stratosphere. Such a system is, however, dynamically unstable, so if it is perturbed—for instance by disturbances resulting from air flow over mountain barriers, by irregularly distributed heat sources, or by moving disturbances already in existence—this great hemispherical vortex will break down. The pattern of the breakdown will depend very little upon the form of the initial perturbation but rather on the properties of the large-scale circulations. Of all possible developments, the unstable three-dimensional disturbance having the largest growth rate will usually become dominant.

The large-scale breakdown of the tropospheric flow gives rise to the slowly-moving long waves in the troughs of which the air moves from low levels in low latitudes upwards and polewards along gently sloping surfaces, while air from above the polar regions moves downwards and equatorwards in the ridges. Thus heat is continually transported from the equator towards the poles as is demanded by the fact that the average temperatures of the tropics and the poles are not changing, despite the fact that the tropical atmosphere continually receives more heat from the Sun.

In a frontal region, where there are usually strong horizontal temperature and density gradients (i.e. where the atmosphere is strongly *baroclinic*), and particularly where the extensive cloud systems provide a relatively unstable layer, disturbances may develop with a wavelength (along the front) of typically 500 miles. These are the depressions of middle latitudes. Initially they are confined to the vicinity of the frontal zone and are comparatively shallow (perhaps 2 to 3 miles), but later they may penetrate the whole depth of the troposphere.

The long waves and cyclones are not, however, completely independent systems. The development of long waves usually gives rise to strongly baroclinic zones which are suitable for the growth of the smaller cyclone waves. Distortions of the jet stream aloft are often associated with perturbations of the polar front on which so many of our mid-latitude depressions develop; conversely, the appearance of families of depressions and anticyclones on the surface chart are often associated with the major features of the long-wave pattern. Also, growth of the long waves often leads to the formation of closed circulations—cold cyclonic vortices on the equator side and warm anticyclones on the poleward side (see Fig. 2)—these being important agencies in the large-scale poleward transfer of heat.

Both species of disturbance grow initially at the expense of the potential energy of the system in which they develop, but at a later stage the kinetic energy of the large-scale atmospheric circulation feeds the kinetic energy of the growing disturbances. In time these reach maturity, and are then gradually worn down by friction; eventually friction and the continuing radiative processes re-establish the unstable zonal current and prepare the way for the growth of new disturbances.

Synoptic Analysis and Preparation of the Forecast

Having briefly tested the attractive but not altogether satisfying fruits of the theoretical meteorologist, let us return to the bread and butter problems of the forecaster. The preparation of the forecast begins with a study of the existing atmospheric conditions as represented on the surface and upper air charts in the manner described above. During his study of these maps the forecaster continually compares his analysis with that shown on the charts for other levels and for earlier hours, ensuring that they are mutually consistent. In forming his mental picture of the structure, motion and state of evolution of the weather pattern, he will pay particular attention to the signs of impending changes in the existing system. Analysis of the existing situation is followed by construction of forecast charts for 12 or 24 hours ahead showing, first of all, the expected surface pattern of pressure, and the expected contour and thickness patterns (which are closely related to the distribution of pressure and temperature), at several upper levels.

Ever since scientific forecasting began about 100 years ago, the basic technique has been the extrapolation of the changing pressure field—the judicious extrapolation for some hours ahead of the tracks of pressure centres, the movements and development of ridges, troughs, fronts, etc.—modified as necessary on the basis of general experience. This technique is still widely practised and under certain conditions it is difficult to improve. It has, however, serious limitations, particularly in rapidly developing situations when the changes are non-linear; and it is from his experience and physical understanding of when and how extrapolation will break down that the forecaster demonstrates his skill. In these circumstances, he will be guided by his knowledge of the structure and development of weather systems based, perhaps, on typical models describing a type of dynamical evolution, which he will adjust to the needs of the current situation. Some forecasters will make what use they can of the few tools provided by the dynamical meteorologist—for example, rules expressing the tendency for cyclonic or anticyclonic development in terms of certain measurable properties of the wind field between 1000 and 500 millibars—but, for the most part, the forecaster will probably fall back on his accumulated experience of more or less similar situations which have occurred in the past, making due allowance for local and seasonal influences.

Besides predicting the pressure or contour patterns from which the general wind field may be derived and the areas of widespread rain inferred, it is necessary to forecast the positions of the fronts which separate the principal air masses and link the depressions; and also the small-scale features of weather, for example, the occurrence of cloud, showers, thunderstorms, fog, local visibilities and temperatures which, because of the coarseness of the observational network or the small scale or short period of the changes themselves, cannot be represented in detail in the evolution of the broad synoptic pattern.

Accurate prediction of the movement of fronts, which requires a very accurate forecast of the pressure field, and which is essential for predicting the arrival of cloud and precipitation, is one of the major practical problems. Fronts, being subject to continual modification, vary greatly in structure and in magnitude and sharpness of the temperature and wind changes associated with them. Being individualistic, they defy rigid classification and show great reluctance to conform to the highly idealized models which appear in the text books.

In forecasting the weather, as distinct from the general distribution of pressure and temperature, particular attention is paid to the distributions of temperature and humidity within the various air masses and how these, and hence the stability of the air, might be modified by general ascent or subsidence of the air, or by its travel over colder or warmer surfaces. In deciding the evolution of weather in the frontal zones, the forecaster will be guided by certain models of the structure of fronts and their associated cloud systems, and by the fact that convergence of the air is the main factor in causing sharpening of fronts and the upward air currents which produce cloud and precipitation. In all of this, the role of topographical and other local effects, for example, the influence of hills on the intensity and persistence of rainfall, has to be borne in mind.

The forecasting of showers and thunderstorms provides one of the few examples of theory being of some direct practical value. By plotting the vertical distributions of temperature and humidity as measured by the radio-sonde on a special diagram, and using certain thermodynamical criteria for the onset of instability, it is often possible to predict for a *few hours ahead* the likelihood of showers and thunderstorms. These techniques have their limitations, however, and it is also necessary to take into account the synoptic type, the locality and season, the effects of diurnal heating and nocturnal cooling in promoting or damping convection, and above all, the effect of subsidence or ascent of the air on its stability. Beyond a few hours ahead, the vertical profiles of humidity and temperature became modified by thermal and dynamical processes to an extent which can only be roughly estimated at present.

Although a good deal of attention has been given to the study of the turbulent transfer of heat, water vapour and momentum near the Earth's surface, the subject is poorly developed from a quantitative point of view. For this and other reasons, the forecasting of such phenomena as surface wind, temperature, humidity, visibility and cloudiness is almost entirely empirical, being largely based on some qualitative appreciation of the physical factors involved, on statistics, and on general experience.

This very brief account of the methods and problems of synoptic forecasting barely describes the mechanics involved— the mere canvas, brushes and paint. It can convey little of how the forecaster examines his material, decides the composition, sketches the outline and finally, fills in the details of his picture. Implying that forecasting is something of an art is not to underestimate the large amount of physical insight required by a good forecaster; an instinctive feeling for the ways of the atmosphere, which can be acquired only through experience, is invaluable. The time factor is of over-riding practical importance and the analysis and forecast must be made as quickly as possible to reduce the interval between the observed and the predicted weather, thus improving the utility of the forecast.

It is not apparent that marked improvements in the accuracy and range of forecasts are likely to be realized in the immediate future; what hope there is lies mainly in the use of high-speed electronic computers to *calculate* the broad patterns of pressure and temperature from the raw observational data. This is an exciting new development which we shall now pursue in a little more detail.

Forecasting with Machines

We recall that the preparation, by conventional methods, of a weather forecast may be divided into two stages: prediction of the main features of the pressure field—the cyclones, anticyclones, troughs and ridges; location of the fronts, and mapping the weather, cloud, temperature, etc., which is likely to accompany the larger-scale developments. It is only with the first of these stages that the new numerical techniques are at present concerned.

The idea of using the hydrodynamic equations which describe the motion of the atmosphere, to calculate the changes in the distribution of pressure from one day to the next is not new. Indeed, an attempt along these lines was made by the late L. F.

N

Richardson in his remarkable book *Weather Prediction by Numerical Processes*, published in 1922. Because Richardson's calculations predicted some quite impossible changes in pressure, and because of his conclusion that some 64,000 computers would be required to keep pace with the weather of the world, interest in his ideas lapsed. They were 30 years ahead of their time! The notion of computing the broad features of a weather map became feasible only a few years ago. It resulted from the development of routine upper air observations, the increased knowledge of the structure and behaviour of weather systems, the realization that useful answers might be obtained by using a simplified model of the atmosphere, and above all, the advent of electronic high-speed computing machines which allow the several million numerical operations involved in a 24-hour forecast to be performed in a reasonable time. Research along these lines which is now being carried out in a number of countries, including the United States, Sweden and Britain, is being followed with the greatest interest. The forecasts being prepared in the Forecasting Research Division of the British Meteorological Office are based upon a model which supposes the atmosphere to be contained between two constant pressure surfaces located at 1,000 millibars, corresponding roughly to sea level, and at 200 millibars corresponding roughly to the tropopause. The mathematical complexity of the problem is greatly reduced by making an assumption, based on observation, that changes of wind, which increase in strength at greater heights as a result of the existence of horizontal temperature gradients, occur in the same direction at all levels. Furthermore, the vertical motion of the air is assumed to vary parabolically with height, being zero at the ground and the tropopause, and a maximum at 500 millibars.

The state of motion of the model is studied by considering the contour pattern of the 500-millibar pressure surface which gives the geostrophic wind at this level. Special attention is also given to the thickness of the 1000 to 500 millibar layer which, of course, is related to the temperature distribution and hence to the variation of wind with height (the so-called relative or thermal wind). Computations are carried out in terms of two parameters, the height of the 500-millibar surface and the thickness of the 1000 to 500 millibar layer.

The analysis leads to two differential equations for the

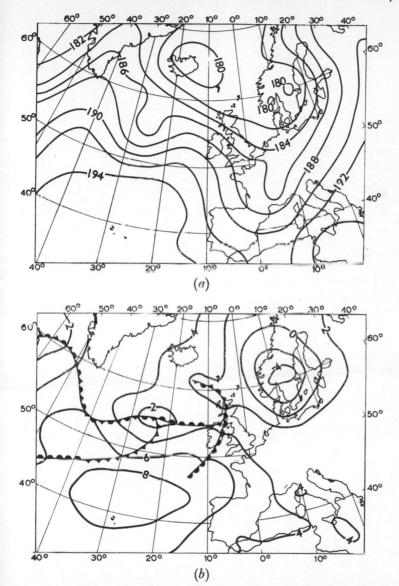

FIG. 3.   (a) Contours of the 500-millibar surface for 1500 G.M.T. on August
             10, 1951, from which the calculations were started (units 100's of
             feet).
          (b) Contours of the 1000-millibar surface for 1500 G.M.T. on August
             10, 1951, from which the calculations were started.

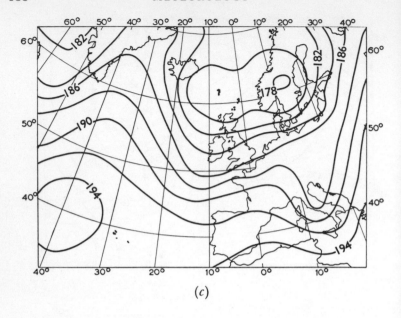

(c)

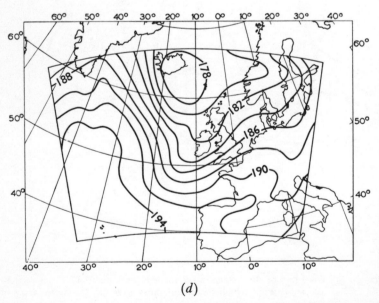

(d)

(c) Contours of the 500-millibar surface *as observed* 24 hours later.
(d) Contours of the 500-millibar surface *as calculated* for the same time.

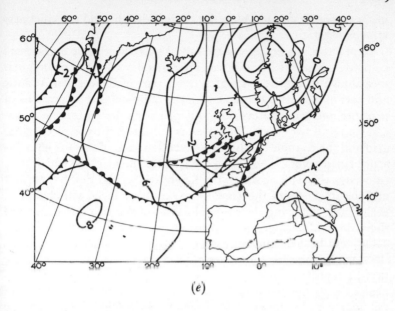

(e)

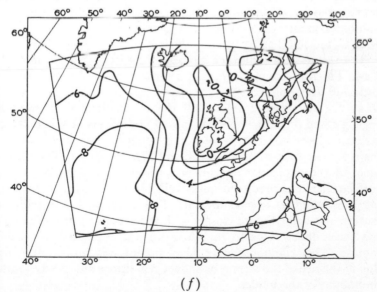

(f)

(e) The 1000-millibar chart *as observed* at 1500 G.M.T. on August 11 1951.

(f) The 1000-millibar chart as *computed* for the same afternoon.

instantaneous rates at which the contour height and the thickness are changing.

In practice, the equations are solved by an electronic high-speed computer. The British forecasts are carried out for the rectangular area shown in Figs. 3 a–f which cover part of the eastern Atlantic and part of western Europe. Using the radio-sonde observations of pressure and temperature, contour maps are drawn for the 1000– and 500-millibar levels. The area is subdivided by a rectangular grid and the contour heights are read off at each of the 192 equally-spaced grid points. These data are fed into the machine which then calculates the rates at which the height of the 500-millibar surface and the thickness of the 1000 to 500 millibar layer will change at each point. Knowing the original values of the two quantities and their rates of change, it is possible to predict what their new values will be, say, one hour later. These new values then become the starting point for a new computation; and the whole procedure may be repeated, say, 24 times to give contour heights and thick-nesses for 24 hours ahead at the 192 points from which the fore-cast map may be drawn. The forecast 1000-millibar chart may be constructed by subtracting from the forecast height of the 500-millibar contours at each point the predicted thickness of the 1000 to 500 millibar layer.

The results of a computed 24-hour forecast are shown in Figs. 3 a–f. The first two maps, Figs. 3 a and b, give the contours of the 500- and 1000-millibar surfaces for 1500 hrs, 10 August, 1951. They are the maps from which the calculations were started. Figs. 3 c and d compare the computed and observed 500-millibar contour charts for the following afternoon, the corresponding maps for the 1000-millibar level being Figs. 3 e and f. The move-ment of the depression originally centred at 54°N 24°W on the surface chart was predicted quite well, but the amount of deepen-ing was slightly over-estimated. The computed 500-millibar pattern also agreed quite closely with the actual pattern, although the 500-millibar ridge in mid-Atlantic was computed to be too intense. This computed over-development was probably partly due to the use of the wrong boundary conditions and partly to the limitations of the model.

The computation of such a 24-hour forecast takes less than half an hour on the fastest machines now available.

It must be emphasized that by these methods it is possible to compute only the large-scale pressure distribution, and that the weather has to be filled in by the forecaster. Nevertheless, a realiable estimate of the former is of great value because many of the major failures in forecasting arise from erroneous forecasts of the pressure field. At the present time, using rather crude models of the atmosphere, the forecast charts produced by numerical methods for 24 hours ahead, have a standard of accuracy comparable with those produced by an experienced forecaster, but have the virtue of being independent of the personal judgment of any individual. With improved methods and data it may prove possible to do rather better.

Apart from the limitations of the models employed, errors arise from the fact that the computations are made for only a limited area and that changing conditions on its boundaries, which cannot be taken fully into account, may effect developments inside the area during the forecast period. Furthermore, experience shows that in order to keep down computational errors, the calculations should be carried out in time steps of not more than one hour with grid points not more than 150 miles apart. The errors can be reduced by extending the area under consideration and by having a closer network of radio-sonde stations.

But in trying to extend the forecast beyond 24 hours, other difficulties arise. The slowing effects of friction, the driving energy of the Sun's radiation, the release of latent heat during cloud formation and the warming and cooling of air masses as they travel over warmer or colder surfaces (effects which are ignored in the present computations), may be neglected over 24 hours, but having a cumulative effect over long periods, will ultimately cause gross errors in the forecast. It is not easy to express these processes numerically and there is no immediate prospect of incorporating them fully into the calculations.

Future Developments in Forecasting

To what extent may it be possible to improve the accuracy and range of forecasts in the future? Although with present data and methods the accuracy usually falls off quite rapidly after 24 or 48 hours, will improved observations and techniques make it possible to do much better? One can only speculate on such a question, but as far as we can see at present, it seems that some improvement may be expected, but that progress will be rather slow; spectacular advances are not likely. This is not only because of the enormous complexity of the problem, but because there would appear to be a limit to the accuracy ultimately attainable, set by the fact that small disturbances which are below the threshold of observation at one time can grow rapidly into large systems within a day or so. These instability processes cannot be predicted, even in theory, unless the small beginnings can themselves be predicted with a high order of accuracy. In other words, there is an effective time barrier beyond which the detailed prediction of a weather system may well remain impossible. The time barrier may intervene after only a few minutes if we are concerned with the occurrence of a shower, it may be a few hours for a small secondary depression, and perhaps a few days for the large disturbances associated with the long-wave patterns. Beyond these time limits the behaviour of systems appears to be indeterminate in the sense that they cannot be located with precision in space and time, but only in a statistical sense, that is, in terms of probabilities.

Extension of forecasts in time can be made only by sacrificing precision and detail. Thus forecasts for 3 or 4 days ahead, based on the persistence and coherence of the long-wave pattern, are useful in indicating whether it will be generally cold or warm, wet or dry. However, the timing of changes will usually be poorly predicted and the evolution of the smaller systems which determine the detailed weather can only be treated schematically or statistically.

For periods further ahead than a few days, the outlook is very uncertain. Because of the obvious economic importance of being able to predict whether, say, the following winter will be abnormally cold or mild, a good deal of effort has been devoted to developing techniques for long-range forecasting but so far with little success. Study of the development of individual systems now has to be replaced by consideration of the general circulation of the atmosphere, the mechanism of which is poorly understood. The exchange of energy between the Sun, the atmosphere, the oceans and the ground, and the redistribution of energy in the atmosphere itself brought about by many inter-related processes, are so complicated that the prospect of tracing a direct path between cause and effect seems remote. But in time it may be possible to acquire sufficient physical insight into the processes at work to suggest relationships which can be explored by statistical techniques and machine methods of handling the enormous quantity of data which will be involved.

THE PHYSICS OF RAIN CLOUDS

We shall now look at a different aspect of meteorology and from a rather different view point. Cloud physics, which is concerned with the structure and development of clouds and with the physical processes which go on inside them, has achieved considerable prominence in recent years, largely through the activities of physicists equipped with radar, highly-instrumented aircraft, and and imposing array of laboratory techniques including cloud chambers, electron microscopy, X-ray and electron diffraction and a wide range of electronic devices. Considerable progress has been made in the study of the microphysical processes of condensation, the supercooling and freezing of water droplets, the growth of ice crystals and the mechanisms of raindrop, snowflake and hailstone formation; but of equal importance are the little-studied dynamical processes which control the larger-scale features of cloud development (the distribution, dimensions, life and vigour of cloud systems) and which, in turn, govern the time and space scales of the microphysical events.

This interrelation between processes working on different scales, which is the key to understanding of atmospheric behaviour, has always to be borne in mind when applying the results of small-scale laboratory experiments to the atmosphere. The important role of clouds in the dynamics of the general circulation of the atmosphere may be gauged from the fact that clouds reflect back nearly one quarter of the incoming solar radiation to outer space and so considerably reduce the amount of energy available to drive the atmospheric machine.

In the release of precipitation (hail, rain, snow) from clouds, the factors of prime importance are the motion of the air, its water vapour content, and the numbers and properties of those particles which it contains and which act as centres of condensation and freezing. Because of the great complexity of atmospheric motions and the enormous variability in the vapour and particle content of the air, it is not possible to construct a detailed, general theory of the manner in which cloud and precipitation will develop. However,

considerable progress has been made in recent years with calculations, based on simple models of the air motion, of the growth of
individual cloud particles. These give a reasonable explanation of
the formation of precipitation in the different kinds of clouds.

Mechanisms of Precipitation Release

Clouds are formed by the lifting of damp air which cools by
expansion under continuously falling pressure. The relative
humidity increases until the air approaches saturation, when
condensation occurs on some of the wide variety of aerosol
particles which are present in average concentrations of several
hundreds per cubic centimetre. A proportion of these are hygroscopic and promote condensation at relative humidities below
100 per cent, but for continued condensation leading to cloud-
droplet formation the air must be slightly supersaturated. Among
the highly efficient condensation nuclei are the salt particles produced by the evaporation of sea spray, but it now appears that
particles produced by man-made fires and by natural combustion
(such as forest fires) make a major contribution. Condensation on
to the nuclei continues as rapidly as the water vapour is made
available by cooling of the air and gives rise to droplets of order
one hundredth of a millimetre in diameter. These droplets,
present in concentrations of a few hundreds per cubic centimetre,
constitute a non-precipitating water cloud. Now we shall see how
the transformation into a rain-bearing cloud takes place.

Growing clouds are sustained by upward air currents which may
vary in strength from an inch or so per second to several yards per
second. Considerable growth of the cloud droplets, which have
falling-speeds of only about half an inch per second, is necessary
if they are to fall through the cloud, survive evaporation in the
unsaturated air beneath, and reach the ground as drizzle or rain.
Drizzle drops have radii exceeding four thousandths of an inch
while the largest raindrops are a quarter of an inch across and
fall at nearly ten yards per second. The production of a relatively
few large drops from a large population of much smaller ones may
be achieved in one of two ways.

The Coalescence Process

Cloud droplets are not, in general, of uniform size because they
arise on nuclei of various sizes, grow under slightly different con-

ditions of temperature and supersaturation in different parts of the cloud, and some may remain inside the cloud for longer than others before being carried to the drier air outside.

A droplet which is larger than average will fall faster than the smaller ones and so may collide and coalesce with some of those lying in its fall path. Once a drop starts to grow by this process, it will continue at an ever-increasing rate, because after each collision it becomes bigger, falls faster and so sweeps out a given volume of cloud more quickly. If its journey in the cloud is sufficiently long and if the population of smaller droplets is sufficiently dense, it may eventually grow large enough to fall through the base of the cloud as a raindrop.

The Ice-crystal Process

One of the fundamental features of natural water clouds is their frequent occurrence in the supercooled state, i.e. the water droplets exist as liquid at temperatures below zero degrees Centigrade— sometimes down to minus 40 degrees Centigrade. At temperatures above minus 40 degrees Centigrade, small cloud droplets can freeze only if infected with small solid motes possessing certain favourable properties. These minute sub-microscopic particles, called ice-forming nuclei, are very elusive and their nature and origin have not yet been definitely established. At temperatures just below zero degrees Centigrade the probability of a cloud droplet containing an active ice nucleus is very small, but at lower temperatures this probability increases as more and more airborne particles become capable of initiating the crystallization of the supercooled water.

In general, then, that part of the cloud which lies between the zero and minus 20 degree levels initially consists of supercooled droplets co-existing with a much smaller number of ice crystals. Since the equilibrium vapour pressure over water is greater than that over ice at temperatures below zero degrees Centigrade, air saturated with respect to water will be appreciably supersaturated relative to ice. Consequently the ice crystals will grow much more rapidly than the water droplets.

The development of snow crystals, which can be grown artificially in the laboratory, and study of the factors which control their amazing variety of shape and form, are fascinating aspects of cloud physics.

They occur in three predominant forms depending on the temperature—as hexagonal prismatic columns, as thin hexagonal plates, or as delicately branched star-shaped crystals. Several crystals may aggregate to form a snowflake which, on falling through the level at which the temperature becomes zero degrees centigrade will melt to produce one or more raindrops.

Ten years ago, meteorologists were firmly of the opinion that only this second mechanism was of importance and that all rain was produced by the melting of snowflakes. However, recent observations show beyond all doubt that heavy rains often fall in tropical and subtropical regions from clouds which are entirely beneath the zero degree level and thus cannot contain ice crystals. Even in temperate regions, there is now evidence to show that, during warm weather, showers are sometimes produced by the coalescence process.

Here radar working on centimetric wavelengths has proved an invaluable tool. The fact that precipitating clouds may reflect sufficient of the energy in the incident radar beam to be detectable by a sensitive receiver many miles distant allows one to study these clouds in the comfort of the laboratory. The strength of the echo is determined by the size and concentration of the particles in the cloud, the radar wavelength, and the distance of the cloud. The echoes are displayed on cathode-ray tubes from which one can locate the positions of storms in space up to distances of 100 miles or more, and follow their distribution and movement. Such information has obvious practical application to the short-range forecasting of rain, the development of thunderstorms and the probable tracks of hurricanes. More detailed study of the echo allows one to deduce a good deal about the structure, growth and development of the storm, and the nature of the precipitation elements which it contains. For example, the melting of snowflakes produces a very characteristic radar echo, the appearance of which speaks for the activity of the ice-crystal mechanism; on the other hand, the appearance of the cloud echo at levels where the temperature is above freezing affords strong evidence for the coalescence process.

In considering, in a little more detail, the roles played by the ice-crystal and coalescence mechanisms in natural clouds, it is convenient to distinguish between layer (stratiform) clouds and shower (cumulus) clouds.

Precipitation Release from Layer Clouds

The extensive sheets of stratiform cloud, from which falls precipitation of a steady, persistent character, are generally formed in cyclonic depressions and near fronts, and are associated with feeble up-currents of only a few centimetres per second which are maintained for at least several hours. The structure of these great rain-cloud systems can be examined satisfactorily only by observers using aircraft and by radar, and their systematic exploration has hardly begun. But analysis of the available aircraft data shows that while *drizzle* often falls from non-freezing stratiform clouds in which the drops must be growing by coalescence, the majority of these clouds produce *rain* only when their tops are colder than minus 12 degrees Centigrade which suggests that ice crystals may be responsible. This view is supported by the radar evidence; the variation of the strength of the radar signal with height indicates that ice crystals grow in the cold upper regions of the cloud, then they coalesce to form snowflakes as they approach the zero degree level, and finally the snowflakes melt to form raindrops. Because the melting snowflakes produce a very characteristic radar signal, the appearance of the latter shows that the rain is being released by the ice-crystal mechanism, which is responsible for most of the rainfall in temperate latitudes.

The Production of Showers

Precipitation from shower clouds (which may reach the ground in the form of raindrops, pellets of soft hail or as larger hard hailstones), is generally of greater intensity and shorter duration than that from layer clouds, and is composed of larger particles. The clouds themselves are characterized by their great vertical depth, and the strong vertical air currents and high concentrations of liquid water in them; all these factors ensuring the rapid growth of the precipitation particles by coalescence.

In a cloud composed wholly of water, raindrops must grow by coalescence with smaller droplets, and for this process to start some droplets must be larger than average. In layer clouds which may persist for days, these larger droplets may be developed *in situ*: in shower clouds, whose active life may be restricted to only a few minutes, this appears impossible, and the larger droplets have to be introduced ready-made from an external source. Now over the oceans, droplets of sea water formed as spray and having diameters of about one twentieth of a millimetre may be carried up by convection currents to the cloud base without appreciable evaporation, and may thereafter be capable of initiating a shower. While being carried up through the cloud, such a droplet will grow by sweeping up smaller cloud droplets until it is too heavy to be supported by the vertical air currents; it will then fall, continuing to grow by the same process on its downward journey, and if the cloud is sufficiently deep, it may emerge from the base as a raindrop.

In a dense, vigorous cloud of considerable depth, the drop may attain its limiting stable diameter (about 5 millimetres) before reaching the cloud base; it will then break up into several large fragments, each of which may continue to grow and itself attain break-up size. The number of raindrops may increase so rapidly in this manner, that, after a few minutes, the accumulated mass of water can no longer be supported by the upcurrents, and so a heavy shower is released. The conditions which favour this rapid multiplication of water drops occur more readily in tropical regions.

In temperate regions, where the zero degree level is so much lower, conditions are relatively more favourable for the ice-crystal mechanism, although many showers may be released by the coalescence of water drops.

The ice crystals will grow initially by sublimation of water vapour in much the same way as in layer clouds, but when their diameters exceed about a tenth of a millimetre, growth by collision with supercooled water droplets will predominate. The droplets freeze on impact to form pellets of soft hail. Because air spaces are formed between the frozen droplets, the average density of the particle may be as low as 0·3 or even 0·1, so that in a dense cloud it will increase very rapidly in size. However, the growth of the particle is restricted by the fact that it may collect supercooled water at a rate faster than it can be frozen and so acquire a liquid coat which, on subsequent freezing, produces a layer of clear ice. Alternate layers of opaque and clear ice are characteristic of large hailstones. Their formation may be interpreted in terms of alternate periods of wet and dry growth associated, perhaps, with the passage of the hailstones through regions of high and low liquid-water content and of stronger and weaker up-draughts in the cloud.

In a warm, dense vigorous cloud the wet hailstones may accumulate excess water at such a rate that large drops may be flung off and continue to grow by coalescence to disruption size. Thus the water drop 'chain reaction' may be initiated by the shedding of water from a very small population of wet hailstones. The alternative mechanisms for releasing precipitation from both shower and layer clouds are summarized in Fig. 4.

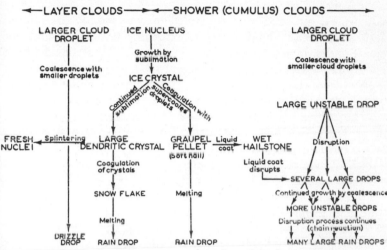

FIG. 4. A schematic representation of precipitation mechanisms.

RAIN-MAKING EXPERIMENTS

We have seen that the presence of either ice crystals or comparatively large water droplets (to initiate the coalescence process), appears essential to the natural release of precipitation. Rainmaking experiments are conducted on the assumption that some clouds precipitate inefficiently, or not at all, because these natural nuclei are deficient; and that this deficiency can be remedied by 'seeding' the clouds artificially with 'dry ice' or silver iodide (to produce ice crystals), or by introducing water droplets or large hygroscopic nuclei.

Three different methods have been tested in rainmaking experiments. In the first method, pellets of dry ice (solid carbon dioxide), about a centimetre in diameter, are dropped from an aircraft into the top of a supercooled cloud. Each pellet cools a thin sheath of air near its surface to well below minus 40 degrees Centigrade and produces perhaps ten thousand million million minute ice crystals, which subsequently grow and coalesce to form snowflakes. Thus only a few pounds of dry ice are required to seed a large cumulus cloud. More than two hundred experiments, carried out mainly in Australia, Canada and South Africa, have shown beyond all reasonable doubt that cumulus clouds in a suitable state of development may be induced to rain by seeding them with dry ice on occasions when neighbouring clouds, unseeded, do not precipitate.

However, for large-scale trials designed to modify the rainfall from widespread cloud systems extending over thousands of square miles, it is very costly to use aircraft. This consideration led to the development of the second technique; silver iodide is released from the ground in the form of a smoke, and air currents carry it up into the supercooled regions of the cloud. Silver iodide was chosen because of the similarity of its crystal structure to that of ice; but an adequate explanation for its particular efficiency as an ice-forming nucleus awaits further research. It produces ice crystals in relatively small numbers at minus 5 degrees Centigrade, and becomes fully effective at about minus 15 degrees Centigrade, when one gramme of iodide can be vaporized to produce a thousand million million nuclei. Of course, with this method, there is no control over the subsequent transport of the smoke. We are unable to make a reliable estimate of the concentration of nuclei reaching cloud level, nor do we know for how long silver iodide retains its ice-nucleating ability in the atmosphere. It is these unknown factors which, together with the impossibility of estimating accurately what would have been the natural rainfall in the absence of seeding activities, makes the design and evaluation of a large-scale operation so difficult. In the data so far published, no convincing evidence can be found that large increases in rainfall can be produced consistently over large areas.

Attempts to stimulate the coalescence process in shower clouds are a more recent development. Aircraft equipped with water tanks and spraying devices have been used to introduce droplets of mean diameter about a twentieth of a millimetre into the bases of growing clouds, thus providing the larger droplets necessary to start the coalescence process. The results of the first Australian experiments were encouraging; ten out of eleven experiments produced rain, and in four cases (where the cloud depth exceeded 5000 feet), the rain was heavy. Some success was achieved in some very recent tests with tropical cumulus clouds in the Caribbean. But in view of what has been said about the probable role of water droplets formed on large salt particles, and the fact that about four ounces of salt may be used instead of one gallon of water, it appears more economical to disperse salt crystals of about a hundredth of a millimetre in diameter instead of water droplets; the salt crystals, being strongly hygroscopic, would grow to droplets of the requisite size while being carried up through the bottom 1000 feet of the cloud. A few 'salting' experiments involving aircraft were made in England in 1952; further trials have been made in East Africa with balloon-borne bombs containing gun-powder mixed with finely ground salt, and in Pakistan where the dry climate has made it possible to disperse salt dust from the ground. The results of these tests are encouraging, and suggest that this may prove an efficient method of releasing showers from warm cumulus clouds.

The Potentialities of Rain-making

The experiments carried out in recent years have created the greatest interest and a good deal of controversy. Although, unfortunately, the significance of the first preliminary results has often been greatly exaggerated, most responsible meteorologists would agree that they suggest possibilities which should not be ignored. To what extent future development of these techniques may allow man to exert some control on the weather is difficult to foresee. As far as one can judge at present, it is more realistic to think in terms of seeding operations effecting a redistribution rather than an over-all increase in the total amount of rainfall.

By inducing a premature release of precipitation, it may be possible, for example, to either augment or reduce the rainfall over land relative to that which normally occurs over the oceans. It may, of course, be much more difficult to arrange for the additional rain to fall in regions where it is most needed.

In temperate latitudes most of the rain falls from deep layer cloud systems whose tops usually reach to levels at which there are abundant natural ice nuclei and in which the natural precipitation processes have plenty of time to operate. It is therefore not obvious that seeding of these clouds would produce a significant increase in rainfall, although marginal effects are always possible. Conceivably, judicious seeding of the cloud system during its early stages of development, when thick layers of supercooled cloud may be present, could forestall the natural release of precipitation and therefore effect some re-distribution of rainfall.

Perhaps more promising as additional sources of rain or snow are the persistent supercooled clouds produced by the ascent of damp air over large mountain barriers. The continuous generation of an appropriate concentration of ice crystals near the windward edge might well produce persistent light snowfall to the leeward, since water vapour is continually being made available for crystal growth by the lifting of the air. The condensed water, once converted into snow crystals, has a much greater opportunity of reaching the mountain surface without evaporating, and might accumulate in appreciable amount if seeding were maintained for many hours.

In attempting to increase or redistribute the rain falling from shower clouds, there will be great difficulty in judging the optimum time for seeding. In the case of large vigorous clouds which will normally grow to levels at which natural nuclei may initiate a shower, it may be possible to anticipate natural events by only a few minutes. Smaller clouds which do not reach these levels may respond to seeding, but will probably produce only small amounts of rain.

However, these statements may apply only to average conditions. There may well be a large number of individual occasions in particular regions where natural rain-producing nuclei are deficient, and when the occurrence or non-occurrence of precipitation is decided by very marginal conditions. By exploiting these marginal conditions cloud seeding may have its greatest application and benefit, particularly in those regions where even a small amount of extra rainfall would be of great economic value.

The feasibility of decreasing the rainfall by 'overseeding' clouds has been discussed from time to time. It seems likely that the introduction of an excessive concentration of ice nuclei into a supercooled cloud would prevent the crystals from growing sufficiently large to fall out of the cloud and that the onset of precipitation would thereby be retarded; but the practical difficulties of doing this over a large area are so great that it has not been seriously attempted. The suppression of large hail and of lightning by the overseeding of incipient thunderstorms are also intriguing possibilities which again have yet to be seriously tested.

The science of cloud modification is, however, still in its infancy. It may well be that further knowledge of cloud behaviour and of natural precipitation mechanisms may suggest new possibilities and improved techniques which will lead to developments far beyond those which seem likely at present. The challenge to find out is too strong to be resisted.

CHAPTER TWELVE

The Ionosphere

J. A. RATCLIFFE

In 1901 G. Marconi made the discovery that it was possible to send radio waves from England to America over the great hill which consisted of the intervening quarter of the globe. Now radio waves are a form of electro-magnetic wave-motion just like ordinary visible light, about which enough was known to suggest at once that Marconi's result was most remarkable and unexpected. It was clear that what determined the behaviour of waves as they passed round obstacles was the ratio of the wave-length to the size of the obstacle, so that if radio waves could go a quarter way round the Earth then light waves could go a quarter way round a sphere which on their scale, was of a similar size. Marconi's result implied that light from a small lamp on the surface of a sphere of radius six inches would travel quarter way round it. Just as it would be absurd to expect that, so it would be absurd to expect Marconi's experiment to succeed. But it did: how could that be explained?

In 1902 it was suggested simultaneously by O. Heaviside in England and by A. E. Kennelly in America, that the only possible explanation involved the existence, high in the atmosphere, of a reflecting surface which acted so as to keep the wave down near the ground and prevent its spreading out into space. Now to reflect radio waves it is necessary to have some free electric charges present, and the rather vague suggestion was made that these charges existed because the air pressure at great heights was a good deal smaller than at the ground. In the words of Heaviside, 'There may possibly be a sufficiently conducting layer in the upper air. If so the waves will, so to speak, catch on to it more or less. Then the guidance will be by the sea on the one side and the upper air on the other'; or in the more precise words of Kennelly, 'At an elevation of about 80 kilometres, or 50 miles, a rarefaction exists in the air which accompanies a conductivity about 20 times as great as that of ocean water.' . . . 'It seems reasonable to infer that electromagnetic disturbances emitted from a wireless sending antenna spread, until the conducting strata of the atmosphere are encountered, after which the waves will move horizontally outwards in a 50-mile layer between the electrically reflecting surface of the ocean beneath, and an electrically reflecting surface, or successive series of surfaces, in the rarefied air above.' . . . 'As soon as long-distance wireless waves come under the sway of accurate measurements, we may hope to find, from the observed attenuations, data for computing the electrical conditions of the upper atmosphere.'

Later we shall make these early ideas of Kennelly and Heaviside clearer. In the meantime, however, we recall that theirs was not the first suggestion that there was an important conducting layer in the high atmosphere. Accurate observations, as early as 1722, had shown that the position of a compass needle went through a regular oscillation once each day, and that the form of this oscillation depended on where, on the Earth's surface, the observation was made. Now it is known that a compass needle will be deflected if it is near a current and if the current is very strong it need not even be near. The currents supplying electric trains have, for example, caused considerable interference at magnetic observatories several miles away. In 1882, Balfour Stewart suggested that the daily oscillations of the compass needle could have been caused by strong electric currents flowing in the high atmosphere. The existence of these currents implied the existence of free electric charges whose movements they revealed.

It became accepted that there was an elevated conducting layer and it was called the *Kennelly-Heaviside layer*, but there was at first no direct proof of its existence. It needed the development of radio technique during the first World War before 'the waves could come under the sway of accurate measurements', and then, in 1924, E.V. Appleton and M.A.F. Barnett, in the Cavendish Laboratory at Cambridge, demonstrated the existence of the layer beyond doubt, by making experiments on waves which had been vertically reflected from it.

The upper conducting region, from which radio waves can be reflected, represents that part of the atmosphere which is appreciably ionized and has been called the *ionosphere*. Since the early experiments of Appleton and Barnett the region has been extensively explored by the use of radio waves and it is the purpose of this chapter to tell something of how these waves are used as a tool of the experimenter and of the knowledge about the upper atmosphere which they have provided. First, however, it is necessary to enquire a little more fully into two fundamental questions which must be answered before our study can begin. One is 'Why should there be conducting layers in the high atmosphere?' and the other is 'How does a conducting layer influence radio waves passing through it?'

PRODUCTION OF IONIZED LAYERS

The tenuous upper atmosphere is irradiated during the day by intense ultra-violet and X-radiations from the Sun. These radiations remove electrons from the air atoms and molecules by the process known as *ionization*, and as they descend into the denser atmosphere they encounter more and more atoms and molecules so that they produce electrons more and more copiously. When the radiations have penetrated a certain depth, however, they become used up, so that at greater depths they produce electrons less rapidly. The rate of production of electrons thus has a peak at some level which depends jointly on the rate at which the atmospheric density increases downwards and on the absorbability of the ionizing radiation. The rate of production at this peak, and the height at which it occurs, also depend on the angle at which the Sun's rays enter the atmosphere, for it is this angle which determines how much air they must pass through before reaching a certain level.

PASSAGE OF RADIO WAVES THROUGH IONIZED AIR

Radio waves are emitted whenever electrons, in a piece of wire for example, are caused to oscillate back and forth sufficiently rapidly. In the wave there is an electric field which repeatedly reverses its direction in sympathy with the oscillating electron. The number of complete oscillations which occur every second is called the frequency: it is very great, in broadcasting waves for example, it is about one million per second (one megacycle per second) and in the waves which will be discussed later in connection with the experiments on the ionosphere it is usually between one and ten megacycles per second (1 Mc/s to 10 Mc/s).

If the radio wave now encounters a free electron it will set it into oscillation with its own frequency. This oscillating electron will then re-radiate a new wave, just as it would if it were oscillating in a wire. The re-radiation from a single electron is extremely small, and is of no importance; but if the electrons become sufficiently numerous their combined re-radiations can be comparable in strength with that of the original radiation, and, when combined with it, can lead to important modifications of the total wave. In particular the speed of the wave can be markedly altered so that, if it is chopped up into a series of morse 'dots', each 'dot' will travel more slowly than it would in ordinary air. This alteration of speed is made use of in experimental methods for investigating the ionosphere.

The alteration of speed is, however, not the only way in which the wave can be affected. If the electrons make collisions with heavier particles such as air atoms and molecules the strength of the wave will also be altered for the following reason. Up to now the electrons have been described as though they were completely free, but that is not quite a true picture. They have, indeed, been freed, by the ionizing radiation, from the atoms or molecules to which they originally belonged, but they are still surrounded by air atoms and molecules which are much heavier than they are. All these heavy particles, and the free electrons, are continuously moving amongst each other with great speeds and in random directions, so that at intervals an electron will make a collision with one of the heavier particles, as a result of which it will be deflected violently and will move off in a new direction. At a height of about 60 miles, which we shall discuss in some detail, the electrons travel about a foot in each free path between collisions, and with a speed of several thousand miles per hour so that they make about a hundred thousand collisions each second. At lower heights there are more heavy air particles to collide with, and the collisions are correspondingly more frequent.

If a radio wave is now traversing the region, the electrons, moving in their random paths between collisions, will be driven into ordered and regular oscillations. These oscillations represent the passing back and forth of energy between the electron and the wave and on the whole no energy is removed from the wave. When, however, a collision occurs, the excess oscillatory energy of the electron becomes converted into excess disordered energy in the random motion of the electron in its next free path, and, on the whole, energy has been absorbed from the wave and given to speed up the electron. At each collision, therefore, the wave loses energy, and is partially absorbed.

The amount of the absorption will depend on the number of electrons present and able to pick up energy, on the number of collisions they make with heavy air particles, and on the energy picked up in the oscillation. The latter quantity is greater when the wave frequency is smaller so that the lower frequency waves are more strongly absorbed. For the future discussion the important points are that

(a) the absorption will be great whenever there are numerous electrons low down in the ionosphere where the collisions occur more frequently, and

(b) the absorption is greater on the lower frequencies.

EXPERIMENTAL PROOF OF THE EXISTENCE OF THE IONOSPHERE

In the experiments made, in 1924, to demonstrate the existence of the Kennelly-Heaviside layer as it was then called, radio waves were sent up into the air and a search was made to see whether they were reflected back towards the ground. Special arrangements were needed to separate and recognize the returned wave in the presence of the stronger original wave. It is interesting to note that Appleton and Barnett, in the tradition of the Cavendish Laboratory, did not build elaborate equipment for their experiments, but hit upon the idea of using an existing transmitter of the B.B.C. and a principle, known as *interference*, taken by analogy from the study of optics. Continuing the analogy they described their results in terms of interference fringes, and were able to show that the waves were, indeed, reflected from a height of about 60 miles. When, as sometimes happened, the down-coming wave was reflected at the Earth to return a second time to the ionosphere and back, the fringes became complicated and their interpretation was not easy.

G. Breit and M. Tuve, experimenting a little later on the same subject in America, separated the weak reflected wave by a method which involved more sophisticated techniques, but which gave results easier to interpret, and their method is the one now commonly used. It consisted simply of sending a regular series of short morse 'dots' up into the air, keeping them so short that each was finished and done with before its reflection was returned to the Earth. In their experiment a measure of the height of reflection involved only a measurement of the time delay in the return of the echo. This time was short, only about one thousandth of a second, but even in those early days their techniques were sufficiently good for accurate measurements to be made.

IONOSPHERE SOUNDINGS

Once the existence of the reflecting region had been established there was an increasing amount of experimenting all directed towards finding out just how the electrons were distributed in the ionosphere. The method of Breit and Tuve has been used all over the world, for sounding the ionosphere by means of morse 'dots' sent upwards, much as the bed of the ocean is sounded from a ship by the method known as *echo sounding* in which short 'dots' of sound are sent downwards. The ionospheric experiment is, in fact, often known as *ionosphere sounding*.

The problem of disentangling, from the results of these sounding experiments, the story of the detailed behaviour of the ionosphere has a peculiar fascination for may physicists, particularly for those like Appleton and Barnett, who delight in using simple apparatus to derive important results. It is largely because the ionosphere, at heights of 60 miles and beyond, is inaccessible to direct investigation, that the possibility of studying it indirectly, by means of the radio waves reflected from it, has proved so fascinating. Recently rockets sent up into the air with measuring equipment which automatically transmits the results to the ground, have added a few items to our knowledge, but to the ionosphere worker of the old school this seems, in some way, not quite fair; the real challenge of the early days was to disentangle the answers through observations made from a distance, and if possible with the simplest apparatus, used with the most detailed and penetrating thought.

The ionosphere investigations of the past 30 years have led to some fairly certain conclusions and to the exposing of some complicated problems. During the International Geophysical Year attention is being directed on a world-wide basis towards the solution of some of these.

The rest of this chapter will be concerned, first with an outline of what is accepted as known about the ionosphere, and second with what the main problems are.

Ionospheric Observatories

If, in Breit and Tuve's method of exploring the ionosphere, the time taken by the morse 'dot' in its travel up and down is measured, then, the speed of radio waves being known, it might be expected that the height of the reflection-point could be calculated. It has already been mentioned, however, that the speed of a wave is altered when it passes through free electrons, and since the number of electrons is not known the speed is not known. If it is supposed, admittedly incorrectly, that the speed is the same everywhere as it is at the ground, then the calculated height may be called the *equivalent height*; it is of considerable theoretical interest, and is usually denoted by the symbol h', but it must always be remembered that it is not the same as the actual height of the reflection.

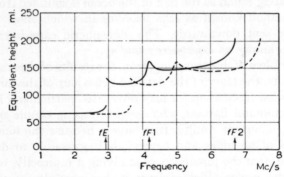

FIG. 1.   Sketch of a $h'(f)$ curve as recorded by an ionospheric sounder.

The equivalent height of reflection changes with the radio-wave frequency, usually denoted by the letter f, and it is of importance for ionosphere investigations to know the form of the curve which shows the observed values of h' plotted against f: this curve is usually called the $h'(f)$ curve. It is desirable that the form of this curve should be known, as far as possible for places situated all over the Earth, and for experiments made at all times of the day, the season and the solar cycle.* For this purpose a series of ionospheric observatories have been set up at about 50 places distributed over the free Western world, and at these $h'(f)$ curves are recorded once every hour at least. Special arrangements are being made during the International Geophysical Year, to augment this series of observatories where desirable.

* The meaning of the expression *solar cycle* is explained on page 218.

The apparatus at the observatories is usually arranged so that the $h'(f)$ curve is automatically drawn out on photographic film. Its essential features are sketched in Fig. 1 and merit detailed examination.

First it is noticed that the trace seems to be doubled over most of its length, as though it had been shifted along the frequency scale a distance corresponding to about 0·7 Mc/s. This doubling occurs because, when free electrons are set into oscillation by the impinging wave, the presence of the steady magnetic field of the Earth causes them to move in circles instead of moving back and forth along the direction of the wave's electric field. The re-radiation from these circling electrons, when combined with the original wave, leads to the propagation of two waves instead of one, so that the original morse 'dot' is split into two. The iono-sphere is then said to have become *doubly refracting* and the phenomenon is closely analogous to that in which a piece of doubly refracting calcite is found to split a single beam of light into two parts.

For our present purpose we may neglect the double refraction and concern ourselves only with the left-hand trace, shown in Fig. 1 by continuous lines, but we may note in passing that detailed examination of the phenomenon of double-refraction has provided clear evidence that it is the light electrons, and not the heavier ions, which are responsible for the reflection of the waves.

$h'(f)$ CURVES AND CRITICAL FREQUENCIES

Examination of the left-hand (continuous line) trace of Fig. 1 reveals that, at certain *critical frequencies* marked fE, fF_1, and fF_2, the trace rises rather sharply and for frequencies greater than these the reflection either persists from a greater height, or disappears completely. These critical frequencies are of major importance. They are explained as follows.

When a morse 'dot' is passing through the ionosphere its speed is reduced, for reasons previously given, and this reduction is greater the greater the electron concentration. The reduction in speed is also greater for the lower frequencies. Suppose now that a wave of low frequency is sent upwards into the ionosphere. As it rises it encounters electrons more and more densely distributed at successive heights, and its speed becomes correspondingly smaller until, at a certain height, it is brought to rest. It is then reflected and returns downwards, increasing its speed as it goes, until it finally reaches the ground with its original speed. It is as though a ball, projected up a slope, rolled with gradually decreasing speed till it stopped, after which it returned, gradually speeding up, to its starting point.

If the radio-wave frequency is now increased, so that the electrons have less effect on its speed, it will penetrate higher before it finds enough electrons to bring it to rest, and the total time of travel will be longer. It is as though the ball were projected up the slope with a greater initial speed. Next suppose that the electron-concentration in the layer does not increase upwards continuously, but that, at some height which may be called the *peak* of the layer, it reaches a maximum. Then, if the wave-frequency is sufficiently great, the wave will nowhere be brought to a stop, not even at the peak, and it will penetrate the layer completely. In the analogy of the rolling ball the continuous slope has become a hill with a peak of finite height, and the ball has rolled over the top, never to return again to the starting point.

If the speed of the ball which just fails to return is known, it is possible to deduce the height of the hill, whatever its shape may be, and, in an analogous way, the lowest radio frequency which just fails to be reflected from a given layer indicates the electron concentration at the peak of the layer. It is these frequencies which are called the critical frequencies. They tell us the concentration of the electrons at the most densely ionized part of a layer.

Ionospheric records of the type shown in Fig. 1 show two clear critical frequences, marked fE and fF_2 which correspond to the penetration of layers situated at heights somewhere near 60 miles and 150 miles. These layers are now called the E and F layers,* the names being chosen to leave letters for the naming of layers which might later be discovered either below or above. Sometimes, as in the example shown, there is a less well-defined critical frequency fF_1, between fE and fF_2, and the corresponding layer, which is less clearly developed, is called the F_1 layer.

If the rolling-ball method were used for mapping the contours of a hill it would be interesting to know, not only the height of the

* The E layer was at one time called the Kennelly-Heaviside layer and the F layer the Appleton layer.

hill, as deduced from the 'critical ball speed', but also the detailed contours of the slope which led up to the peak. It so happens that this can be deduced if the time of travel of the ball, from the moment of projection to the moment of return, is measured for a series of different speeds. In the radio case the analogy is exact and the electron density contours, which show the shape of the electron layer, can be deduced from a knowledge of how the equivalent height h' depends on the wave frequency f, a knowledge which is represented in the $h'(f)$ curve.

Most of our knowledge of the ionized layers is derived from $h'(f)$ curves. Since the critical frequencies are easily observed they have been used widely: the deduction of electron density contours from $h'(f)$ curves is complicated and has been carried out extensively at only one or two places.

The Well-behaved Layers—The E and F1 Layers

If a layer were produced according to simple theory, by an ionizing radiation coming from the Sun, the electron concentration at its peak would be expected to depend on two things. First it would depend on the rate at which electrons were produced, and that would depend, amongst other things, on the slope of the Sun's rays, as measured by the angle which they made with the vertical the so-called *solar zenith angle*. Second, after being produced the electrons would tend to disappear again, by re-attaching themselves to air atoms or molecules, and the number present at any one time would be determined by the balance between these two processes. When production is predominant the number will, on the whole increase, when disappearance is predominant the number will decrease, and when the two balance the number will remain constant.

By making observations at those times when the number in the peak of a layer is found to be constant, and by considering in detail how the electrons disappear, it is possible to deduce how the critical frequency of a simple layer should vary with the solar zenith angle. These calculations can be compared with the results of observation. The solar zenith angle varies with the place on the Earth, with the time of day, and the time of the year, and it is found that, for the E and $F1$ layers there is rough agreement with the simple theory.

As so often happens in any branch of science the agreement is, however, not quite exact, and although the observations establish the fact that the layers are produced in the way suggested, they indicate the importance of certain disturbing factors, probably associated with movements of the layers. These small discrepancies in the behaviour of the layers seem to be different at different parts of the Earth and their examination in more detail during the IGY will doubtless lead to interesting results. On the whole however, the E and $F1$ layers behave much as would be expected on simple theory, they are the 'well-behaved' layers of the ionosphere.

The Peculiar Layer—The F2 Layer

It is quite different with the $F2$ layer. Its behaviour is peculiar and unexpected in many respects and, as with human beings, it is all the more interesting for that reason. The peculiarities are immediately obvious from an examination of its critical frequency. According to simple theory this should reach a maximum value soon after the Sun is highest in the sky at midday, and this midday maximum should itself be greatest on those days and at those places where the midday Sun reaches its greatest height, that is in summer and near the equator. Observation shows, however, that under many circumstances the critical frequency behaves quite differently, so that, for example, there is often a *decrease* near midday; the midwinter maximum is often *greater* than the midsummer; and the values near the equator are markedly *less* than those at some distance North or South.

These anomalies might be explained in more than one way. The peculiar behaviour might be in the ionizing radiation responsible for the layer, in the atmospheric gas which it ionizes, or it might be the result of large-scale movements of the electrons after they have been produced. A decision between these different possibilities is assisted by an examination of the electron distribution contours which can be derived from the $h'(f)$ curves. It then appears almost certain that what makes the $F2$ layer peculiar is not that the processes of electron production are unusual, but that there are large-scale vertical movements of the electrons, as a result of which the layer is 'squashed in' or 'pulled out' with a consequent increase or decrease of the electron concentration at the peak.

Much of the present-day work on the ionosphere is directed

towards investigations of the F_2 layer and deduction of these large-scale movements. It is not, however, yet clear what causes them. They might follow from the heating of the air by the Sun's radiation, and the corresponding cooling at night, or they might be the result of electro-magnetic forces acting on the electrons. The present-day view inclines to the latter explanation, which is considered in more detail in the next section.

ELECTRIC CURRENTS IN THE HIGH ATMOSPHERE

It was mentioned earlier that magnetic observations seemed to show that electric currents flow somewhere in the high atmosphere, and calculation indicates that these are of considerable strength, so that, for example about 50,000 amperes flow overhead between England and the equator. Now electric currents usually need a battery or a dynamo to drive them, and in 1902 A. Schuster set himself to find where this driving force could be. He realized that, in a dynamo, wires, attached to a moving 'armature', are swept by a 'driving force' through a magnetic field produced by a 'field magnet', and he looked around in the atmosphere for the corresponding component parts of an 'atmospheric dynamo'. He came to the conclusion that the atmosphere at a height of about 60 miles was itself a huge dynamo, in which the 'armature wires' were replaced by the conducting layer itself, the 'field magnet' was the Earth and its magnetic field, and the 'driving force' was the gravitational attraction of the Sun and Moon. This force produces a tidal oscillation in the air, just as it does in the sea, and this oscillation carries the ionospheric electrons with it across the Earth's magnetic field, so that currents are caused to flow. Schuster was able to show that these currents would be of the right sort to produce the observed magnetic variations. The ionosphere is thus a huge power station, driven by the action of the atmospheric tides, much as a man-made power station might be driven by the action of the sea tides.

It might be thought that if the tidal movements of the air were to be sufficient to produce the large currents required they would be evident at ground level either as tidal winds, or as variations of the barometric pressure. Usually, however, hour-to-hour variations accompanying the ordinary weather changes are sufficient to mask the small effects occurring, and, if the tidal motion is to be easily noticeable, it is necessary to examine records from a place where the weather conditions are particularly uniform. Another way of showing up the tidal effect on the barometer, even at a place where weather changes are important, is to examine a very long series of records and use a type of analysis in which variations occurring regularly, as in a tide, are caused to show themselves up compared with any variations which are quite irregular, like the ordinary weather. In this way periodic tidal variations of pressure, which were only 0·4 per cent of the mean daily variation, have been discovered by studying the barometric records made at Greenwich over a period of 63 years.

The analogy with a power station is not finished when the atmospheric dynamo has been located. A dynamo is usually connected, by wires, to an electric motor, which is an instrument, just like the dynamo itself, with an armature carrying wires which can move in the magnetic field of a field magnet. When current from the dynamo flows through these wires they move in the magnetic field and the armature rotates. Since the motor and the dynamo are similar in construction the whole arrangement is symmetrical, and each could play the part of the other: if either is rotated the other will rotate in sympathy.

In the atmosphere the place of the dynamo is taken by the E layer at a height near 60 miles, the place of the motor by the F layer near 150 miles, and the 'connecting wires' consist of the intervening conducting ionosphere. The analogy with wires is quite close, because in the ionosphere conduction takes place most readily along the lines of force of the Earth's magnetic field, and these lines lead upwards from the E to the F layer. Then, just as in the power-station model, if either the E or the F region is moved by an outside force it will act as a dynamo, currents will flow into the other region and it will move in turn, acting like a motor. It is thought that, in the ionosphere, the primary driving force is that of the tides in the E layer, the 'dynamo' is there, and the 'motor' in the F region moves because of the currents passing through it from the dynamo.

The calculation of the detailed movements of the two regions is complicated and is not yet at all certain. Enough is known, however, to show that vertical movements produced in this way could be quite important in the F layer, and might explain some, if not all, of its pecularities.

The calculations also show that the tidal forces should produce horizontal movements in the E layer, and that these should be accompanied by *horizontal* movements in the F layer, so that it is next of interest to see whether the reflected radio waves carry any evidence of movements of this kind.

HORIZONTAL MOVEMENTS OF THE IONOSPHERE

If a radio wave reflected from the ionosphere is observed simultaneously at several points on the ground, it is found that its strength is continually varying, and the variations are appreciably different at points more than about one wavelength* apart. The strength of the wave is distributed over the ground in the form of an irregular pattern which is continually changing and moving. From this it is deduced that the ionosphere which reflects the waves also contains irregularities which are always on the move, and from a study of the irregular pattern on the ground it should be possible to determine their shapes and movements.

It is as though light was reflected from the rippling surface of a pond or stream on to a ceiling where it produced an irregular pattern of darker and lighter patches, from which it was required to make deductions about the nature of the water surface. The ionospheric problem is one stage more complicated because there the reflection is not all from the surface and variations in depth have to be taken into account. It is not easy to deduce the ionospheric structure in detail and there are still serious doubts about some of the conclusions which have been drawn, but one deduction seems fairly clear and useful. If the wave-pattern on the ground is found to move, on the average, with a smooth drift then it can be supposed that the ionosphere itself is also drifting horizontally. In the same way if the irregular pattern reflected from the water were found to drift steadily across the ceiling it could be deduced that the surface of the water was moving in the same direction.

There are other methods of observing horizontal movements in the ionosphere. One of these makes use of the fact that radio waves are reflected from the short-lived ionized trails which meteors leave behind. when they traverse the E layer (Chapter 15). Another depends on the existence of large-scale irregularities in the

* Experiments of this kind are most commonly made on a frequency of about 3 Mc/s for which the wave-length is 100 metres.

layer, of the order of 5 to 50 miles in size, and provides a means of measuring their movements.

All these measurements show that horizontal drifts occur in both the E and F layers, and that these are similar at different places on the Earth. The drift in the E layer is found to contain a component which rotates twice in twenty-four hours, and is probably related to the atmospheric tidal motion which drives the E layer 'dynamo'. More wide-spread observations during the IGY should make this relation more precise.

The drift in the F layer varies differently through the day and has not yet been properly explained. Part of it, at least, is probably caused by the 'motor effect' previously discussed. It is quite possible that the movements of the large irregularities do not represent bodily movements of the electrons, but constitute a compressional wave-motion travelling through them. It would then be as though, in our previous analogy, the movements of the irregular light-pattern on the ceiling were the result, not of bodily movement of the reflecting water, but of a wave moving over its surface under the action of a wind. The cause of the possible wave in the F layer is a matter of considerable discussion, but no satisfactory explanation has yet been offered.

THE SUN AND THE IONOSPHERE

Since it is established that the ionosphere owes its existence to the ionizing radiation coming from the Sun it is to be expected that any disturbances of that radiation would cause detectable disturbances in the ionosphere, and that a study of the effect of these radio waves would provide a powerful method for investigating the Sun, even when it was obscured by cloud. Now if the Sun is examined in visible light, either directly or by means of a spectrohelioscope which selects light of one wave-length, it is sometimes found that there are disturbed regions on its surface over which the emission is either stronger or weaker than usual. Those which are too weak are visible in ordinary light and are called sunspots: the total area which they occupy on the Sun's disc is represented by a number called the sunspot number. It is well-known that this number varies cyclically having maxima once about every eleven years and the year 1957–58, chosen for the IGY, is expected to be near one of these. The variation in the spottedness from minimum through maximum and back to minimum again is termed the *solar cycle*.

When the Sun is observed in light of a certain wave-length emitted by hydrogen, it is often found that a bright flash, starting suddenly and lasting for five or ten minutes, is visible over a limited area on the disc. These flashes are called *solar flares*; they usually occur near large sunspots, and are of particular importance for the present discussions.

The ionospheric phenomena accompanying disturbances on the Sun are of two kinds, one called a *sudden ionosphere disturbance* (S.I.D.) and the other an *ionosphere storm*. Both types are likely to be intensively studied during the IGY. Their characteristics are described below.

S.I.D's frequently accompany solar flares. They start suddenly, last for about 15 to 30 minutes, and are noticeable all over the sunlit side of the Earth. It is believed that they are caused by an increase in the Sun's output of ionizing radiation, probably in the ultra-violet, accompanying the increase in the visible radiation observed in the spectro-helioscope. The particular ultra-violet wave-length involved is rather more penetrating than the normal ultra-violet and forms most of its electrons low down, below the peak of the *E* layer. The relatively great increase of electrons at these low levels, where collisions are more frequent, produces strong absorption of radio waves, and the most obvious effect of an S.I.D. on radio waves is a great decrease in their strength. This decrease is called a *fade-out* and it can be exceedingly troublesome for commercial users of radio, who find that all their communication channels on the sunlit side of the Earth go out of action simultaneously. Fortunately, however, they usually return to service within about one half or three quarters of an hour.

If very low frequency waves are observed during an S.I.D. it is found that, instead of being more strongly absorbed they are increased in strength, a phenomenon which is ascribed to the fact that they are reflected from, rather than absorbed by, the increased layer of electrons produced at low levels by the flare. This phenomenon is made use of by recording the strength of the very low frequency waves, known as *radio atmospherics*, which are emitted by the electrical discharges of lightning flashes. The occurrence of an S.I.D. shows itself on these records as a sudden increase of the recorded strength. Many astronomical observatories make use of records of this kind to supplement their visual observations of the Sun, since the radio observations are not interfered with by the presence of cloud.

The other type of ionospheric disturbance, known as an ionosphere storm, is quite different. It occurs equally frequently by day and by night, and is of longer duration, lasting for hours or even days. In low and medium latitudes this type of storm is mainly evidenced by a radical change in the distribution of electrons in the F layer, and an accompanying alteration in the F critical frequency. In high latitudes it is also accompanied by a marked increase in the electron content at low levels, so that the absorption of waves is increased, sometimes catastrophically, and the event is spoken of as a *polar black-out*. Both these occurrences, the reduction of the F layer critical frequency, and the polar black-out, can have damaging effects on the performance of commercial communication channels and, since a storm can occur both on the light and the dark side of the Earth, and can sometimes last for days, the disturbances to the world's communications can be serious.

It often happens that an ionosphere storm is accompanied by an irregular movement of the compass needle quite different in type from the smaller regular movement which occurs each day. These *magnetic storms* as they are called, are sometimes said to 'cause' the disturbance of radio communications; it is more reasonable to say that both are results of some other underlying 'cause'. There is evidence that this primary cause has its greatest effect near the poles of the Earth; we have already seen that the polar black-out occurs there, the magnetic storm is found to be most intense there, and often the aurora occurs there at the same time. It is believed that all these polar disturbances are caused by a stream of charged particles, emitted from the Sun, and guided towards the polar regions by the Earth's magnetic field (Chapter 14). The rapidly moving particles ionize the air through which they pass and produce both the visible light of the aurora and the electrons responsible for the polar black-out. These same electrons add considerably to the conductivity of the lower ionosphere so that the atmospheric dynamo is seriously upset, and the resulting changes in the current system are manifested as the magnetic storm. The disturbance in the 'dynamo' also leads to different movements of the 'atmospheric motor' so that the F layer is also seriously distorted at these times.

Although the two types of disturbance, the S.I.D. and the ionosphere storm, are so different in their effects, they are, on some occasions, closely related. It often happens that an ionosphere storm follows a large S.I.D. after an interval of about 36 hours, and on these occasions it seems that the stream of charged particles which caused the storm left the Sun 36 hours earlier, simultaneously with the occurrence of the solar flare which produced the S.I.D. This association of an S.I.D. and an ionosphere storm is not always observed, but when it is it is very striking. It has sometimes been used to warn commercial radio users of the imminence of an ionosphere storm which might disrupt their communications.

WORLD-WIDE STUDIES AND THE INTERNATIONAL GEOPHYSICAL YEAR

The formation and movements of the ionospheric layers take place on a world-wide scale, and if they are to be properly understood they must be studied over a period of at least one year, at several places simultaneously. It is planned to make use of the IGY to conduct this study.

The simplest form of study, that of recording $h'(f)$ curves, is already in progress at many places: what is required in addition is the analysis of many of those curves to give electron density contours, and arrangements are being made for this to be done. From those contours the knowledge of the detailed behaviour of the $F2$ layer should be much improved, so that the theories of vertical movement can be properly tested and the correct ones selected and refined.

The horizontal movements of both the E and F layers have, so far, only been studied in two or three places in detail; an extension of the observations during the IGY should clarify their world-wide distribution.

The most interesting result of the ionospheric observations will probably relate to the world-wide nature of S.I.D's and ionosphere storms. The proper understanding of both these phenomena requires the making of frequent observations of a detailed nature, at many places on the Earth. A simultaneous study of the happenings on the Sun, and of the disturbances of the Earth's magnetic field at several places should enable a detailed picture to be built up.

Although the E and F_1 layers are, on the whole, well behaved, they do, none the less, show some interesting anomalies of a comparatively small magnitude, and if these are studied on a world-wide basis their explanation will probably be found.

CHAPTER THIRTEEN

The Airglow

D. R. BATES

EVEN IN the absence of the Moon the sky is not completely black during a clear night, it is instead faintly luminescent. This is partly due to the stars but mainly to an emission from the atmosphere known as the *airglow*. The emission occurs throughout the twenty-four hours. It is customary to refer to the nocturnal part as the *nightglow* and to make analogous use of the terms *twilight airglow* and *dayglow*.

The nightglow and the twilight airglow have been studied extensively, but the dayglow has as yet received little attention.

NIGHTGLOW

The nightglow is extremely feeble, the illumination it gives to the ground being only of the same order as that from a candle at a height of 100 yards. In contrast to the much more intense aurorae* (Chapter 14) it does not exhibit structure (such as arcs) and covers the entire sky at all latitudes.

The principal questions to be answered are as follows: What are the characteristics of the luminescence? From what region of the atmosphere does it originate? To what is it due?

Spectrum†

Most light is a blend of different colours, that is, it contains components of different wave-lengths. In investigating a source it is important to determine the precise blend emitted. The determination may be carried out with the aid of a spectroscope. This gives what is called the *spectrum* of the light which is simply a record of how the intensity varies with the wave-length. If the source is a hot solid, such as the filament of an electric light bulb,

---

* An aurora may be 10,000 or more times brighter than the nightglow.
† See Appendix VI.

223

the variation is slow and smooth. However, if the source is gaseous the variation is much more interesting, for there are then sharp peaks in the intensity at certain wave-lengths, which show in the spectrum as *lines* or *bands* according to whether the emission is due to *atoms* or *molecules*. From the wave-lengths of these spectral features it is possible to identify the radiating atoms or molecules provided adequate comparison data for known sources are available. Thanks to this astronomers have been able to determine the compositions of distant stars and nebulae.

The nightglow was not analysed at all fully until recently. There are two main reasons for the lack of early success. Firstly, the intensity of the nightglow is so weak that even with modern instruments extremely lengthy exposures are required to obtain a good spectrum; and secondly, at the time of their discovery many of the emissions had not been produced in a laboratory source so that they could not be recognized immediately.

Towards the end of the last century a feature, called the auroral green line because of its prominence in aurorae, was detected in the nightglow. Its origin was for long a mystery. Many theories were advanced—amongst them that the upper atmosphere contains a hitherto unknown gas, geokoronium. In 1923 a vital contribution towards the solution of the problem was made by H. D. Babcock, who by very accurate measurements showed the wave-length to be $5577 \cdot 350 A$. Scientists were then unaware of any line having precisely this wave-length, but within a year J. C. McLennan succeeded in proving that atomic oxygen possesses such a line. A simple source is an electrical discharge through a mixture of oxygen and argon (or other inert gas).

As is now realized the auroral green line belongs to a special class which is termed *forbidden* in contradistinction to the more usual class which is termed *allowed*. An excited atom does not radiate instantaneously, it remains in the excited state for a time. The average time it so remains when free from external disturbance is called its *radiative life*. If an allowed line can be emitted the radiative life is extremely brief—perhaps of the order of 1×10^{-8} (one hundredth of a millionth) of a second. However, if only forbidden lines can be emitted, the radiative life may be several seconds or even several hours. Such lines are therefore not easy to produce in the laboratory, since before the atoms can radiate they are likely to be removed from the excited state through striking some surface, or through making collisions with other atoms; but the emission of forbidden lines from the upper atmosphere is not hindered to any very marked extent, surfaces of course being absent and collisions between atoms being relatively rare at the low gas densities prevailing there.

Atomic oxygen also possesses a pair of forbidden lines called the *nebular red lines*. In 1928 V.M. Slipher found that these contribute to the nightglow. Indeed, apart from the auroral green line the stronger of the nebular red lines is the most prominent feature in the visible part of the spectrum. The occurrence of emissions from *atomic* oxygen is consistent with the conclusions that have been reached regarding the constitution of the upper atmosphere (cf. Chapter 7).

In the year in which he discovered the presence of the nebular red lines, Slipher noticed a yellow feature in the nightglow spectrum and commented on its closeness to a pair of allowed atomic sodium lines, of wave-lengths 5890 A and 5895 A, known as the D-doublet.* The proximity was originally thought to be a coincidence, for it did not seem probable that a chemically reactive metallic element like sodium could be an atmospheric constituent. However, in 1938 R. Bernard, J. Cabannes and other French workers reported a careful series of observations establishing beyond doubt that the yellow feature is to be attributed to the D-doublet. As we shall see later the amount of sodium present is minute.

All the features mentioned so far are atomic lines. The first generally accepted identification of molecular bands was not made until 1943 when P. Swings showed that the principal features in the ultra-violet part of the spectrum are due to a forbidden system of oxygen (O_2), named the Herzberg system. Progress then became more rapid mainly as a result of the work of A. B. Meinel at Yerkes Observatory, who in 1948 identified a prominent infra-red feature as a band belonging to another forbidden system of oxygen; and in 1950 proved that a forbidden system of hydroxyl (OH) accounts for the remaining infra-red features (which, incidentally, are far more intense than the auroral green line), and in addition for many visible features.

Contrary to early beliefs, bands of nitrogen (N_2) appear to be too

---

* It may be remarked that the D-doublet is the principal emission from the sodium vapour lamps that are widely used for street lighting.

weak to be detected with present techniques. The nightglow
spectrum obviously give no indication of the relative abundance
of the atmospheric constituents.

Seat of Luminescence

In principle it is possible to find the altitude of a thin uniform
luminous layer from observations made on the ground. As is
apparent from Fig. 1 a vertical line of sight passes through a

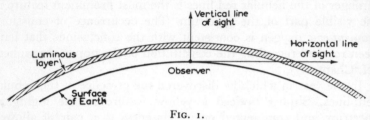

FIG. 1.

smaller thickness of such a layer than does a horizontal line of
sight. If there were no absorption by the lower atmosphere, a
light-meter pointed vertically would record correspondingly less
intensity than would one pointed horizontally. The ratio of the two
intensities can be expressed as a function of the altitude of the layer.
This altitude may therefore be calculated if the ratio is measured.

Much effort has been devoted to the method but unfortunately
it has proved of little practical value: thus the luminosity is not
strictly uniform; the influence of extra-terrestrial light is difficult to
eliminate completely; the correction for atmospheric absorption is
considerable and rather uncertain, and the calculated altitude is
unduly sensitive to the measured ratio of the intensities. The
altitudes obtained differ widely—they range from less than 50
miles to more than 500 miles. No reliance can be placed on them.

An important advance was made in 1955 by R. Tousey and his
associates of the U.S. Naval Research Laboratory using light-
meters mounted on an Aerobee rocket flown at night. From the
changes in the recorded intensities of the spectral features studied,
they were able to tell when the rocket penetrated the luminous
layers concerned. They succeeded in showing that the auroral
green line of oxygen originates from near the 60 mile level, and that
the D-doublet of atomic sodium originates from near the 55 mile
level. It seems not improbable that the luminous layers responsible for the other spectral features lie in the same general region

of the atmosphere. Further measurements are planned. Light-meters will be included in the equipment carried by some of the Skylark rockets to be launched from the Woomera range in Australia.

Theory

We require to know how the energy that is used in the night-glow is stored and how it is converted into light.

Since energy is needed to break an oxygen molecule into atoms it follows that energy is released when a pair of oxygen atoms unite to form a molecule. The atomic oxygen in the upper at-mosphere (Chapter 7) thus acts as a chemical reservoir of energy. Many years ago S. Chapman pointed out that the total amount of energy in this reservoir is sufficient to maintain the nightglow at the observed, approximately constant intensity from sunset to sunrise—when the reservoir is replenished owing to the disrup-tion of molecular oxygen by the solar ultra-violet radiation (Chapter 7). Chapman also gave reasons for believing that other reservoirs which have been suggested do not contain enough energy. His views are now generally accepted.

Controversy still exists concerning the detailed mechanisms by which excitation is produced. However, it is certain that at least two types of mechanism are involved. There must be a rapid type for the rare constituents, hydroxyl and atomic sodium; and there must be a slow type for the plentiful constituents, atomic and molecular oxygen. Otherwise, the relative intensities of the emissions could not be as observed.

Chemical reactions result from collisions between atoms and molecules. For present purposes it is sufficient to consider only the following classes:

(i) *Rearrangement collisions*—e.g. an atom A and a molecule BC collide yielding a molecule AB and an atom C, either or both of which may be excited.

(ii) *Association collisions*—e.g. an atom X and an atom Y collide with each other *and* with an atom or molecule T yielding a molecule XY, which may be excited, and leaving T unchanged except that it also may be excited.*

* If the so-called third body T did not take part in the collision, the atoms X and Y could not stick together to form the molecule XY—they would instead bounce off one another.

Reactions of class (i), many of which are very fast, account fo the occurrence in the nightglow spectrum of the hydroxyl band and of the D-doublet of atomic sodium. Members of this class are highly selective in the excitation they produce. Some may contri bute to the emissions from atomic and molecular oxygen, but reactions of class (ii) are mainly responsible for these emissions The relatively great abundance of atomic and molecular oxygen in the upper atmosphere offsets the infrequency of the *triple* col lisions involved.

It may be noted that the amount of excitation energy that can be supplied in a collision is quite low. Since the bands of molecula nitrogen and the allowed emissions from the major constituents have rather high excitation energies their absence from the night glow spectrum is at once understandable.

The presence of the hydroxyl bands is probably due to ozone (O_3) reacting with atomic hydrogen (H) to give molecular oxygen (O_2) and excited hydroxyl (OH). After emission the hydroxy reacts with atomic oxygen (O) giving more molecular oxygen and liberating the atomic hydrogen which is thus not consumed. Both reactions are of class (i). The energy for the sequence comes from the indirect conversion of *odd* oxygen atoms (free or in ozone into oxygen molecules.

It is possible that all the oxygen emissions arise from a simple reaction of class (ii), since the oxygen molecule formed when two oxygen atoms unite may be in an excited state, and since, in addi tion, an excited oxygen atom may result from such union if the necessary third body happens to be an oxygen atom.

Other reactions are of importance, but an account of them would be too long to be given here.

TWILIGHT AIRGLOW AND DAYGLOW

The spectrum of the *twilight airglow* is the same as that of the nightglow except that the D-doublet of atomic sodium and the nebular red lines of atomic oxygen are much more intense; and except also that bands of ionized molecular nitrogen* and prob ably a forbidden line of atomic nitrogen occur. It is clear that the additional emissions must be caused by the action of sunlight. We shall confine ourselves to discussing the enhancement of the

* An ionized nitrogen molecule is an ordinary nitrogen molecule with one electron removed.

D-doublet, this being the simplest, and perhaps the most interesting, effect.

When the Sun is just below an observer's horizon, part of the upper atmosphere is illuminated. The solar radiation passing through cannot, of course, be detected. However, all does not pass through. Radiation in the immediate wave-length region of the D-doublet is absorbed by the atomic sodium present, which then emits it again in random directions so that some reaches the observer. In effect each sodium atom acts like a tiny mirror suspended far above the Earth's surface, the mirror having the peculiar property of reflecting light of a certain yellow colour and being transparent to light of all other colours.

The absorption and emission sequence is so simple that it may be treated mathematically, and a formula has been derived relating the amount of atomic sodium in the upper atmosphere to the intensity of the D-doublet in the spectrum of the twilight airglow. From the measured intensity it is found that atomic sodium forms only about 1×10^{-12} (one millionth of a millionth) of the atmosphere above the 50 mile level. A constituent so rare might originate in a number of ways—it might for example be deposited by meteors.

The *dayglow* cannot be studied from the ground, because of interference from sunlight scattered by the lower atmosphere. Its spectrum is expected to be rather similar to, but far richer than, that of the twilight airglow. Attempts have been made to carry out observations with rocket borne instruments, but these have not met with much success.

ARTIFICIAL AIRGLOWS

A cubic mile of the upper atmosphere contains less sodium than would go on the head of a pin. Nevertheless, the D-doublet is emitted strongly at night and very strongly during the twilight periods. This suggested that a glow intense enough to be seen easily with the unaided eye would be produced if a few pounds of sodium were vaporized and ejected into the upper atmosphere from a rocket. The experiment was first carried out in 1955 by a group of American scientists working under the direction of J. F. Bedinger. An intense yellow glow that was visible even at great distances from the firing site resulted. From the motion of the glow it was found that there was a wind of 180 miles per hour from the north-west near the 50 mile level, and a wind of 100 miles per hour from the south-east near the 7⊚ mile level.

Clearly a man-made sodium cloud is a useful tool for the exploration of the upper atmosphere. In their rocket research programme, the British plan to exploit this new tool further; thus with its aid they hope to obtain information on the temperature, turbulence and certain other properties of the air at great altitudes. In addition, the British intend to study the effect of ejecting the metallic element potassium in vapour form. Instead of glowing *yellow* like a sodium cloud, a potassium cloud would glow *red*.

Recently M. Zelikoff of the U.S. Air Force Research Directorate arranged for the gas nitric oxide (NO) to be released from a night flown rocket at an altitude of about 60 miles. A spectacular glow lasting about 10 minutes ensued, due to the fact that the presence of nitric oxide facilitates the conversion into radiation of the energy stored by the atomic oxygen in the atmosphere. The observations made on the glow provided valuable information concerning several chemical reactions.

CHAPTER FOURTEEN

Aurorae and Magnetic Storms

V. C. A. FERRARO

THE STUDY of the Earth's magnetism dates from the sixteenth century. In 1600 William Gilbert, physician to Queen Elizabeth I, put forward the hypothesis that the Earth is a great magnet in his book *De Magnete*. Henry Gellibrand, a London instrument maker, discovered in 1635 that the Earth's magnetism was not constant, but showed a slow variation from year to year, now called the *secular variation*. In the eighteenth century George Graham discovered the transient variations. His discovery was confirmed by Andreas Celsius at Upsala in 1740 and his observations were continued by Olav P. Hiorter. Edmund Halley described in the *Philosophical Transactions of the Royal Society* the remarkable aurora of March 6, 1716, and prophetically put forward the view that aurorae are caused by 'magnetic effluvia' which are constrained to move along the direction of the Earth's magnetism.

The connection between the polar aurora and magnetic disturbances, that is, periods when the magnetic needle becomes greatly agitated, was discovered by Hiorter in 1741. 'Who could have thought,' he writes, 'that the northern lights would have a connection and a sympathy with the magnet, and that these northern lights . . . could within a few minutes cause considerable oscillations of the magnetic needle through whole degrees? The first time that I saw an aurora to the south and noted simultaneously a great movement of the magnetic needle was on March 1, 1741, in the evening. . . . When I announced this to the professor (Andreas Celsius) he said that he had noted such a disturbance of the needle in similar circumstances, but had not wished to mention it in order to see . . . whether I, too, would light on the same speculation.'

The polar aurorae are amongst the most beautiful of natural

phenomena. They were known to the ancient Greeks and Romans, and are mentioned by Aristotle, Pliny and Seneca. The aurorae are most frequently seen in high latitudes, north and south; they may last a few minutes but more often the display lasts for several hours or even the whole night. They vary greatly in form, colour and intensity and change rapidly in position. Yet their brightness seldom exceeds that of the full Moon.

There are vivid descriptions of the aurorae by Norwegians as early as the thirteenth century, such as the following passage from *The King's Mirror* written in 1250.

'This is the nature and constitution of the northern light, that it is always the brighter, the darker the night, and it is seen only at night, never by day, and especially in the profound obscurity and rarely by moonlight. It appears like a flame of strong fire seen from afar. Pointed shafts of unequal and very variable size dart upward into the air, so that now the one and now the other is the higher, and the light is floating like a shining blaze. So long as these rays are highest and brightest, this sparkling fire gives so much light, out of doors, one can find one's way about and even hunt. . . . But this light is so variable, that it sometimes seems to grow obscure, as if a dark smoke or a thick fog is breathed on it, and soon the light seems to be stifled in this smoke and near extinct. But as soon as this fog grows less thick, the light is pierced and brightens again, and sometimes it seems to shoot out big sparks, like a red-hot iron taken from the forge. As night ends and dawn approaches, the light begins to pale, and disappears when day breaks!'

The first observation of an aurora in the southern hemisphere appears to have been made by Captain James Cook in 1773 who gave it the name of *aurora australis*; the northern light had long been known as the *aurora borealis*. Observations show that there is little difference between the northern and southern lights. Both are accompanied by disturbances of the Earth's magnetic field; at times when these disturbances are intense, aurorae are seen from many parts of the world and even in low latitudes.

One of the most striking features of these intense disturbances, or *magnetic storms*, is that they begin suddenly and almost simultaneously all over the Earth. They show great variety in detail but there is nevertheless a certain regularity about their average characteristics.

MAGNETIC STORMS

The Variations of the Earth's Magnetic Field

A small bar magnet freely pivoted about its centre of gravity takes up a definite position at any point of the Earth's surface, thus indicating the presence of magnetic forces around the Earth. The magnetic state which surrounds a magnet is conveniently referred to as its *magnetic field*. The direction of the field can be made visible by iron filings which show that 'lines of force', that is, lines drawn such that the tangent at any point is in the direction of the magnetic force at that point. A force has magnitude and direction and can therefore be represented, on a suitable scale, by a directed segment, or *vector*. This vector is called the *intensity* of the magnetic field and requires three elements for its definition. In the case of the Earth's magnetic field the elements usually used are the horizontal and vertical components of the intensity, which are denoted respectively by H and V, and the angle made by the *magnetic meridian*, that is, the vertical plane through the vector, with the geographical north. This angle is called the *declination* and is denoted by D, whilst H and V are conveniently referred to as the *horizontal* and *vertical* forces.

In the last century, mainly due to the efforts of the German mathematician C. F. Gauss, magnetic observatories were built to obtain systematic observations of the intensity of the Earth's magnetic field and its variation. At first this was done by continuous visual records; later these gave way to photographic recording,

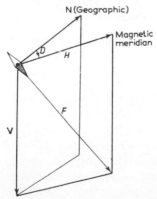

FIG. 1.   Illustrating the horizontal and vertical forces H and V which together make up the resultant intensity of the field F. The declination is the angle D made by the magnetic meridian and geographic north.

the three elements most frequently recorded being the horizontal and vertical forces H and V and the declination D. The magneto-grams (as these recordings are called) show that each element is not constant but on some days undergoes smooth regular variations, while on others the elements are more or less disturbed (Fig. 2).

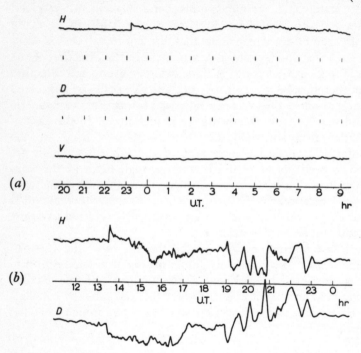

FIG. 2.   Variation in the elements H, V, D on a calm day, and slightly disturbed day.

The annual means of these variations at an observatory show that the Earth's field undergoes changes over long periods of time. This is called the *secular variation*. It is almost certainly of internal origin, though no satisfactory explanation of this variation has as yet been put forward (Chapter 6). The transient variations, on the other hand, are of external origin. Days of magnetic calm are called *quiet* days; days when the variations in these elements are more intense and regular are called *disturbed* days.

Except for periods of extreme activity, it appears that magnetic disturbances may be regarded as due to the superposition on a regular daily variation with a period of 24 hours, called the *diurnal variations*, of an additional disturbance field D (which is not to be confused with the declination). The intensity of the disturbance varies greatly with latitude and time. But intense disturbance is a world-wide phenomenon affecting both the northern and southern hemispheres simultaneously. Such intense world-wide magnetic disturbances are called *magnetic storms*. When extremely violent, they interrupt telegraphic and radio communication over great distances owing to currents induced in cables and to ionospheric effects.

Storm-time Variations

A comparison of magnetograms at different stations shows that magnetic storms are not only world-wide but that they often begin suddenly and almost simultaneously—within two or three minutes at most—all over the world. The sudden onset of the storm is called the *sudden commencement* and is usually characterized by an increase in the horizontal force over a period of a minute.

Most magnetic storms show marked differences, as well as similarities, at different stations, and these differences are likely to be of local origin.

The average characteristics of magnetic storms were first analysed by the Indian geomagnetician N. F. Moos, for a number of magnetic storms recorded at Bombay. A more extensive analysis was subsequently carried out by S. Chapman, who analysed forty magnetic storms chosen from three groups of observatories situated in low, middle and high latitudes, and whose times of commencement were fairly well distributed over the twenty-four hours of the day. The arithmetic mean of each of the three elements representing the disturbance one hour, two hours, etc., from the beginning of the storm are called the *storm-time variations*, and denoted by the symbol D_{st}, the *storm-time* being reckoned from the time of the sudden commencement. The results obtained by Chapman are illustrated in Fig. 3; it will be seen from this that by far the largest variation occurs in H the horizontal force. This is increased for the first few hours of the storm, and thereafter it decreases to a minimum some ten hours later, after which there is a slow recovery to the undisturbed mean. This minimum in H is deeper than the earlier maximum increase. The period of recovery may last for several days—indeed the Earth's magnetic field may truly be said to be constantly recovering from the effects of magnetic disturbance.

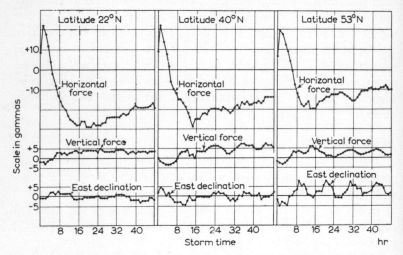

FIG. 3.   Illustrating the average storm-time variation in different latitudes for the three elements *H*, *V*, *D*.

The storm-time variations in the vertical component are similar but smaller and of opposite sign; they also differ in sign in the northern and southern hemisphere, unlike the variations in the horizontal force which shows no such reversal in the two hemispheres. The variations in the declination shows no systematic trend.

The period of increase in the horizontal force is called the *first phase* of the storm; the longer period of decrease is called the *main phase*. It is found that the more intense the storm the quicker it goes through its two phases.

These results indicate that there is practically no variation in the declination during a magnetic storm, so that normally the magnetic vectors representing this variation lie in the magnetic meridian planes. Since the variations in *V* are small compared with those in *H* the disturbance vector is nearly *horizontal*. During the main phase this vector is directed from North to South along magnetic meridians and it has the opposite sign during the first phase.

Disturbance Daily Variations

Owing to the nearly uniform distribution of the commencements over the twenty-four hours of the day of the storms chosen, the storm-time variations will not depend on local time.

If hourly means for this variation are subtracted from the hourly values for each successive hour of the day following the commencement of the storm, and the differences rewritten in columns corresponding to the local time, the mean in each column will give the mean solar daily variation of the element considered. This mean still contains the solar diurnal variation: when this is subtracted the residual is the *disturbance daily variation* denoted by S_D. It should be noted that this is not a diurnal variation in spite of its dependence on local time. In fact, some great magnetic storms are over in less than a day, and Chapman proposes to distinguish the disturbance daily variation for these cases by the symbol D_s.

The disturbance daily variation for the three groups of observatories considered by Chapman is shown in Figs. 4–6, for each of the elements H, V and D.

Chapman's analysis was confined to zones in middle and low latitudes. In high latitudes the disturbance field is more intense and complex than in lower latitudes, and the data indicates that there is a flow of currents along the auroral zones (see page 249), which Chapman has called the *auroral electrojets* (e.g. electric current limited laterally), and which clearly extend over the day as well as the night hemisphere. The flow is eastward over one half of each auroral zone, namely, lying over the post meridiem hemisphere, and is westward over the remaining half. The fact that this electrojet coincides with the auroral zones strongly suggests that part of the magnetic disturbance is due to currents flowing in the atmosphere. Magnetic and radio evidence point to a height of the electrojet of about 60 to 95 miles.

THE AURORAE

The Aurorae: Their Forms and Colour

We have already mentioned that magnetic storms are usually accompanied by striking displays of the aurorae. In the following sections we shall consider some of their characteristics.

Most aurorae appear to be composed of one or more principal

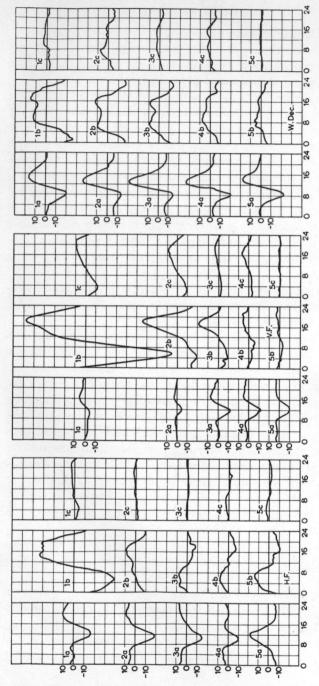

In FIGS. 4, 5, and 6, (a) represents the permanent diurnal magnetic variation which on quiet days appears alone; and (b) and (c) respectively represent the average diurnal effect of moderately strong and of relatively weak magnetic disturbances which are superimposed on this permanent variation. The numbers refer to the observing station: (1) Sitka, (2) Pavlovsk, (3) Greenwich, (4) Cheltenham, (5) Honolulu.

The vertical scale variations are in gammas

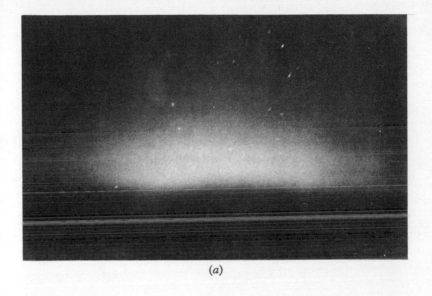

(a)

(b)

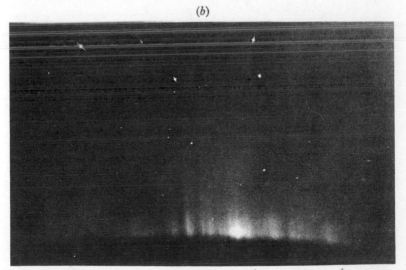

Fig. 7. Photograph of a homogeneous auroral arc (a) and rayed arc (b).

forms falling under two main types, namely, forms without ray structures and those with ray structures (Fig. 7).

Forms of the first type include the *homogeneous quiet arcs* which are sharply bounded at their lower edges but more diffuse along their upper borders. When near the horizon they have the semblance of a low bow. This is because the lower borders are very high, usually at an altitude of about 60 miles, and when seen from a distance of several hundred miles the arcs appear to follow the curvature of the Earth. The *homogeneous* bands are less regular than the arcs, but are more rapidly moving; usually they have one or more folds. The arcs may flash up and disappear regularly within a period of a few seconds; they are then called *pulsating arcs*. Or again, a diffuse veil or glow may appear over the greater part of the sky: this is called a *diffuse luminous surface*. On other occasions, a diffuse patch of light may appear and disappear at the same place with great rapidity forming a so-called *pulsating surface*.

The forms with ray structure consist of short or long rays which seem to converge towards the magnetic zenith along the lines of force of the Earth's magnetic field. These forms include the *rayed arc* and *rayed band*, which resemble the homogeneous arcs and bands but are formed of a series of rays which may be close together; *draperies*, which consist of one or more bands with very long rays giving the appearance of curtains; *rays*, which may be narrow or broad, short or long, either stationary or moving slowly from east to west or vice versa; the *corona*—often one of the most striking forms of the aurora—consisting of rays radiating from the magnetic zenith and terminating in a central ring of light.

An auroral display usually begins after sunset in the northern sky as a quiet homogeneous arc which slowly moves southward across the whole sky during the night. Gradually the arc splits into rays and draperies and at the height of the display develops a corona.

The predominant colour of the aurora is greenish yellow but sometimes it is bluish white or red; and at times of maximum solar activity it is of deep red. Draperies are greenish yellow with reddish blue streamers.

The Height of the Aurora. Sunlit Aurorae

The height and position of the aurora cannot be found from observations at a single station; it can be obtained by methods used in geodetic surveys, that is, from the azimuth and angular heights of an identifiable point of the aurora photographed from two stations at some distance apart, usually from 6 to 250 miles. Most of our knowledge of the height of the aurora is due to C. Störmer and L. Vegard. The relative frequency of the lower borders of the aurora at different stations is shown in Fig. 8 (after Störmer). All curves show pronounced maxima at heights around 65 miles; the figure also shows that the heights of the lower borders of the various forms of the aurora differ by only one or two miles. Occasionally the aurora descends to lower levels but the lower borders of draperies are seldom higher than 100 miles.

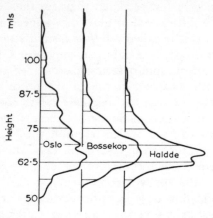

Fig. 8. Relative frequency of lower borders of aurorae for Haldde, Bossekop and Oslo.

Whilst the heights of the upper limit of arcs do not often exceed 100 miles, rays can extend to a height of 250 miles or more. On March 22–23, 1920, Störmer observed rays as high as 500 miles with a base at a height of 250 miles. On September 8, 1926, an auroral curtain of violet-grey colour, was seen from Oslo at a height of 200 to 300 miles, and this later became a diffuse cloud extending to 600 miles. Störmer found that these very high rays are situated in the sunlit part of the atmosphere over parts where the atmosphere is in the Earth's shadow up to 250 miles. Some rays consist of two luminous halves, one situated in the sunlit part of the atmosphere, the other in the dark portion along the continuation of the same line. The ray is thus divided by a dark segment along the shadow boundary (Fig. 9). These very high auroral rays are called *sunlit aurorae*; their distinguishing feature, apart from their great height, is the greyish-violet or blue colour.

Geographical Distribution

In 1881, Hermann Fritz drew a map showing the average relative frequency of nights with aurorae, using data from his catalogue of aurorae. This was reduced to a common epoch to eliminate yearly variation. He expressed the frequency as M nights per year. This diagram was revised by E. H. Vestine in 1945 and is

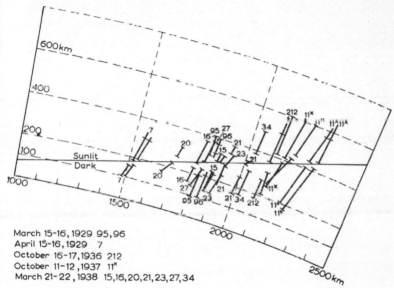

March 15-16, 1929 95,96
April 15-16, 1929   7
October 16-17, 1936 212
October 11-12, 1937 11ˣ
March 21-22, 1938 15,16,20,21,23,27,34

FIG. 9.   Sunlit aurora, showing divided auroral rays along the Earth's shadow line.

shown in Fig. 10. The curves represent the *isochasm* or lines of equal auroral frequency beginning with M equal to 0·1, that is, the line of one aurora in ten years. They are nearly circular with a line of maximum auroral frequency, called the *auroral zone*, of mean angular radius 23° centred near the pole of the geomagnetic axis.

Observations of the southern light are scanty and the corresponding diagram of isochasm for the Antarctic is incomplete. The radius of the auroral zone for this region appears to be smaller than for the arctic regions, being about 18°.

Diurnal Variation

In non-polar regions aurorae appear to be most frequent in the early night hours with a maximum usually one or two hours before midnight. The more brilliant displays occur prior to the times of maximum auroral frequency whilst faint glows are more frequent near morning. Aurorae are also more frequent at the time

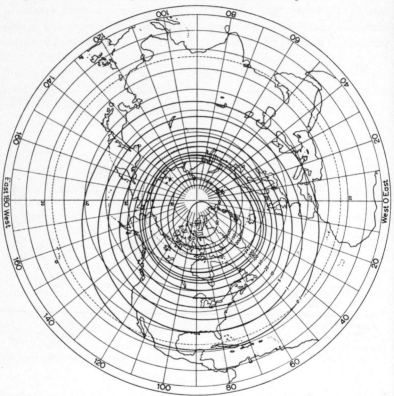

Fɪɢ. 10. Estimated annual frequency of days of visible auroral display, northern hemisphere (based on Fritz's data, 1700–1872, and later data, 1872–1942).

of the equinoxes but this equinoctial maximum is not so marked at polar stations. Fritz found a tendency for aurorae to recur after a period of about 27 or 28 days.

Connection with Geomagnetism

We have already noted the fact that auroral rays align themselves along magnetic lines of force of the Earth's field and that the mean

direction of arcs lies nearly parallel to the magnetic parallels of
latitude. The close connection between aurorae and magnetic
storms was noted as early as 1716 by Halley. Strong auroral
displays always accompany magnetic storms and when these are
intense the auroral zones widen and in the northern hemisphere
aurorae are seen in the tropics. It would appear that forms with
ray structures are more likely to be accompanied by magnetically
disturbed conditions than quiet homogeneous forms.

The Auroral Spectrum

As early as 1733 M. de Mairan gave good reason for rejecting
the hypothesis that the aurora is due to reflection of sunlight from
ice crystals. No strong polarization of the auroral light has indeed
ever been found so that the aurora is not due to reflected or
refracted light. It must therefore be self-luminous; the spectrum
of the aurora was first observed by A. J. Ångström in 1867 who
noted a strong line near 5570 Å in the yellow green region.
Much early work on the spectrum is due to Vegard and
later measurements in the visible portions were made by Lord
Rayleigh, V.M. Slipher, J. Kaplan and others. The spectrum
consists of the green and red forbidden lines of atomic oxygen
(Chapter 13); the first positive band of molecular nitrogen in the
red and infra red region; the second positive band of molecular
nitrogen in the ultra-violet region; the Vegard-Kaplan bands of
molecular nitrogen in the blue-violet and ultra violet region; and
the first negative band of singly ionized molecular nitrogen in the
blue-violet and ultra-violet regions. More recently, A.B. Meinel
has noted bands in the infra-red region, which are named after him.

The apparent absence from the auroral spectrum of hydrogen
lines was long considered as evidence of the absence of hydrogen
from the upper atmosphere. In 1939, Vegard noted an occasional
appearance of hydrogen Balmer lines in auroral spectra. These
observations were confirmed by both C. W. Gartlein and Meinel.
During the intense auroral display of August 18–19, 1950, Meinel
noted that the spectrum of an auroral homogeneous arc in the
magnetic zenith showed emission of the first hydrogen line
strongly asymmetric to the violet. As the spectrograph was then
pointed parallel to the magnetic lines of force, Meinel concluded
that protons must be approaching the Earth's atmosphere with a
speed which he estimated as over 2000 miles per second. This

AURORAE AND MAGNETIC STORMS

observation provided for the first time evidence that fast protons, probably of solar origin, are entering the upper atmosphere. The primary incoming protons will eject electrons in sufficient numbers and with moderate energy, on impact with atmospheric atoms and molecules to give rise to the greater part of the auroral luminosity.

Several detailed theories of the emission of the auroral spectrum have been put forward by Vegard, Chapman, Ta You Wu, D. R. Bates and H. S. W. Massey. Most of these depend on some collision process in which a secondary electron liberated from an atmospheric molecule or atom by the incoming particles, gives up its kinetic energy to excite another molecule or atom; this excitation is then followed by emission.

SOLAR RELATIONSHIPS WITH MAGNETIC STORMS AND AURORAE

Connection with Sunspots and Solar Flares

Galileo de Galilei made the first systematic study of dark markings on the Sun's surface called sunspots; he showed that their passage across the solar disc indicates that the Sun, like the Earth, revolves on an axis, refuting the notion that sunspots were but the visible transits of planets close to the Sun. Observations of the motion of sunspots and other surface markings across the solar disc gives the period of rotation to be about 27 days.

It was later discovered that the number and size of sunspots visible varied from year to year, and this was taken to imply that the Sun's activity waxes and wanes with a period which S. H. Schwabe, in 1843, found to be eleven years. This periodic variation of the Sun's activity is referred to as the *solar cycle*.

Magnetic activity follows a parallel eleven years cycle, disturbance is more frequent, and on the whole, more intense near the epoch of maximum sunspot activity than near the minimum sunspot epoch. Aurorae are likewise more frequent at sunspot maximum. On the other hand, periods of magnetic quiet sometimes coincide with a period when there are many sunspots, and conversely, magnetic disturbance may occur when there are no sunspots. It is seen, therefore, that sunspots themselves are not the direct cause of geomagnetic disturbance; there is general, but not detailed, correlation with sunspots. Nevertheless, as was first noted by E. W. Maunder in 1904, the greatest disturbances coincide, in general, with the presence of great spots near the centre of the Sun. Maunder was able to show that the onset of the storm occurred, on the average, about 26 hours after the central meridian passage of the spot. This was confirmed by statistical analysis carried out by G. Abetti and also by W.M.H. Greaves and H.W. Newton.

Bright chromospheric eruptions, or *solar flares*, are regions of the Sun's surface of 1,000 million square miles in extent which suddenly flare up to ten times the normal intensity of the hydrogen light. They are not long-lived and seldom last for more than half-an-hour. In 1944, Newton found a detailed relationship between magnetic storms and intense solar flares. He found that far more often than could occur by chance, an intense solar flare is followed about a day later by a great magnetic storm. This strongly suggested that the statistical relationships found between large sunspots and magnetic storms was one between flares and magnetic storms; in fact solar flares often occur during the development of a complex sunspot group.

Newton also found that the statistical mean time-interval between the occurrence of a flare and the onset of the associated magnetic storm is about 26 hours; but the most intense magnetic storms give a shorter time-interval of about 20 hours.

Not all solar flares, however, give rise to magnetic storms. Newton found that there was a greater association between magnetic storms and flares occurring on the solar disc within an angular distance of 45° from the centre of the disc than flares outside this zone. Moreover, not all magnetic storms are due to the action of solar flares; weak and moderate storms occur during periods of minimum sunspot activity when bright solar flares are not observed.

The 27-day Recurrence Tendency of Magnetic Storms

By considering the times of recurrences of magnetic storms, Maunder was led to conclude that the recurrence of magnetic disturbance was connected with the period of the solar rotation. He found that magnetic storms tended to recur at an interval of 27·3 days, which is very nearly the same as the period of the solar rotation. The identification of the two periods however, was an independent step; it was proved beyond doubt by Charles Chree in 1922.

This tendency for magnetic disturbance to recur at intervals of one solar rotation affords a strong presumption, that, as was noted by Maunder, the Sun emits streams of particles from disturbed areas on its disc, the emission lasting for one or more rotations, and that each time the stream encounters the Earth a magnetic storm develops.

Chree established the recurrence tendency for moderate and weak storms. In 1928, Greaves and Newton extended the work of Maunder and Chree to still more intense storms and they found a general lack of recurrence. It would thus seem that the recurrence tendency is characteristic of small storms. In no way does this conflict with the conclusion drawn by Maunder from the recurrence tendency that magnetic storms are due to the action of solar streams of particles. In the case of great magnetic storms their close connection with solar flares leads us to suppose that particles are emitted in isolated blasts from these flares. In the case of weak or moderate disturbances J. Bartels suggested that one must suppose that the streams are continuously emitted from 'magnetically active' regions on the Sun which he called M-regions. They appear to be more long-lived than sunspots or other solar phenomena. Many attempts have been made, albeit without success, to identify the hypothetical M-regions with characteristic features on the Sun's surface. C. W. Allen and later H. von Klüber, have tentatively suggested that M-regions are to be identified with the long coronal streamers seen at times of solar eclipses.

There is considerable evidence of clouds of matter on the Sun's surface being accelerated away from the Sun. The time lag of about a day, noted by Abetti and confirmed by Greaves and Newton, between the passage of notable sunspots across the central meridian of the Sun and the beginning of a great magnetic storm, also suggests that the solar agent causing magnetic storms and aurorae cannot travel with the speed of light and so cannot be in the form of electromagnetic radiations. Furthermore, during an intense solar flare a simultaneous variation in the magnetic elements is observed, lasting for the same period as the duration of the flare and called a *crochet*. The dissimilarity of this effect, which is due to ultra-violet radiation from the flare, with the magnetic storm variation, is unfavourable to an ultra-violet light theory of magnetic storms and aurorae. The fact that aurorae occur most frequently in polar regions and that auroral rays tend to dispose themselves along the magnetic lines of force of the Earth's field also supports the hypothesis, first suggested in 1881 by Goldstein, that the solar agent is corpuscular, and not electromagnetic, radiation.

For a long time the evidence in favour of this hypothesis was largely indirect; more definite evidence has been adduced from the spectroscopic observation of Vegard, Gartlein and Meinel indicating that fast protons are entering the upper atmosphere with speed exceeding 2000 miles per second.

In 1896, K. Birkeland had pointed out that a stream of electrons emitted from the Sun would be deflected polewards by the Earth's magnetic field. He supported this hypothesis by showing in the laboratory that when a stream of cathode rays (electrons) are projected towards a magnetized sphere, the rays are deflected by the magnetic field over two circular zones, one around each pole of the sphere. Sir Arthur Schuster in 1911, and F.A. Lindemann (later Lord Cherwell) in 1919, pointed out that the particles of a solar stream could not all be of one sign, for in that case they would be greatly dispersed by their mutual electrostatic repulsion by the time they reached the Earth's orbit. Lindemann therefore suggested that the streams would be electrostatically neutral, but ionized.

Because of the criticism directed by Schuster and Lindemann against one-sign theories many theorists now consider that theories of magnetic storms and aurorae must be based on the neutral stream hypothesis of Lindemann. Several theories have been proposed, by S. Chapman and V.C.A. Ferraro, by H. Alfvén, and more recently by E.O. Hulbert and W.M. Bennett.

The Neutral Ionized Streams

We do not know from what level or by what mechanism the neutral ionized gas is emitted from the Sun. The time interval of about a day between the occurrence of a solar flare and the onset of a magnetic storm may be interpreted as indicating a speed of travel from the Sun to the Earth of about 650–1400 miles per second and an angle of emission as wide as 50°. The composition of the stream is likely to be that of typical solar gas, consisting mainly of protons and electrons with a small admixture of other solar constituents. The density and temperature of the gas at emission are also unknown but may be presumed to be that corresponding to the level of emission, *viz.* ten thousand million particles to the cubic

inch and 5700 degrees Centigrade, respectively, for a photo-
spheric level emission with correspondingly higher temperature
and lower density if the gas is emitted at higher levels. Recom-
bination of ions and electrons during the passage of the streams
from the Sun to the Earth is certainly negligible.

Because of its high temperature the gas will expand rapidly, the
speed of the surface being comparable with the molecular speeds.
For a temperature of 5700 degrees Centigrade these are of the
order of 7 miles per second. In a day the gas will therefore expand
to dimensions of a million miles and on reaching the Earth's orbit
the dimensions of the gas will therefore greatly exceed those of the
Earth. The expansion of the gas is, in fact, even greater on account
of the divergence of the directions of emission from the source on
the surface of the Sun. For a stream of angle 10°—such as seem
characteristic of the recurrent streams—the breadth at the distance
of the Earth from the Sun is 16 million miles. For the great
magnetic storms the linear dimensions of the gas may be of the
order of a hundred million miles.

This expansion will greatly reduce the density of the gas by a
factor of from five to eight powers of ten depending on the original
size and density of the gas.

The inclination of the front surface of the gas will be different
for the flare-burst stream of gas thought responsible for great
magnetic storms, and for recurrent, long-continued streams. In the
former case there will be a 'head-on' encounter with the Earth.
In the case of the recurrent stream, the surface of the stream is
inclined to the direction of travel because of the rotation of the
Sun. The curve of the streams will, in fact, be bent backwards in
the same way as for a stream of water issuing from a rotating
garden hose (Fig. 11).

THEORIES OF MAGNETIC STORMS AND AURORAE

The Birkeland-Stormer Theory of Aurorae and Magnetic Storms

As we have already mentioned, this theory ascribes auroral
phenomena to the action of the Earth's magnetic field on a solar
stream of particles of one sign. Birkeland supposed these to be
electrons. Carl Störmer, who developed the mathematical theory
of Birkeland's experiments with cathode rays projected towards a
magnetized sphere, made no definite hypothesis regarding the

nature of the particles. Restricting his investigation to the motion of a single charge in the Earth's magnetic field, he showed that such a particle projected from the Sun into the Earth's magnetic field could reach the Earth only along two narrow zones centred round the two poles of the geomagnetic axis. Störmer identified these as the *auroral zones* and showed that the angular radius of the zone depended on the charge and the momentum of the particle.

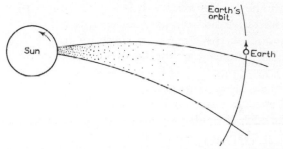

FIG. 11. Showing the form of a corpuscular stream of corpuscles emitted from the Sun.

But to account for the observed angular radius of the zone, about 23°, Störmer found that the speed of the particle would have to be higher than appeared possible at the time. Now, by calculating a large number of orbits, Störmer showed that a bundle of particles projected from the Sun on the Earth's magnetic equatorial plane would be deflected round the Earth at several hundred Earth-radii from it, the negative particles flowing eastward, the positive particles westward, so as to produce roughly a westward ring-current. Such a ring-current would produce a world-wide decrease in the Earth's magnetic field, such as is observed during the main phase of a magnetic storm. Furthermore, as Störmer showed, this decrease could draw out the auroral zones equatorwards to the observed value, and that during great magnetic disturbances, aurorae would be seen even in very low latitudes. However, it seems doubtful whether such a ring-current could hold together against the mutual repulsion of its parts.

Though the Birkeland-Störmer theory contains many valuable suggestions, some of which may be incorporated in an eventual theory of magnetic storms and aurorae, the neglect of electrostatic forces makes it difficult to accept the theory in its original form.

R

Theories Based on the Neutral Stream Hypothesis

(a) *The Chapman-Ferraro theory of magnetic storms*—Chapman and Ferraro made the first attempt to develop a theory of magnetic storms, based on Lindemann's hypothesis that their cause is to be sought in the phenomena accompanying the advance of a neutral ionized stream in the Earth's magnetic field.

On arrival near the Earth's orbit we have seen that the dimensions of the stream are so great compared with the diameter of the Earth, that the stream surface will appear almost plane as seen from the Earth. An ionized gas, however, is a good conductor of electricity and as the stream advances on to the Earth's field, current will be induced within the stream by its motion across the magnetic lines of force. The dimensions of the stream and the speed of the particles are so large that the resistance of the stream can be neglected and the stream will behave as if it were a perfect conductor. As such it tends to reflect completely the magnetic field outside it, so that the induced currents are practically confined to the surface. These will shield the main body of the stream from the Earth's magnetic field. It is as if the ionized gas were impervious to the interpenetration of the magnetic lines of force, which are thereby pushed forward by the stream. Now, Michael Faraday, when studying the curvature of the lines of force of a magnetic field, had noticed an apparent tendency of adjacent lines to repel each other, as if each line of force were inherently disposed to expand laterally. Hence, the lines of force which are pushed forward by the stream surface will react by exerting a lateral pressure on the surface, tending to repel it away from the Earth. The force of repulsion will be greater for those points of the surface that are nearer to the Earth. Since the gas in the stream is highly distortable, these points will suffer the greatest retardation and this will cause a hollow space to be carved out in the stream (Fig. 12). The crowding of the lines of force into this hollow by the surface of the stream will increase the field within it and this will manifest itself as an increase in the horizontal force at the Earth's surface. This increase is identified as the first phase of a magnetic storm. Its intensity will depend on the closeness of approach of the front surface of the stream to the Earth.

Since the interior of the stream is shielded from the magnetic field of the Earth outside, the particles in the main stream are able to move with the undisturbed speed of emission until they penetrate the surface current layers; here they are subjected to the full brunt of the action of the magnetic field, and part of the momentum of the gas is thus taken up by the lateral pressure of the tubes of force until eventually the stream surface is brought to rest. The distance from the Earth of the nearest point, can be calculated by equating the rate at which the momentum is destroyed, to the magnetic pressure which the lines of force exert on the surface of the stream. This condition enables an estimate to be made of the density of the stream required to produce an increase in the

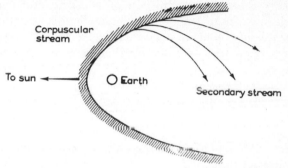

FIG. 12.   Hollow formed in the stream surface by the Earth's magnetic field as the stream advances towards the Earth.

horizontal force comparable with the rise observed during the first phase of a storm. Assuming that the speed of the particles is about 600 miles per second, it is found that a moderate magnetic storm could be produced by a stream for which the particle density is only of the order of a few tens of particles per cubic inch.

On account of the high speed of approach of the stream, the increase in the horizontal force produced by the induced currents at the Earth's surface will be rapid—the order of a minute; this is of the same order as the observed duration of a sudden commencement movement, and this sudden increase would seem to provide a simple and direct explanation of this phenomenon.

During the main phase of a magnetic storm the Earth is surrounded by a nearly uniform external magnetic field over the entire surface directed from North to South. The simplest explanation is that this external field is produced by a westward electric current encircling the Earth, as was first suggested by Störmer (page 249). Adolf Schmidt revived this idea on purely observational evidence;

he supposed that the ring had a continued existence, being rein-
forced from time to time during the storm, and that it decayed
during periods of magnetic calm. He expressed no views as to the
size and form of the ring but suggested that the positive charges
would circulate westward and the electrons eastwards.

Chapman and Ferraro attempted to explain how such a ring
might be formed once the hollow space in the stream became
stationary, but their suggestion is only tentative and unsupported
by detailed mathematical analysis. However, they discussed in
detail the mechanical equilibrium of the ring and showed, as
follows at once from Ampère's right hand rule, that this equilibrium could only be maintained if the current in the ring is westward, as is required to account for the decrease in the horizontal
force during the main phase. Because of the low resistance of the
ionized gas, they also showed that there would be no difficulty in
accounting for the long continued existence of the ring over many
days.

(b) *Martyn's theory of the aurora*—The charges which are induced
on the surface of the ring by the magnetic field are unstable and
are accelerated away from the surface by the action of electric fields
set up during the period of formation of the ring. These leakage
charges are thence guided along the magnetic lines of force towards
the polar regions with speeds which D. F. Martyn has shown to be
considerably in excess of the streaming velocity of the charges.
This is in accord with Meinel's observations that incoming protons
from outside the Earth have speeds greater than 2000 miles per
second; the increase in speed is in any case necessary in order that
the particles may penetrate to the observed auroral levels.

Martyn also showed that in the case of a ring-current which could
produce a moderate decrease in the horizontal force during a
magnetic storm, we may expect the escaping particles to be pre-
cipitated over a zone of the Earth's surface of angular radius 23°—
agreeing with the observed value for the auroral zone. As Martyn
suggested, the precipitation of these charged particles may be the
cause of strong excitation on impact with atmospheric molecules
necessary to produce the aurora luminiscence.

(c) *Alfvén's theory of magnetic storms and aurorae*—The theory
put forward by Alfvén is also based on the hypothesis that the Sun

emits a stream of neutral ionized gas, but differs from the Chapman-Ferraro theory as regards the evolution of the effects near the Earth.

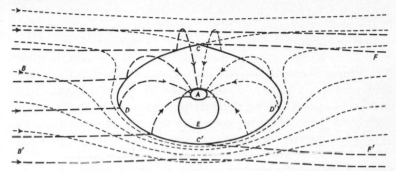

FIG. 13. Perspective drawing of paths of ions and electrons near the Earth. paths of ions— — —: paths of electrons- - - - - - -:
E is Earth: Curve A is north auroral zone: BB' are ions and electrons approaching Earth in equatorial plane: CDC'D' is boundary of forbidden region: CF and C'F' are boundaries of shadow of Earth where no ions are present.

A characteristic feature of Alfvén's theory is the important part played by the solar magnetic field or its extension into interplanetary space whereas Chapman and Ferraro thought that the influence of the solar magnetic field was relatively unimportant. Alfvén also requires that the electrons in the stream should have higher energies than the positive ions. On arrival near the Earth the motion of the charged particles are profoundly modified by the Earth's magnetic field. The electrons, which in the absence of the field would impinge on the Earth, are deflected towards the evening side of the Earth, skirting a forbidden region whose dimensions depend on the electric field generated by the motion of the stream across the solar magnetic field (Fig. 13). Because the ions have smaller energies than the electrons they are undeflected until they reach the forbidden region for the electrons. On arrival at this boundary they produce a positive charge there which is then discharged along the magnetic lines of force to the polar regions on the sunlit side of the Earth. This leaves an uncompensated negative charge along the border of the forbidden region facing the night side of the Earth. This is also discharged along the lines of force towards the polar regions; thus the projection of the boundary of the forbidden region for the electron along the lines of force over the polar regions of the Earth form a narrow zone which Alfvén identified with the auroral zone. This is, briefly, Alfvén's theory of the aurora.

The electrons in the equatorial plane flow eastwards and their motion is therefore equivalent to a westward ring current situated in the magnetic equatorial plane; this produces a decrease of the magnetic horizontal force at the Earth's surface which Alfvén believes to be the cause of the main phase of a magnetic storm. By a proper choice of two parameters, one of which is the electric field mentioned earlier, it is possible to get agreement with a number of features of magnetic storms and aurorae. In spite of this agreement, the theory is open to a number of objections, one of which concerns the neglect of the mutual interactions of the charges in the stream, such as the electric forces produced by the space charges at the borders of the forbidden region.

(d) *The Theory of Bennett and Hulburt*—W.H. Bennett and E.O. Hulburt have recently attempted to revive the Birkeland-Störmer theory by proposing a new variant of the neutral stream hypothesis. They suppose that a conical jet of approximately equal numbers of fast moving ions and electrons emerge from the Sun with approximately the same speed. As the jet passes through the outermost layers of the solar atmosphere the lighter electrons tend to be scattered out of the stream by collisions with the solar ions and electrons. The loss of electrons from the stream leaves an excess positive charge in the jet which is then supposed to be neutralized electrically by slower interplanetary electrons. Consequently, the positive ions have a greater speed than the electrons, and the jet carries a current directed radially away from the Sun. The deflection of the jet by the Earth's magnetic field will then be similar to that of a stream of charged particles continuously emitted from the Sun. But because the jet is electrically neutral, it no longer meets with Schuster's criticism of the original form of the Birkeland-Störmer theory.

Atmospheric Theory

The atmospheric dynamo theory of geomagnetic storms originally proposed many years ago by Schuster has been revived in recent years by Oliver Wulf, S.B. Nicholson and L. Davis, and E.H. Vestine. The solar agent responsible for the occurrence of magnetic storms and aurorae is supposed to be ultra-violet light.

One effect of the absorption of this radiation by the Earth's atmosphere is to energize the air currents, increasing their speed and modifying their circulation. It is supposed that the flow would become unstable and eventually a sudden change is triggered off. This is taken as the beginning of the magnetic storm. The enhanced air flow moving across the magnetic lines of force produces increased electromotive forces which set up additional electric currents. In this way potential differences of the order of 10,000 volts can be produced across two circles of latitudes between which the zonal airflow is 170 feet per second in a vertical magnetic field of about half a gauss. In such a field an electron could gain energy to excite an oxygen atom to emit the wave-length of the auroral green line. However, according to Chapman, this energy is insufficient to produce the extra ionization that accompanies auroral displays.

It is also difficult to account on this theory for the simultaneous world wide change in the airflow which would be needed to explain the fact that magnetic storms begin almost simultaneously all over the globe; and to account for the existence of auroral zone electric currents.

ACKNOWLEDGMENT

We gratefully acknowledge permission given by the *Royal Society* to publish Figs. 4, 5, and 6 from the Proceedings A 1927, vol. 115, and the Editors of the *Journal of Geophysical Research* for permission to reproduce Figs. 10 and 13 from *Terrestrial Magnetism* 1942, vol. 47 and 1944, vol. 49.

CHAPTER FIFTEEN

Meteors

A. C. B. LOVELL

IT IS, perhaps, not generally appreciated that the Earth is constantly being bombarded at an exceedingly high rate by pieces of stone and metal. Occasionally the pieces are so big that they penetrate the entire atmosphere and strike the ground—these are the *meteorites*. More familiar are the smaller pieces which burn away in the upper atmosphere at a height of about 60 miles and appear as shooting stars when the sky is clear at night. These are the *meteors*. Recently pieces have been discovered which are so small that they do not get hot enough to evaporate before they are slowed down; they fall quietly to the ground as very fine dust. These are the *micrometeorites*. Altogether, the Earth collects many thousands of tons of material a day in this manner. We shall discuss where the material comes from and how it can be used as a tool to explore the upper atmosphere.

SHOOTING STARS

First of all we consider the particles of intermediate size—the shooting stars, or meteors—because we know more about these than about either the meteorites or the micrometeorites. There are records in antiquity of the appearance in the sky of shooting stars sometimes in great numbers, but not until the late eighteenth century was it appreciated that the phenomena were due to particles entering the Earth's atmosphere from great distances. Then it was quickly realized that the meteoric particles must be revolving in orbits around the Sun in the same way as the Earth, as shown in Fig. 1.

The Earth, moving in its orbit at 18·5 miles per second, sweeps up any material which it encounters. During an average day and night the Earth collects so much material that a single observer looking at a clear dark sky with the naked eye, can see about 5 or

10 shooting stars per hour. The exact number depends on the season and the time of night. These meteors which can be seen throughout the year appear to be distributed at random in the sky and are known as *sporadic meteors*. Occasionally, however, the numbers seen increase sharply for a few nights and if their paths in the sky are plotted they all appear to diverge from a single point or small area. These are the *shower meteors*, and they occur when the Earth sweeps through a concentration of the meteoric material

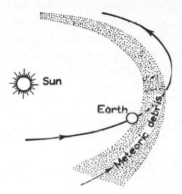

FIG. 1. Production of a meteor shower as the Earth traverses a stream of debris.

all moving in the same orbit around the Sun. Usually showers last for a few nights only, because although the debris might extend for many millions of miles in space, the Earth is itself moving at 18.5 miles per second and so quickly passes through the stream. The meteors as seen in the sky appear to diverge from a point as mentioned above. This is known as the *radiant*, and the position of the radiant amongst the background stars by convention gives the name to the shower. Thus the Perseid shower which is well known in the August sky is so called because its radiant lies in the constellation of Perseus. All the meteors in such a shower are, of course, moving in nearly parallel paths in space and the appearance of divergence from a point is entirely a matter of perspective.

METHODS OF INVESTIGATION
Visual and Photographic Methods
When the true nature of the shooting stars was realized, many scientists in the eighteenth and nineteenth centuries gave their attention to the problem of their origin. The issue is still only

partially resolved, one reason for this being the inherent difficult
of making accurate observations. Even in a very active shower th
individual meteors appear without warning and last only for
fraction of a second. In order to calculate the orbit of the particl
around the Sun it is necessary to measure its velocity and it
direction of flight in the atmosphere, determined in relation t
the background stars. Until the twentieth century, scientists had n
other means of making these measurements than by the unaide
eye, and their results, particularly of the velocity of the meteor
were subject to large errors. Even so, most remarkable result
were achieved, and it was shown that the meteors in some of th
well-known showers must be moving in the same orbits around th
Sun as certain comets. Although new techniques have now bee
developed the visual observers still play a prominent part i
recording meteors. In Great Britain they form an amateur grou
of the British Astronomical Association.

At the beginning of the twentieth century, photography wa
applied to the problem. If the photographic plate is sensitiv
enough to record the meteor then the flight path in relation to th
background stars can be measured with accuracy. The problem o
measuring the velocity was solved by W. J. Elkin of Yale who ro
tated a shutter in front of the camera lens so that the lens wa
occulted many times per second. The bright streak of a meteor o
the photographic plate is then segmented as shown in Fig. 2, an

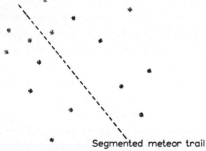

Segmented meteor trail

FIG. 2. A drawing of the appearance of a meteor trail photographed with
camera using a rotating shutter. The occultation of the lens at the rate of man
times per second causes the breaks in the trail from the length of which th
meteor velocity can be calculated.

by measuring the length of the segments the velocity can be calcu
lated. Of course a single camera used in this way gives only th

angular velocity of the meteor, since its height is unknown. In order to measure the actual velocity of the meteor, two such cameras must be used simultaneously, separated by several miles. From the apparent change in position of the trail against the stellar background the height of the meteor and its linear velocity may be calculated.

In principle, this photographic method can be very accurate, but it proved particularly difficult to collect many results because the photographic materials were not susceptible enough to the action of light and could only record the occasional bright meteors; and further, the most sensitive cameras had relatively confined fields of view. As an illustration of these difficulties it might be mentioned that in the photographic meteor programme at Harvard Observatory up to 1948 the average yield of photographic meteors was one per hundred hours of exposure time. Add to this the effects of cloud and moonlight and it is easy to appreciate what a frustrating occupation meteor research could be. During the last few years these difficulties have been largely overcome by the development of cameras known as Super Schmidts. These have special correcting plates which give the camera a very wide field of view (between 50 and 60 degrees) coupled with large apertures, so that the fainter meteors (which, as we shall see later, are more plentiful), can be recorded.

Radio Methods

Before the advent of the Super Schmidt cameras, an entirely different method of studying meteors had revolutionized the subject. When a meteor burns away in the atmosphere it creates the streak of light by which we see it, but in addition it leaves behind a trail of ionized atoms and electrons. This ionized material quickly diffuses and recombines to the neutral state—often in a fraction of a second—but before it does so the free electrons are capable of scattering back energy from a radio wave which is directed at them. The technique is very similar to radar. A transmitter on the ground sends out short pulses of radio waves through a suitable aerial system. In the radar case these are reflected from aircraft, the reflected wave is picked up on a receiver tuned to the frequency of the transmitter, and the aircraft is seen as an echo on a cathode ray tube. In the meteor case, the radio waves are scattered from the electrons in the meteor trail and a similar echo can be seen on a cathode ray tube. These meteor echoes are very transient, and although occasional bright meteors may give echoes lasting for several seconds, the majority are over in about a tenth of a second. The general arrangement is shown in Fig. 3. In principle,

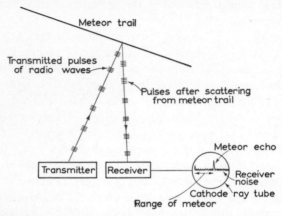

Fig. 3.   Schematic general arrangement of radio echo apparatus for recording of echoes from meteor trails.

the technique is the same as that used in the investigation of the ionospheric layers, but the wave-length of the system must be shorter in order to avoid confusion with echoes from the E layer, which happens to be at about the same height as that at which the majority of meteors evaporate. Experience has shown that wavelengths of about 4 to 8 metres are most suitable. Specialized techniques have been developed involving photographic recording of various forms of cathode ray tube displays, and it is now possible to measure the velocity and direction of the meteor with precision, without even looking at the sky. The radio techniques have two other outstanding advantages. They are independent of sky conditions and thus can continue to give systematic information about the entry of meteors into the atmosphere under all sky conditions, and even by day. Also the systems can be made so sensitive that there is no difficulty in recording meteors which are far too faint to be seen by eye or to be photographed.

THE ORIGIN OF THE METEORS

There has been violent dispute about the interpretation of the results of the observations in terms of the origin of the meteors, but many of the uncertainties have been resolved during the last few years by the radio echo and Super Schmidt camera work. In this section the generally accepted current views on these issues will be summarized.

The Shower Meteors

A list of the more interesting and important meteor showers is given in Table 1 together with their approximate dates of occurrence. Some of these showers, particularly the Quadrantids, Perseids and Geminids, are very regular in their appearance and give nearly the same hourly rate from year to year. This leads to the view that the meteoric debris is well scattered around the orbit, so that the Earth sweeps up the same amount of debris at whatever

TABLE 1

The major meteor showers

Shower	Date of maximum	Remarks
Quadrantids	January 3	Very regular shower with a short maximum of 50 to 100 visible meteors per hour.
Lyrids	April 21	Has given big displays in the past but now only of low activity.
Eta-Aquarids	May 4–6	Regular shower giving 10 to 20 visible meteors per hour.
Summer day time streams	May, June, July	Great series of showers of very high activity observable only by radio.
Delta-Aquarids	July 28	Prominent stream in the southern hemisphere.
Perseids	August 10–14	Very regular shower of unusually bright meteors, giving 50 to 100 visible meteors per hour.
Giacobinids	October 10	Periodic: provided a great meteoric storm in 1946.
Orionids	October 20–23	Regular shower, now of low activity.
Taurids	November 3–10	Another regular shower, now of low activity.
Leonids	November 16–17	Famous for the great storms of 1799, 1833, and 1866. Now of very low activity.
Geminids	December 12–13	Very regular shower with a maximum of 50 to 100 visible meteors per hour.
Ursids	December 22	Recently discovered shower of low activity.

point it intersects the orbit. Others, such as the Lyrids, Leonids and Giacobinids, are quite different. Occasionally these give great meteoric storms and in the intervening years the activity is very low. For example, the spectacular displays of the Leonids in November of 1799, 1833 and 1866 are famous in history, and in more recent times the Giacobinid shower of October 10, 1946 was similar. In these cases it is possible that the debris is localized in one region of the orbit. Another interesting shower is the Bielids which gave great displays in the nineteenth century and which no longer exists. The streams of debris moving around the Sun are subject to perturbing forces of the planets, particularly of Jupiter, and in the case of the Bielids, and probably to a lesser extent in the case of the Leonids and Lyrids, the main bulk of the debris has been forced away from the plane of the Earth's orbit.

In 1866 G. V. Schiaparelli was able to show that the meteoric debris of the Perseids and Leonids must be moving in the same orbit around the Sun as do two well-known comets. Subsequently the close relationship between some of the meteor streams and other comets was established, and in addition to the Perseids and Leonids it is now accepted that the Lyrids, Bielids, Giacobinids and Taurids are associated with known comets.   The problem as to whether the meteoric material is (a) the debris of the comets; (b) the primeval material from which the comets are building up; or (c) just happens to be moving in the same orbit is, however, unresolved. There are two further puzzles. No associated comets are known for some of the most active and prominent showers in Table 1—for example, the great daytime streams of the Arietids and Zeta-Perseids, or the Geminids—and there are many comets whose orbits are intersected by the Earth and which have the other necessary characteristics, but which do not give rise to meteor showers.

The Sporadic Meteors

Although there are many outstanding questions about the shower meteors it has always been recognized that the particles responsible move in closed orbits (ellipses) around the Sun, and hence are essentially members of the solar system. On the other hand there has been much controversy about the origin of the sporadic meteors. The opposing views were, (a) that the orbits of the sporadic meteors were similar to the shower meteors in that they were confined to the solar system; (b) that the orbits of the sporadic meteors were unclosed (hyperbolae) so that these meteors were visitors from interstellar space, moving temporarily under the influence of the Sun. It proved difficult to settle this problem because the change from a hyperbolic to a long period elliptical orbit involves only a slight change in velocity. The general contemporary view is that this issue has been settled by the radio echo and the Super Schmidt photographic measurements, which show that the orbits are all elliptical. In fact, 10,000 orbits of sporadic meteors measured at Jodrell Bank by radio echo methods do not show a single case of a hyperbolic orbit. On the contrary, the majority of the sporadic meteors are moving in orbits with particularly short periods (that is, like some of the inner planets).

Although this particular point is settled, the general relation of the sporadic meteoric material to the solar system remains an enigma. The problem of whether the material is the debris of a comparatively recent disintegration in the solar system, or whether it is some of the primeval matter from which the solar system was formed, remains to be settled.

METEORS AND THE INVESTIGATION OF THE UPPER ATMOSPHERE

The Process of Evaporation

The process by which the meteoric particle evaporates is believed to be as follows. The velocity of entry of the particle into the atmosphere is compounded of the Earth's velocity in its orbit around the Sun (18·5 miles per second), and the velocity of the particle in its own orbit, which could attain a maximum of 26 miles per second if it remains a member of the solar system. Hence the velocity of entry varies from about 7·5 miles per second to 44·5 miles per second, depending on whether the meteor encounters the Earth when travelling in the same or opposite direction, with all intermediate possibilities. As the meteor enters the atmosphere, it will collide with the air atoms and most of these will be trapped in the meteor. The energy of impact will appear as heat which will be sufficient to evaporate several atoms from the meteoric body. These evaporated atoms move away from the meteor and suffer collisions with the air atoms in the vicinity of the meteor's path. It is in these latter collisions that the light and ionized trail are formed.

The height at which evaporation occurs depends on the mass and velocity of the meteor. However, it seems certain that above about 70 miles the atmosphere is too attenuated for any appreciable evaporation to occur. In fact, measurements show that the majority of the meteors are completely evaporated in the height range of about 50 to 70 miles. In this range the atmosphere is dense enough to cause complete evaporation by the above process, and this takes place without any large deceleration of the meteor. The fundamental point is that the size of the meteor is small compared with the average distance between the atoms of the atmosphere at these heights. On the other hand, occasional larger meteors will penetrate below 50 miles before evaporation is complete. Then the atmosphere becomes so dense that the air atoms begin to pile up in front of the meteor. Appreciable retardation occurs but the heat transfer problems are complex and are the subject of much contemporary study.

It will be evident from the above summary that studies of the evaporation of the meteors can give information about fundamental physical processes occurring at these heights. Research work is in progress along these lines, in which the amount of light and ionization are measured as functions of the meteor's velocity and height in the atmosphere.

The Measurement of the Physical Properties of the Upper Atmosphere

The extent to which a meteor of given mass and velocity has evaporated at a particular height, clearly depends on the air density at that height and hence provides the basis for a radio echo method of measuring densities in the upper atmosphere. In this method the velocity and height of the reflection point from large numbers of meteors are measured. Although the masses of individual meteors cannot be determined, the distribution of the masses in a large sample can be inferred. These data make it possible to find the density at various heights in the 50 to 70 mile region. There is also a photographic method of measuring the air densities in the meteor region, which involves the precise measurement of the very small decelerations which the meteor suffers as it evaporates. Both the radio echo and photographic meteor results agree very well with the similar determinations using rockets as shown in Fig. 4.

The presence of considerable winds blowing at great altitudes was inferred many years ago from the behaviour of the long enduring visible trains left behind by occasional very big meteors. A radio echo method has recently been developed which enables these winds to be measured accurately and systematically. The

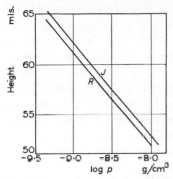

FIG. 4. Atmospheric densities in the 60 mile region as determined by the radio-echo meteor technique (J). The line R shows the densities measured in New Mexico by the rocket and photographic meteor techniques.

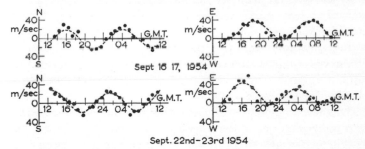

FIG. 5. The N-S, E-W components of the wind at 60 miles as determined by the radio-echo meteor technique for two days in September 1954.

method measures the distance which the ionized trail moves away from, or towards, the observing station in the fraction of the second during which the echo is present, and the collection of enough data to determine a wind speed and direction at a given height takes only about 30 minutes. Some typical results for a day are shown in Fig. 5, from which it is seen that the wind has a semi-diurnal variation. The changes in this wind system throughout the year and its variation with height are complex and are still being studied. These winds are probably the results of the Sun's tidal influences and may well have some connection with the wind movements nearer the Earth's surface.

s

THE NUMBERS AND MASSES OF THE METEORS

The astronomer uses a scale of magnitudes to define the brightness of the stars. Under very dark clear sky conditions stars which are just bright enough to be seen have magnitudes of $+6$. Those of magnitude $+5$ are 2·5 times as bright as those of magnitude $+6$, and so on so that a star of magnitude $+1$ is 100 times brighter than the 6th magnitude star. Very bright stars have negative magnitudes (e.g. Sirius $-1·4$). Meteor observers use the same convention, and the meteors which can be seen by eye are all brighter than magnitude $+5$ or $+6$. The radio methods can readily detect meteors down to magnitude $+10$ and fainter which cannot, of course, be seen by the naked eye under any conditions. Meteors of zero magnitude and brighter are very rare. In fact even a short acquaintance with observing meteors shows that there are far more faint meteors than bright ones. The detailed investigation shows the interesting fact that in the case of sporadic meteors there are 2·5 times more meteors for each fainter magnitude: that is, an observer will see on the average, only one meteor of magnitude o for every 100 meteors of magnitude $+5$. Also, the relation between the mass of the meteor and its brightness is such that these relations mean that the decrease in mass as the meteors get fainter is compensated for by the increase in numbers: that is, in each magnitude range the total meteoric mass entering the atmosphere is the same.

Although a single observer sees rather few meteors per hour, the total number entering the atmosphere is very great. In the range of visible magnitudes these numbers can be obtained if the area of sky covered by the observer is estimated, and for the very faint meteors below the visibility limit the number has been obtained from telescopic and radio echo measurements. By this means it is found that at the limit of naked eye visibility about a hundred million meteors enter the entire atmosphere daily. The factor of 2·5 per magnitude, mentioned above, means that at the 10th magnitude there are about ten thousand million per day, whereas for very bright meteors of magnitude zero there are only one million per day.

There is a good deal of uncertainty about the masses of the individual meteoric particles. The commonly observed shooting stars are certainly very small contrary to popular belief; indeed many are little more than grains of sand. It is thought that a very bright meteor of magnitude o weighs not more than 100 milligrams and one of magnitude +5 not more than 1 milligram.

This information about numbers and masses is summarized in Table 2 for the sporadic meteors.

TABLE 2

Numbers and masses of sporadic meteors

Meteor magnitude	Mass of individual particles	Number per day over the entire atmosphere	Mass per day (in kilograms*)
−10 to −8	500 grams to 100 grams	300	60
−7 to −6	100 to 10	2,500	40
−5 to −4	10 to 1	18,000	40
−3 to −1	1 gram to 100 milligrams	400,000	60
0 to +1	100 milligrams to 10 milligrams	1,000,000	40
2 to 4	10 to 1	36,000,000	60
5 to 6	1 to 0·1	190,000,000	40
7 to 9	0·1 to 0·01	3,300,000,000	60
10 to 12	0·01 to 0·001	65,000,000,000	60

* A kilogram is equivalent to about a thousandth of a ton.

It is an interesting fact that although the showers are far more spectacular than the sporadic meteors, they exist for such a short time that during the course of a year they bring into the atmosphere only about a quarter of the mass brought in by the sporadic meteors. For example the well-known Perseid shower in August probably accounts for only about 12 tons, whereas addition of the last column of Table 2 shows that several hundred tons of sporadic meteors enter during the course of a year. Even great meteoric storms like the Giacobinids probably only account for about 70 tons. Of course, the Earth sweeps up only a minor amount of the material which must be moving around the Sun in the orbit of one of these showers. From the size of the orbit it is possible to calculate how much this material must weigh and the answer comes to about one thousand million tons.

Those interested in space travel sometimes wonder if these vast amounts of material would hit space ships very frequently. The answer is that a space traveller would be exceedingly unlucky to be hit by a particle of any appreciable size. As far as sporadic meteors are concerned, a particle with a mass of a gram occurs on the average in 10,000 million cubic miles of space. Even one as small as a milligram occurs only on the average in 7 million cubic miles of space. If the space traveller ventured out when the Earth was sweeping through a shower orbit, the chances of encountering particles would, of course increase, but even for the great Giacobinid shower the corresponding figures are 1 million cubic miles (for a gram particle), and 1,000 cubic miles (for a milligram particle).

METEORITES

Even a meteor of zero magnitude is a brilliant transient object in the night sky, and those at the head of Table 2 would appear as spectacular fireballs easily visible in the daytime sky. Such objects are so rare that we know little about them; in fact there is a gap in our knowledge until we get to particles which are so big that they penetrate the entire atmosphere without evaporating complete, and land as solid objects. These meteorites are very rare, probably not more than half a dozen enter the atmosphere per day. We can only guess at the size and weight which such a particle must have before it enters the atmosphere. In one sample of 400 falls, the average mass of material collected was 40 pounds, and this probably indicates that the original bodies in space had an average mass of about 200 pounds. Even allowing for large errors in these estimates they indicate that, in spite of the spectacular nature of some falls of meteorites, the total mass accreted by the Earth in this way is rather small—probably only a ton or so per day.

The Composition of Meteorites

Meteorites provide man with a unique opportunity to handle and study material which has recently come from interplanetary space. Consequently there is great interest in the analysis of meteorites with a view to any light which they might throw on the composition of interplanetary material. It is estimated that about 500 tons of meteorites exist in museums throughout the world, and about 25 falls are recovered yearly. These form the basis of the chemical analysis which is peculiarly difficult and is a lively branch of independent research. Some broad conclusions are well established. For example, about 90 per cent of all known meteorites are essentially stony. Nearly 10 per cent are a nickel-iron alloy, and a few are half silicate and half metal. The nickel-iron alloys may contain anything from 4 to 40 per cent of nickel. The stony meteorites are quite unlike the rocks of the Earth's crust; they are veined with nickel-iron alloy and have a very high content of magnesium and a low content of aluminium and alkalies. Structurally, too, the meteorites are quite different from the terrestrial rocks. They are composed of small rounded silicate grains called *chondrules*, embedded in a matrix of broken chondrules and miscellaneous material. There are departures from these generalizations, and many curious rarities such as the *tektites*—small glass meteorites with a most peculiar distribution on the Earth's surface, which indicates that they may have fallen in localized showers at certain epochs.

A great deal is now known about the composition and the structure of these various forms of meteorites, but—as we shall see—there is little agreement as to how they are formed. As an example, we may mention the problem of the chondrules. Either they were formed where we find them now or they are inclusions. If the former is the case it is very hard to see how they could attain shapes and structure when immersed in a mass of splintered crystals. It could be assumed that the crystals were shattered after the formation of the meteorite, in which case it is difficult to see why the chondrules were not shattered as well. The alternative view that the chondrules are inclusive gets over these difficulties but leaves unanswered the problem of how the inclusions occurred in such a mass of material.

The Fall of Meteorites and Large Craters

The meteorites must be moving in orbits around the Sun in the same way as the meteors discussed earlier in this chapter. They enter the atmosphere in the same range of high velocities and rapidly penetrate to a region where the air is so dense that a compression cap forms in front of the meteorite. Melting of the surface takes place and the passage of the meteorite through the atmosphere is often accompanied by detonations. Although appreciable retardation occurs, the impact velocity on the Earth is still many miles per second and the meteorites often plunge yards into the ground. On the other hand, especially in the case of large meteorites, great explosions may occur at impact, leading to fragmentation of the meteorite. Typical of the latter is the case of the great Siberian meteorite which fell on June 30, 1908. The explosion on impact broke windows 50 miles distant and created devastation over a radius of many miles. The mass of this meteorite is estimated at several hundred tons.

Even more recently on February 12, 1947, another great meteorite crashed to earth in the Sikhote-Alin mountains a few hundred miles north of Vladivostok. This one made over a hundred craters with diameters up to 28 yards, and again created extensive devastation in the surrounding districts. Two large pieces of 700 pounds each were recovered from this fall as well as many tons of smaller pieces.

Many large craters have been discovered which must have been formed by impacts of great meteorites at unknown times in the past. There are arguments as to whether some of these craters were actually formed by meteorites, but in many cases the conclusive test is the discovery of pieces of the meteorite with the characteristic heavy nickel content. For example, the famous Arizona crater discovered in 1891, is 1200 yards across with the rim 37 yards above the plain, and the crater depth is 175 yards. Tons of meteoritic material have been discovered in the vicinity. Estimates of the time of fall of this meteorite have been made from the rate of the erosion of the crater—it may have been anything from 5 thousand to 75 thousand years ago.

The biggest crater known was discovered as recently as 1950 at Ungava in Canada. It is 2 miles across, but although no meteoritic material has been located, the general shape and structure of the crater makes it highly probable that it was formed by a huge meteoritic impact.

The Origin of the Meteorites

Earlier in this chapter we discussed the origin of the meteors. Apart from the cometary association of some of the shower meteors there is no solution, although it is known that all the showers and sporadic meteors move in closed orbits around the Sun and hence probably have some cometary or asteroidal association. Can we assume that the meteorites have a similar origin—whatever that is—and that they are the extreme mass range of the meteors? The weight of contemporary evidence is against this conclusion. For example, no meteorite has been known to be associated with any of the great meteor showers. There is also evidence accumulating that meteors may be very fragile and often break up on entering the atmosphere. The small amount of spectral evidence also indicates that meteors have a radically different composition from the meteorites.

The whole subject offers much scope for speculation, and it is only possible here to indicate the kind of opposing views about the origin of the meteorites which are current today. The suggestion that the meteorites have originated from the disintegration of a large body in the solar system has much to support it. For example, if a body somewhat larger than Mars collided in the remote past with a small minor planet, then it seems likely that the large body would be shattered. On this view the disintegrated planet might well be the parent of the asteroids as well as the meteorites. Variants of this view are that the parents of the meteorites are themselves asteroids not larger than about 600 miles in diameter. On the other hand, there is a contemporary school which takes the extreme view that the meteorites are the primeval matter from which the Earth and the Moon were formed by accretion. If this is the case, then the present bombardment of the Earth is simply the tail end of the process by which it was formed.

MICROMETEORITES

Finally we consider the particles which lie beyond the other extreme of Table 2—those which are so minute that they are stopped by the resistance of the atmosphere before their evaporation is complete, and which drift slowly to Earth as exceedingly fine dust. If we extrapolate Table 2 by another 20 magnitudes to +30 we are probably in the region of particles whose size may be only a thousandth of a millimetre. These are so light that they will be blown away by the radiation pressure from the Sun. The tails of comets, which always lie away from the Sun, must be composed of particles like this, and unless the Earth passes through the tail of a comet, such exceedingly small particles will not enter the atmosphere. Particles which are a little heavier and measure, perhaps, a few thousandths of a millimetre will not be driven away in this manner. These are presumably moving in orbits around the Sun like the brighter meteors and are swept up by the Earth in the same way. However, such small particles have the peculiar property that they dissipate the heat generated when they enter the atmosphere, without getting hot enough to evaporate. Their initial energy is used up in this way until they are effectively stopped in their path, and then they drift to the ground, probably taking a day or so in the process.

The evidence for the existence of these micrometeorites comes from several sources. Particles of a few thousanths of a millimetre in diameter have been collected from roofs and rain water and on specially prepared plates. These are distinguished from ordinary fine terrestrial dust by their singular shapes and by their composition, which makes it highly probable that they have an extra-terrestrial origin. Also, sample cores taken from ocean beds show quantities of dust with a very high nickel content. The total weight of dust which the Earth sweeps up in this way is very high— probably a million tons per year, greater than the weight of all the meteorites and meteors together.

CONCLUSION

There is one consistent trend about the particles discussed in this chapter which bombard the Earth. In any section of the size range it is always the smallest and most insignificant particles which are most plentiful. The naked eye sees vastly more faint meteors than bright ones, small meteorites are far more plentiful than large ones, and all of these meteors and meteorites together contribute relatively little compared with the micrometeorites. There is still a gap in the range of sizes about which we know nothing at all. It is the range of faint meteor magnitudes beyond +10 until the dust gets small enough to fall as micrometeorites. Efforts will certainly be made to explore this range of magnitudes between +10 and +20 in the future, because it seems likely that particles of this size in interplanetary space may be responsible for scattering the Sun's light to give the Zodiacal light. If this is the case, then the numbers must be far greater than indicated by the extrapolation of Table 2 by 2·5 times per magnitude. This, and the possibility of studying the impact of the micrometeorites on the artificial satellites, are two of the the many important problems which face meteor research in the immediate future.

CHAPTER SIXTEEN

Cosmic Radiation

J. G. WILSON

AT ALTITUDES attainable by unmanned balloons, it is possible to detect the energetic electrically charged particles which form the primary cosmic radiation, before these have been seriously contaminated with the secondary products of collisions with matter in the atmosphere. The distribution of the primary cosmic radiation has at this stage already been distorted by the presence of the Earth, in particular by its magnetic field; but for this distortion the general flux of particles would be nearly *isotropic*, that is, independent of direction. The particle stream consists of about 79 per cent of hydrogen nuclei (protons), 20 per cent helium nuclei and 1 per cent of heavier nuclei. It is known that the energy of an individual particle may be as much as a hundred million GeV;* and there are no grounds for supposing that this represents a true limiting value.

Within the atmosphere, primary cosmic radiation gives rise, through encounters with atomic nuclei, to a succession of events leading to the formation of a secondary cosmic radiation, with which all observations except those at extreme altitude are concerned. It was in investigations of this secondary radiation that pioneer work on nuclear collisions at high energy was accomplished, the results being so significant that they provided stimulus for the construction of large expensive machines for accelerating particles. With these, controlled experiments lead to a precision of understanding not easily attained using naturally occurring particles; hence as any energy range comes within the scope of machines, the physics of those collisions effectively passes from the sphere of cosmic radiation to the laboratory.

* One GeV equals one thousand million eV, that is, equals one thousand million times the energy an electron would gain in falling through a potential of one volt.

Emphasis in this chapter will incline to the geophysical and cosmological problems, the physics of energetic nuclear encounters being used merely to give features important for this purpose.

NUCLEAR ENCOUNTERS AT COSMIC RAY ENERGIES

At the energies encountered in radioactive transformations, and attainable by the simpler machines, collisions of *protons* and *neutrons*, that is of *nucleons*, are *elastic*, the whole energy initially present remaining with the colliding particles. In the energy range of cosmic radiation this is no longer true: energy is emitted by colliding particles very much as atomic systems emit light waves and moving electric charges in a transmitting aerial emit radio waves. However, the carriers of this energy, which have been named *mesons*, differ from the *photons* which are concerned in electromagnetic radiation (light or radio waves), insofar as they have mass.

The mesons emitted in nuclear collisions form an unexpectedly complex group (in contrast to photons which are all of a kind), with the common property that all are unstable, decaying spontaneously into two or more lighter particles. The dominant species is the *pi-meson*, a particle about 270 times as heavy as an electron, but a second family of mesons, all about 960 times as heavy as an electron, apparently comprises several distinct types. While we do not yet know how the relative abundance at formation of different mesons depends upon the energy of collision, there is no general feature of the secondary radiation which suggests the presence of a substantial proportion of the heavier mesons, and we shall omit them from consideration.

Positively charged, negatively charged and neutral pi-mesons are produced in comparable numbers. The decay products of these mesons form the main components of the secondary cosmic radiation.

Decay Products of Mesons

The charged pi-meson has a lifetime of only about two hundredths of a millionth of a second; it decays to two particles, the almost undetectable *neutrino* and the *mu-meson*, which is of mass roughly three-quarters that of its parent *pi-meson*. This mu-meson occupies a curious, rather isolated position in our picture of the physical world. It reacts only weakly with other particles, playing little part in the physical changes which seem important to us. However, it also is unstable, its decay products being an electron and two neutrinos, but its life—about two millionths of a second—is long enough (when account is taken of the relativistic change of time scale) for many of those formed high in the atmosphere to reach the surface of the Earth. Moreover, these will not be prevented from travelling so far by collisions with nuclei, for the weakness of their interaction with nucleons allows them to pass unhindered through the nuclei they meet while traversing the atmosphere.

Neutral pi-mesons decay within about a hundred-million-millionth of a second into two photons which have energy many orders of magnitude greater than photons encountered in radioactivity. At this energy the important mechanism for the absorption of protons is *pair production*, in which the whole energy of the photon is absorbed in forming a pair of electrons, one of positive, the other of negative charge. A minimum amount of energy is required for the mass energy of these electrons, the remainder appears as their kinetic energy. Considerations of relativity require that the two newly-formed electrons shall follow closely the trajectory of the absorbed photon.

This formation of electron pairs is only the first step of a characteristic process. The electrons, themselves of great energy, in turn lose energy almost solely by emission of further photons, and the two steps we have detailed are capable of repetition. The sequence leads to a forward-moving stream of electrons and photons, the number of these increasing from one generation to the next, but the total energy which they carry slowly diminishing by dissipative processes which we have not described. This represents the growth of an electron *cascade* or *shower*, the most striking feature of the secondary cosmic radiation.

Cascade growth depends upon the dominance of the processes of pair production and of photon emission. Neither of these remains dominant at lower energies; dissipative absorption grows from a minor correction to a controlling feature, the cascade ceases to grow and is in due course absorbed.

SECONDARY DEVELOPMENT FROM A PRIMARY PROTON

We now describe the secondary development from a single

proton of rather high energy incident vertically on the atmosphere. We take this to have an energy of one thousand GeV, an energy perhaps one hundred times greater than that attained by protons in the largest machines. About one out of every two thousand particles in the primary cosmic radiation has greater energy.

There develops in the first place, as a sort of skeleton, the *nucleon cascade*, the stream of protons and neutrons arising from the first collision made by the primary with the nucleus of an air atom and from the later collisions, which these in turn make lower in the atmosphere. The nucleon cascade is itself a multiplicative process at high energy: when a proton or neutron strikes a small nucleus, most of the energy, apart from that diverted to the meson system, will be carried forward by a few nucleons. These undergo similar collisions and the nucleon cascade grows: like that of the electron cascade, this growth involves wider distribution of initial energy; the average energy of each nucleon falls, until a dissipative phase is reached in which low energy products of nuclear collisions finally distribute the remaining energy.

At each nuclear encounter involved in the growth of the skeleton, and until the collision energy gets too small, a fraction of this energy, perhaps as much as 30 per cent, is removed from the nucleon cascade as mesons. Each nuclear collision may accordingly be the source either of a charged meson sequence or of an electron cascade or of both.

The result is a system of associated particles moving down through the atmosphere. For a primary of the selected energy the electron cascade will grow to about 100 electrons at about 30,000 feet altitude and will then tend to die away, while perhaps six mesons will reach sea level, although it is unlikely that any two will strike within twenty yards of each other.

Observations on the Secondary Cosmic Radiation

The description of this particle complex formed in the atmosphere from a single primary draws attention to two modes of observation which are applicable to the secondary radiation.

(i) Individual secondary particles may be detected most easily by the familiar methods of nuclear physics; particles are recorded separately and the average flux at any point is described in terms of the distribution in energy and direction of each type of particle:

(ii) If large enough detecting systems are used it is possible to detect simultaneously two or more secondaries derived from a single primary. The possibility of detection relates the density of secondaries in the shower (and, rather indirectly, the energy of their primary), with the dimensions of the detecting system; so *shower detectors* may be set out to respond selectively to the products of primaries of at least a certain chosen high energy.

We now summarize the description of the secondary radiation as it is observed in these two ways in our latitude (say 50°N). Clearly, from the figures given in the last section, the secondary radiation from the 99.95 per cent primaries of energy less than one thousand GeV cannot normally be detected as a shower of associated particles. Only about one in a million of the primaries leads to an easily detected shower.

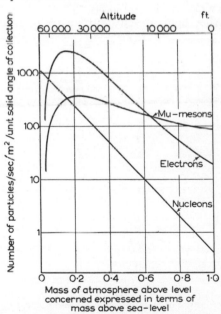

FIG. 1. Vertical flux of the main components of the secondary radiation near latitude 50°N.

The variation of the vertical intensity of the three main components through the atmosphere is shown in Fig. 1, where the electron and meson components, absent in the primary radiation, are seen to develop to maximum values and then to be partially absorbed in the lower atmosphere. At high altitudes the electron component is most intense, but it is more strongly absorbed than are mu-mesons and at sea-level these are three or four times as abundant as electrons. We have considered the electron component as arising from the decay of neutral pi-mesons, and the main part of the electron component in the high atmosphere indeed comes from this source. Near sea-level, however, few of these electrons remain and most of those observed are derived from decay of the slower mu-mesons.

Except in the topmost layers of the atmosphere, nucleons are less numerous than electrons and mesons, and at sea-level they form fewer than 1 per cent of all particles. The diagram refers to particles coming in the vertical direction; the spread of directions over which particles come varies with altitude. At sea-level all components are rather strongly concentrated near the vertical, at high altitudes they come much more nearly in all directions.

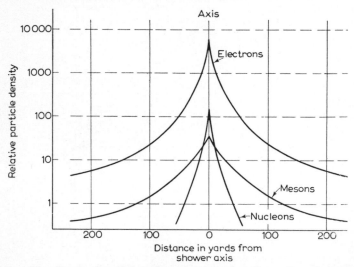

FIG. 2.   The distribution of electrons, mesons and nucleons about the axis of a shower of the secondary cosmic radiation.

The observation of showers, associated secondary particles derived from a single primary, is more complicated than that of the general intensity, for the particles forming a shower are spread over a great area. Fewer than half fall within an area of an acre, and even the most extensive apparatus cannot well receive more than a small sample of the shower particles. A general description of the distribution of particles within a single shower has only recently become possible. Fig. 2 shows the distribution of electrons, mesons and nucleons as a function of distance from the axis of a shower of moderate size at sea-level. At other altitudes the proportions of these particles would be rather different. In the central region, where the particle density is greatest, only about 2 per cent of particles are mesons or nucleons; away from the axis the percentage of nucleons falls right away but that of mesons increases to nearly 10 per cent at the limit of the diagram. At still greater distances the majority of particles are probably mesons, and in large showers about 8 per cent of all particles are mesons. In sheer numbers the electrons dominate the shower, and particularly the central region where the particle density is high; estimates of the size of showers and of the energy of the primaries from which they come are almost always based on counts of electrons. These electrons are, however, of lower energy than the nucleons and mesons in the shower, and the total energy carried by each of the three components is probably about the same.

The most significant measurement of a shower is its total size: if the number of particles at, for example, sea-level is determined, this can be related, although with difficulty, to the energy of the primary from which the shower has developed. In this way the energy spectrum of the primaries can be followed to great energies. No limiting energy has yet been reached beyond which primary particles are not found, but if there is such a limit, it is certainly greater than a hundred million GeV, and probably greater than a thousand million GeV.

The size of these numbers tends to obscure their meaning, and it is useful to consider the observable features arising from the very energetic primaries which arrive at a rate of the order of one per square mile per hour. The energy of such a particle, say a hundred million GeV, would be sufficient to raise a one ounce weight by one inch. The secondary development from this primary will lead to about ten million cascade electrons at sea-level, and over an area of some hundreds of square yards these will fall at a density of more than 1000 per square yard. Almost a million mesons will also reach sea-level, spread over an area of as much as a square mile. These, in contrast to the electrons, are extremely penetrating, and from such large events energetic mesons have been detected forming showers of associated particles at depths of more than 1000 feet underground.

ENERGY DISSIPATION AND IONIZATION IN THE ATMOSPHERE

The energy falling on the Earth as primary cosmic radiation is about equal to that incident as starlight, and amounts to about 10 watts per square mile. Most of this is dissipated in the atmosphere, mainly by the process of ionization, about one-fifth passes in meson decay to neutrinos, and is for practical purposes lost to observation, and only a small part is carried into the ground at sea-level as detectable particles.

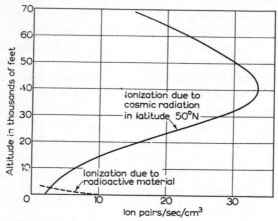

FIG. 3.   Ionization by cosmic radiation through the atmosphere.

The actual number of particles at different levels of the atmosphere has been shown in Fig. 1; in Fig. 3 the rate of ionization by these particles is given as a function of altitude. The greatest number of ions is formed at about 40,000 feet; the number of cosmic ray particles is still increasing as we go to greater altitudes, but this increase is offset by lower ionization by each particle in the less dense air. At sea-level the rate of ionization is about 2 ion pairs per second per cubic centimetre, being usually considerably smaller than the ionization arising from local radioactive matter. In the diagram this is shown as 10 ion pairs per second per cubic centimetre at ground level, but it is very variable. At an altitude of about 2000 feet the total ionization reaches a minimum value, and at greater heights the local contribution is insignificant compared with that due to cosmic radiation.

A small fraction of the energy dissipated in the atmosphere is absorbed in nuclear transformations, and one of these, leading to radioactive carbon, is of general interest. Radioactive carbon is formed in the capture by nitrogen nuclei of slow neutrons which are a normal product of the more energetic nuclear encounters of the nucleon cascade. Its formation takes place on a scale which maintains a measurable proportion of it in the carbon dioxide of the atmosphere, and so in freshly grown vegetable products. The life of radioactive carbon is about 5600 years. Vegetable material which has been undisturbed for times at all comparable with this is found to contain a correspondingly diminished quantity of radioactive carbon. Measurement of this quantity forms the basis of a method of dating which promises to be of considerable value to archeologists.

VARIATIONS OF THE COSMIC RADIATION

Much of the geophysical and cosmological interest of cosmic radiation concerns observed variations of intensity in space and time. Interest relates in particular to the condition of the primary radiation in the neighbourhood of the Earth, but beyond its immediate disturbing influence, and to its significance. However, profitable investigation of this problem can only follow an understanding of the main terrestrial effects. We distinguish (i) geomagnetic effects, and (ii) atmospheric depth effects.

Geomagnetic Effects

The nature of the geomagnetic effects is illustrated in Fig. 4. This diagram (after H. V. Neher) shows the flux of ionizing particles as measured in an instrument known as a *Geiger counter telescope*, flown at an altitude of 30,000 feet. It refers to North-South flights extending from the equator to high latitudes, and gives measurements with a vertical telescope, and also with telescopes inclined at 45° towards the East and West respectively. The tendency for the particle beam to become collimated through the atmosphere is shown by the greater intensity of the vertical measurements as compared with those in inclined directions.

T

The latitude effect shown by the vertical telescope arises from the deflection of primary particles in the Earth's magnetic field. To a first approximation, this field is that of a dipole at the centre of the Earth, but with its axis slightly inclined to that of rotation (Chapter 6). This inclination leads to a difference between geographical and geomagnetic latitudes, and in Fig. 4 the latter are used. For the dipole field, particles approaching the Earth in the equatorial plane, and so at right angles to the field direction, are most strongly deflected. It can be shown to be impossible for a

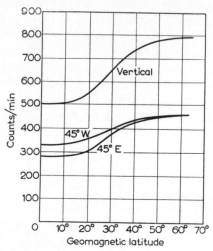

FIG. 4.   Intensity of the secondary cosmic radiation as a function of geomagnetic latitude at 30,000 feet altitude, measured with a Geiger counter telescope.

charged primary to strike vertically at the equator, from whatever initial direction it may come, unless its energy is at least 15 GeV. In higher latitudes the direction of approach of primaries is to some extent along the direction of the field, and accordingly these are less strongly deflected. The minimum energy with which primaries can strike vertically is lower than at the equator, and the total vertical flux therefore greater. This increase does not extend to very high latitudes; there is a *knee* in the latitude-intensity curve which from the earliest studies of the subject has attracted interest. The reason for at least part of the knee phenomenon is trivial, for the primaries of low energy, which would cause the intensity to go on increasing at still higher latitudes, produce secondaries with sufficient penetration very inefficiently. This explanation is not complete, however, and there is little doubt that these low energy primaries are often prevented from approaching near to the Earth.

This feature draws attention to complications in the magnetic deflection of particles approaching the Earth. Measurements of the latitude effect at balloon altitudes (about 100,000 feet), in high latitudes, tend to show considerable variations; low energy primaries appear to be at one time present and at another absent. There is some indication that this is a solar effect and related to the eleven year sunspot cycle; it may be associated with the screening action of entrained magnetic fields carried by gas streams emitted from the Sun.

Referring again to Fig. 4, the intensity at low latitudes in the West-inclined telescope exceeds that in the one pointing to the East. This *East-West effect* is to be expected if the primary particles are positively charged; qualitatively it indicates that positive primaries are in excess, quantitatively it is in accord with 100 per cent of positive primaries. Other evidence, which we will not detail, has demonstrated the virtual absence of electrons from the primary radiation.

Atmospheric Depth Effects

All components of the secondary radiation are subject to absorption by the atmosphere and so all exhibit a negative barometric effect, their intensity diminishing when the barometric pressure rises. This effect is large for the nucleonic component and for the extensive showers, which are developed on a nucleonic skeleton. For these it corresponds to the attenuation of nucleons in collisions with atomic nuclei and is about $2\frac{1}{2}$ per cent per tenth of an inch change of pressure. For mesons, which are only weakly absorbed in the atmosphere, and for the sea-level electronic component which is mainly secondary to the mesons, the barometric effect is still negative but only about one-fifth as great.

The passage of the secondary radiation through the atmosphere is not entirely governed by the mass of air traversed: insofar as decay processes are involved, notably in the pi-meson to mu-meson to electron sequence, the actual distance travelled is relevant to the probability of decay, and so to transmission of the particle beam. Variations in the distance travelled for the traversal of a given mass of air arise from changes in the general temperature of the atmosphere: if the temperature increases, the linear scale of the atmosphere is lengthened (Chapter 7) and, in particular, the chance of decay of mu-mesons before they reach a specified level is increased. There arises in this way, as was first pointed out by P. M. S. Blackett, a negative temperature effect, strictly for the mu-meson intensity, but actually for the total sea-level intensity. This is a small effect, rather less than 0·2 per cent per degree Centigrade. A second temperature effect which must take place, but for which the experimental data are less satisfactory, involves the local temperature at the levels where pi-mesons are created. These mesons, which lead by decay to the observed mu-mesons, can also make nuclear collisions. The probability of these collisions as against decay is increased by an increase of local density and so by a decrease of local temperature. In terms of sea-level meson intensity, this is a positive temperature effect.

Atmospheric changes, of which the effects discussed in the last two paragraphs are particular examples, lead to periodicities of intensity of the secondary radiation at any place. The tide-like pressure waves in the atmosphere and the daily changes of atmospheric temperature give regular daily variations of intensity, while through the year the amplitude, phase and harmonic content of these variations will themselves change. In addition, normal movements of air lead to changes of intensity for the explanation of which meteorological data are usually inadequate. Together, these variations form a partially understood background against which extraterrestrial effects are studied.

Solar Effects

Variations of intensity having their origin outside the Earth can be divided into those arising from solar activity and those related to more distant causes. Events of short time scale, extending over periods of up to perhaps one year, are generally attributed to the first category and operate preferentially in the low energy, latitude-sensitive primary range.

The effects of solar activity appear to be of two kinds. On rather rare occasions, hardly oftener than once every four or five years, a strong emission of low energy primary radiation from the Sun is received at the Earth. The period of emission is short, almost certainly less than an hour, and the mechanism of particle acceleration is not known. The emissions are associated with solar flares which also give rise to magnetic storms and ionospheric disturbances. But very few flares give significant increases of cosmic radiation, and whether the emission of particles of cosmic ray energies is uncommon, or whether the conditions allowing them to escape towards the Earth and to reach it do not often occur, is not understood.

More frequent variations are attributed to modulation of the general primary flux by solar effects. These appear to involve the inter-relation of gas clouds emitted from the Sun and entrained in the solar system (and the associated magnetic fields), with the large scale movement of matter and field in the galactic arm where we lie. The study of these features is in a very early stage, and here we merely indicate four examples:

(i) The screening of the Earth from low energy primaries, which leads at certain times to a cut-off in high latitudes even at balloon altitudes:

(ii) Decreases of general cosmic ray intensity which occur in association with some intense magnetic storms:

(iii) The *Forbush* decreases of intensity, in which the nucleonic component at sea-level may decrease by as much as 15 per cent in one or two days and then recover rather more slowly: and

(iv) Trapping of particles from the rare solar flare emissions, leading to a more or less isotropic distribution near the Earth for many hours after flare emission has ceased.

These features are of great interest in themselves, for increasing attention is being given to the problems of moving interstellar and interplanetary matter; they also act, however, to obscure the characteristics of the external primaries over the whole range of energy for which they are important.

ORIGIN OF THE PRIMARY RADIATION

There is now little doubt that the main primary cosmic radiation reaches us from outside the solar system. It is characterized by its rather high energy density, the presence of heavy nuclei (for example, iron), in an abundance comparable with that in stellar envelopes, the absence of electrons and a high degree of isotropy. The degree of isotropy is determined by an analysis in sidereal time of intensity records of detectors scanning by virtue of the motion of the Earth. The general flux is isotropic to within about

0·05 per cent and the primaries of very large showers within perhaps 2 per cent, a figure entirely set by statistical weakness of the
data.

The presence of heavy nuclei (which are of large collision cross-
section), in considerable abundance, sets an upper limit of only a
few million years to their life since acceleration, and greatly
restricts possible mechanisms of acceleration. It is now widely
accepted that diffusion through turbulent interstellar matter provides a plausible mechanism of acceleration which also leads to
isotropy of the main particle stream. These particles are moreover
effectively trapped within the galactic structure, and the high energy
density need extend only over a restricted region. The primaries of
the largest showers present graver problems. It is unlikely that any
reasonable restraint can bring them to isotropy within the galaxy,
and it can be strongly argued that these must extend at the intensity which we observe through extragalactic space. Little can yet
be said as to the time scale of this extragalactic component or as to
the mechanism of its acceleration.

CHAPTER SEVENTEEN

Genesis of Life

J. B. S. HALDANE

THIS IS not the place to attempt either a definition of life or a history of theories of its origin. But a few points are worth emphasizing. Three hundred years ago it was generally believed that the first living beings on Earth were supernaturally produced, but that new life was constantly arising, for example, mites in cheese and maggots in decaying meat, by natural processes. Careful work by Francesco Redi, Lazaro Spallanzani, Louis Pasteur, and others showed that this was not the case. And even the simplest bacteria proved to be immensely complicated, including hundreds or thousands of different species of large molecules, so that their direct origin from non-living materials was an exceedingly improbable event and presumably miraculous if it occurred.

But while there was little doubt that a bacterium or yeast cell was alive, and an enzyme extracted from it was not, even if it could catalyse a process previously regarded as a prerogative of living things, W. M. Stanley's discovery of molecular viruses made the distinction between living and dead systems dubious. A molecular virus is a nucleoprotein which, when injected into a suitable living cell, is copied by this cell, and may either increase so as to kill its host or, like a normal cellular constituent, only increase at the same rate as the rest of its host. In this case its presence is shown by its attacking other hosts. It has the characteristic of life that 'descendants' or 'copies' usually, but not always, resemble 'ancestors' or 'models'; but it cannot reproduce in a non-living medium. It is, however, quite conceivable that a system of organic substances, such as nucleotides, amino-acids, catalysts, and energy sources such as organic pyrophosphates may be produced which will copy molecular viruses, without being alive in the sense that it can copy itself. If so there will be some sense in saying that molecular viruses are alive. If then we knew the history of the genesis of life on Earth, it might well be impossible to state just when life had originated. It might be possible, however, to say that the essential steps had been taken between certain dates, as we can in the case of the evolution of reptiles from amphibia, even though the status of some intermediate forms is doubtful. As will be seen, I suggest that the origin of life was, in fact, a sudden event.

From the point of view of this book a fundamental division of living organisms is into strict aerobes, which require molecular oxygen, facultative anaerobes, which can live with or without it, and strict anaerobes, to which molecular oxygen is a poison. Most familiar organisms are strict aerobes, even when, like the higher plants, they produce a great deal more oxygen than they use. For the higher plants need molecular oxygen for germination, and for the life of their roots. Yeast is an example of a facultative anaerobe. In the presence of oxygen it oxidizes sugar to carbon dioxide and water; in its absence it ferments sugar to carbon dioxide and alcohol. Some bacteria are strict anaerobes, for example, the tetanus bacillus, though its spores are not killed by oxygen.

FOOD AND ENERGY

All organisms require a supply of food for growth. The main elements needed are hydrogen, carbon, nitrogen, oxygen, phosphorus and sulphur. Potassium is probably always needed; sodium, magnesium, calcium and chlorine are usually needed in fairly large amounts; and other metals, such as iron, copper, zinc, manganese and molybdenum in much smaller quantities. Boron, fluorine, silicon and iodine are needed at least by some. Organisms also need a free energy source. This can be radiation, or the oxidation of organic compounds or ferrous iron, sulphite, thiosulphate, nitrite, ammonium and other inorganic substances by molecular oxygen, or more rarely by nitrate and the like. Or it can be the breakdown of metastable molecules, for example, of sugar by anaerobic yeast.

About 30 years ago it was gradually established that the source of energy in muscular action was the breakdown of glycogen to lactic acid by a process very similar to alcoholic fermentation. The free energy liberated in this process is used to build up an

:ster of pyrophosphoric acid, of which more is said later, and the free energy derived from the hydrolysis of this ester is used for muscular work, and also for luminescence, secretion, organic syntheses, and so on. The energy derived from oxidation is used o build up glucose and its dehydrated polymer, glycogen, from lactate. Similar processes occur in all cells so far studied.

I therefore suggested that the anaerobic metabolic processes, which are found in all organisms, were more primitive than the aerobic ones. That is to say the first organisms had lived by breaking down metastable compounds as a source of free energy, and probably in a medium containing very small amounts of molecular oxygen. At that time the history of the atmosphere was far from clear. Methane had been discovered round the outer planets, but ammonia was only identified after the essay in question was written. I had been compelled to postulate its existence in the Earth's primitive atmosphere. The fact that some of my speculations of thirty years ago were confirmed, encourages me to speculate again.

Geophysicists seem to be agreed that the Earth's primitive atmosphere contained a great deal of hydrogen and methane, and, therefore, little carbon dioxide and practically no free oxygen, the oxygen being almost all in combination with hydrogen as water. They are in agreement that most of the hydrogen was lost, and there must have been a period when there was little free hydrogen or oxygen and probably a good deal more carbon dioxide than at present. In 1953 H. C. Urey calculated that this intermediate stage could have lasted from $2\frac{1}{2}$ million to 100 million years. G. P. Kuiper, (Chapter 2), gives reasons for thinking that 'a steady state with a trace of atmospheric oxygen may thus have developed during part of geologic time', and is inclined to attribute most of the existing oxygen to photosynthesis, as I did. Kuiper adheres to the view that the Earth's crust was once melted. Urey doubts this. If it was melted, the theory which I am supporting will not work unless free oxygen in appreciable amounts only appeared long after the surface cooled down. The absence or rarity of oxygen in the atmospheres of Venus and Mars suggests that it only appeared late on our planet.

A very similar view was developed in much greater detail by A. I. Oparin. J. D. Bernal, J. W. S. Pringle and others have discussed the matter further. However, Pringle thought that the energetic processes which were used by the first life were oxidation processes in a large volume of fluid in which oxygen was diffusing down from above, and hydrocarbons or other reducing substance diffusing up from below. This is the more plausible because in existing aerobic cells there appears to be a gradient of this kind with oxygen diffusing in from the outside. In the rest of this article I shall develop my own views of what seems plausible, rather than deal with those of others as fully as they probably deserve.

MOLECULES IN LIVING ORGANISMS

All fully living organisms contain three types of very large molecule, with molecular weights usually exceeding 20,000, namely polysaccharides, proteins, and nucleic acids. The latter are usually associated with proteins, but probably only by ionic (electrostatic) bonds. Besides this there are some large molecules of mixed type, such as mucoproteins which are intermediate between proteins and polysaccharides.

The polysaccharides consist of hexagonal pyranose sugar residues linked by ether linkages in chains which may occasionally branch. The commonest residue is glucose, but many other sugars and partially oxidized and reduced sugars are found. The proteins consist of amino-acid residues linked by peptide bonds. About twenty different amino-acid are usually found. The backbone of a nucleic acid consists of alternate pentose (five carbon sugar) and phosphoric acid residues. To each pentose residue is attached a nitrogenous base, which may be a one-ringed pyrimidine, either thymine, uracil, cytosine, or methyl- or methoxy-cytosine, or a two-ringed purine, either adenine or guanine. One type of nucleic acid, desoxyribonucleic acid (DNA) occurs in very long chains up to at least 2000 residues in length, which do not appear to branch, and are associated in pairs. The other type, ribonucleic acid (RNA) contains ribose residues and may possibly branch. The peptide chains of proteins are usually united by cystine residues. So large protein molecules have a reticular (netted) structure. Polysaccharide chains may or may not branch. There is very strong evidence that these large molecules are built up in a living cell from the same residues into which they can be broken down by digestive enzymes. This is why, although every species has its own characteristic proteins and nucleic acids, animals can live on the tissues of other organisms.

The main constituents needed, with molecular weights varying from 89 (glycine), to 204 (tryptophan), include perhaps ten sugars, twenty amino-acids, five purine and pyrimidine bases, and phosphoric acid. The fats and lipoids (substances with physical properties like those of fats, but often containing other elements than hydrogen, carbon and oxygen), do not form such large chain molecules, but include one group of large molecules not susceptible of hydrolysis, the steroids, with molecular weights of 280 to 400. Besides the relatively small molecules mentioned a number of others are required in quite small amounts. These are often attached to proteins to form the active groups of enzymes. They include most of the vitamins.

MOLECULAR SYNTHESIS

Organisms differ. Let us take a very simple difference. Some pneumococci (the micro-organisms responsible for most cases of pneumonia) cannot make the equivalent of a hairy coat in which each hair is represented by a polysaccharide chain. Others can, and there are at least 40 different possible types of polysaccharide. In order to enable a pneumococcus to make one of these it is sufficient that it incorporates a single molecule, of molecular weight about 750,000, of *DNA*, derived from a pneumococcus which makes the polysaccharide in question. When this has been done the *DNA* molecule gets copied at each cell division. It also enables the pneumococcus to make a number of molecules of a particular protein, an enzyme concerned in the synthesis of this polysaccharide. The physicochemical basis of heredity in higher organisms is similar, except that the molecules, or parts of a larger molecule, which are copied in this way, and called genes, are generally introduced in very large numbers at a time from a donor organism called a male. But Soviet workers have produced evidence of their occasional introduction by other methods.

With different combinations of the four bases found in *DNA* molecules, it would be possible to construct $2^{2,500}$, or 10^{750} different *DNA* molecules of molecular weight 750,000. Their mass would be 10^{730} grams. That of the known part of the universe is under 10^{60} grams. Probably only a small part of this large molecule is needed for the particular function in question. But if it could be shown that a particular pattern of *DNA*, even of molecular weight 50,000, were needed in the simplest living organism, it would follow that life cannot have originated from inorganic sources, or at most had done so once in the known part of the universe. In any case it is clear that the synthesis of even the smallest living organism would be a very formidable, perhaps an impossible task. Can we imagine how the gap can have been bridged?

Five methods are known by all of which it is reasonably certain that metastable molecules were synthesized when the Earth had a 'reducing' atmosphere containing only traces of free oxygen. Four are described by M. Calvin.

1. Electric discharges through mixtures of hydrogen, methane, ammonia and water vapour generate a variety of organic compounds, including glycine, the smallest of the amino-acids, but one quite capable of chain formation.

2. High energy radiation acting on carbon dioxide and water vapour produces formic, oxalic, and even succinic acid, while glycine is formed in presence of ammonia.

3. Ultra-violet radiation produces amino-acids from formic acid or aldehyde with ammonia or nitrate.

4. The primitive Earth probably contained carbides, yielding acetylene, which polymerizes readily to benzene and other aromatic substances. Oparin stressed this possibility.

5. Heated phosphates lose water to form pyrophosphates and metaphosphates.

When such substances are left about today they are broken down by bacteria and other living organisms, or are actually built up into living matter. In the absence of life I contended that they accumulated in the ocean, or whatever smaller bodies of water may have existed. Urey ventured to suggest that the ocean may have contained as much as 1 per cent of organic substances.

This opinion of Urey's, which coincides with my own in the past, seems to me a little temerarious. All metastable molecules rearrange themselves in the course of time. We have reason to think that even as long as 3 thousand million years ago temperatures were much as today. On the other hand the pH value* of the sea was probably at first high, as the air contained much ammonia and little carbon dioxide. With the loss of hydrogen, the carbon

---

* The pH value of a solution is minus the logarithm to the base 10 of the hydrogen ion concentration in gram equivalents per litre. A solution having a pH value less than 7 is acid and one having a pH value greater than 7 is alkaline.

dioxide increased, and the pH value may have fallen to about 5. Later on it rose again. Before we can say much about conditions in the primitive ocean we should know the half-lives of a number of metastable molecules in aqueous solution at temperatures from 0°C. to 30°C. and pH values from 5 to 9. The stability of some laboratory chemicals shows that many such organic molecules have half-lives of the order of a thousand years or more. Even coal, which is 200 million years old, is not at its lowest energy level. The stability of molecules is probably as important as their rate of formation by the processes considered, in determining the organic composition of the primitive sea.

On the other hand, the half-life of pyrophosphate is small—the work of P. Fleury, J. Courtois and A. Desjobert suggests a half-life of the order of ten years at 20°C. and pH value of 7. It is, of course, possible that some of the metaphosphates are far stabler. If not the supply of polyphosphates may have been a limiting factor in biogenesis.

In a metastable system it is possible for a catalyst molecule C to catalyse not only the breakdown of a substrate system S to provide free energy, but also the formation of another catalyst molecule C' like itself. If so the number of C molecules will increase provided they are not destroyed more quickly than they are formed. The best known examples of C are the free radicals and other activated molecules which are responsible for chain reactions with branching chains. However, I think they are much too unstable to be relevant to the origin of life. We are interested in catalyst molecules which can last for a considerable time in the absence of 'food', and yet multiply their numbers when a suitable substrate is present.

Formally this criterion is satisfied by digestive enzymes such as pepsin and trypsin. Pepsin acts on an enzymatically inactive protein, pepsinogen, converting it into pepsin by removing about a tenth of the molecule. Trypsin has a similar effect on trypsinogen without any appreciable change in molecular weight. This conversion can be, and has been, compared with bacterial infection. However, in these cases the enzyme structure appears to exist ready made in the precursor. Can we find a case where the catalyst molecule builds up more catalyst molecules from smaller molecules?

Such a case is provided by the anaerobic conversion of glucose

to alcohol and carbon dioxide in yeast, or the very similar conversion of glycogen to lactic acid in muscle. Yeast juice will convert
sugar to alcohol and carbon dioxide. At least twelve highly specific
enzymes catalyse the various steps in this reaction. The first three
steps involve the successive transference of two phosphate residues
to the glucose molecule, giving fructofuranose—1 : 6—diphosphate. These residues are transferred from two molecules of
adenosine-triphosphate (ATP). This is a highly metastable
molecule. About 11,500 calories of free energy are liberated when
it is hydrolysed to phosphate and adenosine-diphosphate (ADP).
Fructose diphosphate is broken down by enzymes into two
molecules of 3-phosphoglyceraldehyde which are phosphorylated
by inorganic phosphate, and then dehydrogenated. The two
protons lost in dehydrogenation are transferred to acetaldehyde,
which accumulates at a later stage of the process. The resulting
1 : 3-diphosphoglyceric acid is sufficiently metastable to transfer
both its phosphate residues to ADP, forming pyruvic acid after
a series of isomerizations. The pyruvic acid yields carbon dioxide
and acetaldehyde, which is converted into alcohol by the proton
transfer described above. The net result is that for each glucose
molecule fermented, two ATP molecules are converted into ADP,
and four of ADP converted into ATP.

The process which occurs in muscle, yielding two molecules of
L-lactic acid for each residue of glucose derived from glycogen, is
very similar. The ATP formed in these processes is used up in
muscular contraction, luminescence, secretion, and in the synthesis
of polysaccharides, proteins, and almost certainly nucleic acids.
While the fermentation of a glucose molecule will only yield the
energy needed to add a third phosphate residue to two ADP
molecules, its oxidation by molecular oxygen will probably
phosphorylate forty.

The processes described will only proceed at a measurable rate
when catalysed by enzymes. Among the most interesting of these
are the phosphokinases which transfer a phosphate residue from
ATP to an organic residue, or from an organic phosphoric ester
of high energy content to ADP. They are apparently quite distinct
from the phosphatases, which catalyse hydrolysis of ordinary
phosphoric esters to give inorganic phosphate, and the reverse
reaction. But no systematic search has been made for inorganic
surfaces or heavy metals which might replace these enzymes. Nor

has a search been made for an organic compound which, without
the aid of an enzyme, will receive a phosphate residue from *ATP*,
and will then proceed to isomerize or interact with a later product
of the same reaction, forming a substance sufficiently unstable to
phosphorylate two *ADP* molecules. If such a substance exists it
would be useless or dangerous inside a cell. Life (or at least
contemporary life) is based on reactions whose rates are almost
all controlled by enzymes, and which can, therefore, be integrated
into an orderly system. But the search for such a substance, if
successful, would throw a good deal of light on the origin of life.

ABORTIVE SYSTEMS

   I suggest, then, that in primitive waters, perhaps in the sea, in
fresh water, or in mud, there were chains of phosphoric acid
residues, very probably esterified in a stable manner at one end,
which were capable of esterifying metastable molecules analogous
to glyceraldehyde so that they reacted with an inorganic phosphate
ion to form a still more metastable molecule which could add two
phosphate residues to pre-existing phosphate residue chains. These
chains therefore grew in length, and might divide and thus
effectively reproduce themselves. They had some of the properties
of life, and could be described, in O. W. Stapledon's terminology,
as subvital units. They also phosphorylated other organic compounds which were not prepared to give back more phosphate
residues than they received. But some of them would undergo
synthesis, as, for example, two 3-phospho-glyceraldehyde molecules will condense in presence of two enzymes, to form one
molecule of fructofuranose—1 : 6—diphosphate. Such synthesis
can be very 'life-like'. Thus alpha-glucose-1-phosphate reacts with
pre-existing chains of at least 5 condensed glucose units to form
longer chains containing up to at least 80 glucose residues.
Different enzymes catalyse the production of different types of
chain. And chains once formed may be split. But no chain is
formed except by lengthening a pre-existing one. A glycogen
molecule in one of my muscles and a starch molecule in the
potato which I am eating may have had a common ancestor a
thousand million years ago.
   Some of the large molecules synthesized must have had catalytic
powers. For we know that some 'pure' proteins, that is to say
proteins containing no prosthetic groups such as haematin or

flavin-adenine nucleotide, can act as enzymes. But the sets of processes so catalysed were, I suggest, disorganized. They might go on for hours or days in a suitable pool or mud surface. But, like chain reactions, they came to an end. I disagree with Calvin who contends that chemical evolution was a process lasting for hundreds of millions of years, preceding biological evolution. Such systems as I have sketched 'died' out, and even if one had come very near to being self-perpetuating, no memory of it remained.

PROPOSED HYPOTHESES

I believe that life demands not only self-reproducing molecules, but a self-reproducing system of such molecules. If synthetic enzymes and suitable substrates are available it appears that a large DNA molecule can be accurately copied. It is built up of four types of unit, the nucleotides containing adenine (A), guanine (G), thymine (T) and cytosine (C) in linear order. Two chains of such residues are coiled round one another in a spiral according to J. D. Watson and F. H. Crick so that to A in one chain corresponds T in the other, to G in one C in the other. Thus a sequence $ATGTC$ in one chain corresponds to a sequence $TACAG$ in the other. A and T, G and C fit together, and are probably held together by hydrogen bonds. Provided nucleotides in solution, a suitable enzyme, and probably a free energy source, are available, copying is quite possible as follows.

The double spiral unwinds, and as it does so a new chain is built against each of the old chains. C. Levinthal and H. R. Crane give calculations to show that this is energetically possible. RNA may have a similar structure with uracil replacing cytosine. There is very little doubt that proteins are formed both on DNA and RNA 'scaffoldings', the nucleic acid determining the protein structure to some extent at least.

The minimum living organism which I can imagine would contain a copyable nucleic acid spiral, whose structure enabled it to make at least the following enzymes: a nuclease capable of adding new units to a nucleic acid chain; a proteinase capable of adding new units to a peptide chain; one or two phosphokinases capable of transferring a phosphate residue from a pyrophosphoric ester to amino-acids, sugars and perhaps nucleotides; a nucleosidase capable of forming a nucleotide from bases and a phosphorylated sugar. It would also contain a supply of a self-reproducing pyrophosphoric ester, possible *ATP*. Such a system would automatically synthesize adenosine. It would be surrounded by a monolayer of protein, possibly consisting of the enzymes named.

Such a primitive cell would, I suggest, be able to grow in a medium containing sugars, bases, and amino-acids. It might be able to get free energy from a variety of reactions, but it could only incorporate molecules which fitted its phosphokinases and also its synthesizing enzymes. Both nucleic acids and proteins might be much simpler than modern ones. The former could still yield a vast variety of patterns if it only contained adenine and thymine, and proteins could be built from only eight or ten amino-acids. The joint molecular weight of all the large molecules need not have exceeded 100,000.

Such a cell could arise where there was a fairly dense concentration of organic molecules and pyrophosphoric esters engaged in synthesis. It would slowly grow, and split on reaching a critical size. It was no doubt very inefficient but, provided in a favourable medium, over half the products of fission were viable, it was potentially immortal. Its synthesis, I suggest, was an improbable event, which might have a probability of only a half of happening anywhere on the Earth's surface in several million years, but not an event of the improbability considered earlier. I have elsewhere suggested that it might have been formed by the coming together of several different types of subvital unit.

There is, however, another possibility, which I owe to N. W. Pirie's arguments, though I have no reason to think it will meet with his approval. It is possible that much of the necessary catalysis could have been performed by heavy metals, possibly including rare metals such as vanadium, which are still accumulated by some organisms. If so the formation of compounds which hold them firmly by chelation (i.e. usually as part of a complexion) was one of the main tasks of the primitive organism. The best known group of such compounds is the tetrapyrrolic porphyrin group found in haemoglobin, chlorophyll, the cytochromes, peroxidase, and catalase. If so the primitive organism may have been very different from what I have imagined. Heavy metal catalysis is not very specific. It becomes more so when the active group is attached to a suitable protein. For example, both catalase and peroxidase combine with hydrogen peroxide, but the subsequent

u

fates of the two compounds are very different. Perhaps only later did life 'exploit' the fact that some proteins without prosthetic metal-carrying groups can be efficient catalysts.

On this hypothesis the first organisms may have been simpler than I have suggested, and their synthesis easier. However, it could only be substantiated by a huge programme of research on the catalytic activity of chelated metal atoms, a programme which, by the way, might be of great importance for chemical industry.

Mutation is simply a side reaction to an autocatalytic reaction which generates copyable molecules. The copying process in the first organisms was probably rather inaccurate, and mutation rather common. Perhaps one mutation in ten thousand increased the probability of survival, and was incorporated into the 'species'. Further enzymes, for example one which would make ribose (if that was the sugar in the nucleic acid) from hexoses, as it is made today by hexose-monophosphate dehydrogenase, would have been advantageous. So would greater specificity of existing enzymes.

As the supply of organic molecules was used up, mutations enabling an organism to build them up would have a very high selective advantage. Enzymes with this function exist in plants, but have mostly been lost in animals. I suggest that our first ancestors had a metabolism in some ways more like that of existing animals than existing plants.

Pirie thinks that the first life may have used compounds wholly unlike those now used, perhaps not even carbon compounds. This may be so. I have tried to make a concrete picture of what might have happened, using familiar substances.

Evolution, I suggest, was at first very rapid. Cells sometimes fused, often with disastrous consequences, but sometimes incorporating improvements in each 'parent'. In a few million years the supplies of 'food' ran short, and photosynthesis within the cells became advantageous. Whether the appearance of large amounts of oxygen in the air was due to photosynthesis or to hydrogen loss into space is a matter for argument. Aerobic metabolism led to a far more rapid energy flux, and if haem compounds were first used for photosynthesis they could later be used to fix oxygen, or conversely.

I have suggested that the origin of life was a single 'improbable' event. There may have been several such events, and our present life is derived from the union of their products where these were compatible. The choice between D- and L-antipodal molecules was perhaps a matter of chance. The Crick-Watson model of nucleic acid demands only one antipode of a sugar to ensure regular coiling. Given this the rest may follow inevitably.

The data of H. G. Thode, J. Macnamara, and H. W. Fleming on sulphur isotopes suggest that there was little oxygen in our air before 800 million years ago, and that life did not originate much before this. The earliest organisms which left satisfactory fossils, those of the lower Cambrian, were only about 500 million years old. In work in the press on factors limiting the rate of evolution I give a reason for thinking that evolution may have been a good deal quicker in pre-Cambrian times than later. If so life may have originated only a thousand million or less years ago. This is intelligible if, as Urey thinks, it could not originate till most of the atmospheric hydrogen had been lost. This notion is, of course, quite opposed to that of a prolonged pre-vital period of chemical evolution, against which I have already given another argument. It may be that on any planet there is a relatively short critical period in which life must originate if it is ever to do so. Perhaps, for example, this period is past on Mars and has not yet arrived on Venus.

Many authors would like to think of the origin of life as a gradual process, as its subsequent evolution appears to be. I think this appearance is fallacious. Many higher plant species arose quite suddenly, by allopolyploidy* following on hybridization. All evolution occurs by mutation, which is a sudden event, as the substitution of one molecular species by another must be. Natural selection, which favours a small minority of mutants, is, of course, relatively slow.

These workers, and others, will say that I have made the origin of life a matter of 'blind chance'. In science, at any rate when we get above the level of quantum mechanics, 'chance' is a somewhat rude word which we apply to events which cannot be predicted in terms of the branch of science in which we are interested. I cannot tell that this particular man will die in a railway accident tomorrow. But with sufficient knowledge of the state of British Railway tracks and his intended journey I might be able at least to say that he had a five per cent probability of doing so. Similarly

---

* Hybrids are often sterile because the maternal and paternal chromosomes in the hybrid nuclei will not pair. If the chromosomes divide without a nuclear division each chromosome can find a partner from its own species and fertility is restored. Other more complicated processes lead to the same result.

if the conditions for biogenesis were known, it might be possible to say that the probability that it would occur on a given planet in the next 100 million years was 99 per cent.

Another objection raised is that even if a primitive organism could arise from 'dead' matter in the manner here suggested, mind could not do so. This is certainly true if the account which physicists give of matter is complete. But I have yet to meet a physicist who thinks it is complete. I am personally naive enough to think that matter is at least somewhat like my experience of it, in other words that the 'gulf' between matter and mind is bridged whenever I experience or act.

But for scientists the main value of a hypothesis which cannot be verified in the immediate future, is that it suggests experiments and observations.

The hypothesis as to the environment in which life arose shows the need not only for further calculations as to the past history of the atmosphere and hydrosphere, but for determination of the half-lives of a great variety of metastable organic compounds and some inorganic ones, and a more detailed study of pyrophosphates and metaphosphates. The hypotheses concerning pyrophosphoric esters suggest not only an investigation of the properties of simpler analogues of ATP, but of the possibility that these substances may be able to lengthen their phosphate chains by helping metastable molecules over energy barriers without catalysis by special enzymes. Many of the other problems raised, in particular that of the copying of nucleic acids, and that of the building up of proteins on nucleic acid 'templates', are being actively pursued. I hardly expect a serious attempt at the synthesis of a primitive organism for a century or so. It is wholly possible that long before that time the minimal requirements may turn out to be vastly more complicated than I have suggested. If so our descendants may have to choose between the hypothesis of supernatural intervention and the hypothesis that life is coeternal with matter, and is introduced to planets by spores drifting through space under radiation pressure.

I do not think that either of these hypotheses is needed in the present state of our ignorance. But I know enough of the history of science to have few illusions as to the validity of my own.

OTHER WORLDS

A few words may be said as to the genesis of life outside the

Earth. There may, of course, be types of life with a wholly different chemical basis to our own, for example, a low temperature life on the outer planets which is based on reactions in liquid ammonia. The temperatures of Venus and Mars would probably permit life of the terrestrial type. The absence or paucity of oxygen in their atmospheres shows that photosynthesis of the usual terrestrial type does not occur on any great scale. It further means that animal life, that is to say the life of organisms with a large flux of energy per gram per second, is almost certainly absent. While, as suggested above, life may well have begun without intracellular photosynthesis, it is hard to see how it could continue for very long without this process.

If Type II stars have planets, it is unlikely that they contain enough heavy elements to resemble the Earth at all closely. They are more likely to resemble Jupiter. But a large fraction of Type I stars may have planets, and of these a very large total number per galaxy may be as suited for life as the Earth. Type I stars of the same age as the Sun, and originally belonging to the main sequence, have already started to increase their outputs of radiation considerably if they are much more massive than the Sun. If Aldebaran (to mention a neighbour which has left the main sequence) ever had planets with life on them, this is likely to be extinct long ago. The Sun may leave the main sequence in 5 thousand million years or so. By this time our descendants, if we have not killed one another, may well be able to migrate, either to the outer planets of our system, or to those of a neighbouring star, when a suitable one comes within a fraction of a parsec.

If planets of composition like our own are at all frequently formed at a distance from stars a little less massive than the Sun which would give them suitable temperatures, life might continue on them for much longer times. It may be that the highest biological and mental developments in our galaxy will take place on such stars. If, as is widely held, the synthesis of heavy elements is continuing at the present time, it may be that more recently formed planetary systems are more favourable for the origin of life than those like our own formed about 4 thousand million years ago. The opposite may, however, be true. The next few years of astronomical research may help us to answer such questions. I hope that it is not too early to ask them.

SELECTED BIBLIOGRAPHY

(References of a more advanced nature are marked by an asterisk)

CHAPTER 1: THE INTERNATIONAL GEOPHYSICAL YEAR

Annals of the International Geophysical Year, (Gen. Ed.: Sir HAROLD SPENCER JONES), vol. 1, (Pergamon Press, London, 1957).*

CHAPMAN, S., 'The International Geophysical Year, 1957–8', *Nature*, vol. 175, pp. 55 and 402, (1955).

CHAPMAN, S., 'The International Geophysical Year', *The Advancement of Science*, vol. 13, p. 259, (1957).

CROOME, ANGELA, 'IGY Month-by-Month', *Discovery*, vol. 27, p. 205, (1956), (and subsequent monthly issues).

MARTIN, D. C., 'The International Geophysical Year', *Penguin Science News*, vol. 45, p. 7, (1957).

MASSEY, H. S. W., 'The Earth Satellite Programme', *Space Research and Exploration*, ch. 7, (Ed.: D. R. BATES), (Eyre and Spottiswoode, London, 1957).

CHAPTER 2: ORIGIN, AGE AND POSSIBLE ULTIMATE FATE OF THE EARTH

ALDRICH, L. T., 'Measurement of Radioactive Ages of Rocks', *Science*, vol. 123, p. 871, (1956).

DARWIN, Sir GEORGE H., *The Tides*, (Murray, London, 1911).*

JEFFREYS, Sir HAROLD, *The Earth*, (The University Press, Cambridge, 1952).*

KUIPER, G. P., 'The Formation of the Planets', *Journal of the Royal Astronomical Society of Canada*, vol. 50, pp. 57, 105 and 158, (1956).

PATTERSON, C. C., 'Age of Meteorites and the Earth', *Geochimica et Cosmochimica Acta*, vol. 10, p. 230, (1956).*

PATTERSON, C. C., TILTON, G. R., and INGHRAM, M. G., 'Age of the Earth', *Science*, vol. 121, p. 69, (1955).

SCHILLIBEER, H. A., and RUSSELL, R. D., 'The Argon-40 Content of the Atmosphere and the Age of the Earth', *Geochimica et Cosmochimica Acta*, vol. 8, p. 16, (1955).*

UREY, H. C., *The Planets*, (Yale University Press, New Haven, 1952).

CHAPTER 3: THE DEEP INTERIOR

BULLEN, K. E., 'Seismology and the Broad Structure of the Earth's Interior', *Physics and Chemistry of the Earth*, (Eds.: L. H. AHRENS, K. RANKAMA and S. K. RUNCORN), ch. 4, vol. 1, (Pergamon Press, London, 1956).

BULLEN, K. E., *Seismology*, (Methuen, London, 1954).*

BULLEN, K. E., *Introduction to the Theory of Seismology*, (The University Press, Cambridge, 1953).*

JEFFREYS, Sir HAROLD, *Earthquakes and Mountains*, (Methuen, London, 1950).

JEFFREYS, Sir HAROLD, *The Earth*, (The University Press, Cambridge, 1952).*

CHAPTER 4: THE CRUST

DE SITTER, L. V., *Structural Geology*, (McGraw-Hill, New York, 1956).*

GUTENBERG, B., and RICHTER, C. F., *Seismicity of the Earth*, (Princeton University Press, Princeton, 1954).*

HOLMES, A., *Principles of Physical Geology*, (Nelson, London, 1946).

JEFFREYS, Sir HAROLD, *Earthquakes and Mountains*, (Methuen, London, 1950).

JEFFREYS, Sir HAROLD, *The Earth*, (The University Press, Cambridge, 1952).*

KUIPER, G. P., (Ed.), *The Earth as a Planet*, (Chapters 4, 5 and 6), (University of Chicago Press, Chicago, 1954).*

MASON, B., *Principles of Geochemistry*, (Wiley, New York, 1952).*

MOORE, RUTH, *The Earth We Live In*, (Knopf, New York, 1956).

UMBGROVE, J. H. F., *The Pulse of the Earth*, (Nijhoff, The Hague, Holland, 1947).*

CHAPTER 5: THE OCEANS

COKER, R. E., *This Great and Wide Sea*, (The University of North Carolina Press, Chapel Hill, 1947).

OMMANNEY, F. D., *The Ocean*, (Clarendon Press, Oxford, 1949).

PROUDMAN, J., *Dynamical Oceanography*, (Methuen, London, 1954).*

SVERDRUP, H. U., *Oceanography for Meteorologists*, (Allen and Unwin, London, 1945).

SVERDRUP, H. U., JOHNSON, M. W., and FLEMING, R. H., *The Oceans*, (Prentice-Hall, New York, 1942).

CHAPTER 6: GEOMAGNETIC FIELD

BLACKETT, P. M. S., *Lectures on Rock Magnetism*, (The Weizmann Science Press of Israel, Jerusalem, 1956).

CHAPMAN, S., and BARTELS, J., *Geomagnetism*, (Clarendon Press, Oxford, 1940).*

COWLING, T. G., 'Dynamo Theories of Cosmic Magnetic Fields', *Vistas in Astronomy*, (Ed.: A. BEER), vol. 1, p. 314, (Pergamon Press, London, 1955).

INGLIS, D. R., 'Theories of the Earth's Magnetism', *Reviews of Modern Physics*, vol. 27, p. 212, (1955).*

NAGATA, T., *Rock Magnetism*, (Maruzen Co., Tokyo, 1953).*

RUNCORN, S. K., 'The Magnetism of the Earth's Body', *Handbuch der Physik*, vol. 47, *Geophysics*, (Ed.: J. BARTELS), (Springer-Verlag, Berlin, 1956).*
RUNCORN, S. K., 'The Earth's Magnetism', *Scientific American*, vol. 193, p. 152, (1955).

CHAPTER 7: COMPOSITION AND STRUCTURE OF THE ATMOSPHERE

BATES, D. R., 'Rocket Exploration of the Upper Atmosphere', *Space Research and Exploration*, ch. 4, (Ed.: D. R. BATES), (Eyre and Spottiswoode, London, 1957).
BURGESS, E., *Frontier to Space*, (Chapman and Hall, London, 1955).
GOODY, R. M., *The Physics of the Stratosphere*, (The University Press, Cambridge, 1954).*
MITRA, S. K., *The Upper Atmosphere*, (The Asiatic Society, Calcutta, 1952).*
NEWELL, H. E., *High Altitude Rocket Research*, (Academic Press, New York, 1953).
PANETH, F. A., 'The Chemical Exploration of the Stratosphere', (Hugo Müller Lecture), *Journal of the Chemical Society*, Pt. 3, p. 3651, 1952.

CHAPTER 8: CLIMATE

BROOKS, C. E. P., *Climate Through the Ages*, (Benn, London, 1949).
GEIGER, R., *The Climate Near the Ground*, (Harvard University Press, Cambridge, Massachusetts, 1950).*
MILLER, A. A., *Climatology*, (Methuen, London, 1950).
SHAPLEY, H., (Ed.), *Climatic Change*, (Harvard University Press, Cambridge, Massachusetts, 1950).

CHAPTER 9: THE GENERAL CIRCULATION OF THE ATMOSPHERE AND OCEANS

BJERKNES, V. *et al.*, *Physikalishe Hydrodynamik*, (Springer-Verlag, Berlin, 1933).*
BRUNT, Sir DAVID, *Physical and Dynamical Meteorology*, (The University Press, Cambridge, 1944).*
MALONE, THOS. F., (Ed.), *Compendium of Meteorology*, (American Met. Soc. Boston, 1951).*
MUNK, W. H., 'The Circulation of the Oceans', *Scientific American*, vol. 193, p. 96, (1955).
SVERDRUP, H. U., *Oceanography for Meteorologists*, (Allen and Unwin, London, 1945).*
WEXLER, H., 'The Circulation of the Atmosphere', *Scientific American*, vol. 193, p. 114, (1955).

CHAPTER 10: ICE AGES

BROOKS, C. E. P., *Climate Through the Ages*, (Benn, London, 1949).*
EMILIANI, C., 'Note on Absolute Chronology of Human Evolution', *Science*, vol. 123, p. 924, (1956).

ÖPIK, E. J., 'The Destiny of Life', *The Irish Astronomical Journal*, vol. 2, p. 65, (1952).

ÖPIK, E. J., 'The Ice Ages', *The Irish Astronomical Journal*, vol. 2, p. 71, (1952).

ÖPIK, E. J., 'On the Causes of the Palaeoclimatic Variations and of the Ice Ages in Particular', *The Journal of Glaciology*, vol. 2, p. 213, (1953).*

SHAPLEY, H., (Ed.), *Climatic Change*, (Harvard University Press, Cambridge, Massachusetts, 1953).*

SUESS, H. E., 'Absolute Chronology of the Last Glaciation', *Science*, vol. 123, p. 355, (1956).

UMBGROVE, J. H. F., *The Pulse of the Earth*, (Nijhoff, The Hague, 1947).*

CHAPTER 11: METEOROLOGY

BROWNE, I. C., PALMER, H. P., and WORMELL, T. W., 'The Physics of Rainclouds', *Quarterly Journal of the Royal Meteorological Society*, vol. 80, p. 291, (1954).*

DOUGLAS, C. K. M., 'The Evolution of 20th Century Forecasting in the British Isles', *Quart. J. Roy. Met. Soc.*, vol. 78, p. 1, (1952).*

LUDLAM, F. H., 'The Structure of Shower Clouds', *Weather*, vol. 11, p. 187, (1956).

LUDLAM, F. H., and SCORER, R. S., *Further Outlook*, (Wingate, London, 1954).

MASON, B. J., 'The Physics of Rainmaking', *Discovery*, vol. 26, p. 461, (1955).

MASON, B. J., *The Physics of Clouds*, (Clarendon Press, Oxford, 1957).*

MASON, B. J., and LUDLAM, F. H., 'The Microphysics of Clouds', *Reports on Progress in Physics*, vol. 14, p. 147, (1951).*

PETTERSSEN, S., *Weather Analysis and Forecasting*, (McGraw-Hill, New York, 1956).*

SUTCLIFFE, R. C., 'Principles of Synoptic Weather Forecasting', *Quart. J. Roy. Met. Soc.*, vol. 78, p. 291, (1952).*

CHAPTER 12: THE IONOSPHERE

GAUTIER, T. N., 'The Ionosphere', *Scientific American*, vol. 193, p. 126, (1955).

MITRA, S. K., *The Upper Atmosphere*, (The Asiatic Society, Calcutta, 1952).*

RATCLIFFE, J. A., 'The Physics of the Ionosphere', (Kelvin Lecture), *Proceedings of the Institute of Electrical Engineers*, vol. 101, Part 1, p. 339, (1954).

RATCLIFFE, J. A., 'The Ionosphere', *Nature*, vol. 179, p. 228, (1957).

Report of the Physical Society Conference on 'The Physics of the Ionosphere', (The Physical Society, London, 1955).*

CHAPTER 13: THE AIRGLOW

ARMSTRONG, E. B., and DALGARNO, A., (Eds.), *The Airglow and the Aurorae*, (Pergamon Press, London, 1956).*

BARBIER, D., 'Analyse du Spectre du Ciel Nocturne', *Annales de Géophysique*, vol. 11, p. 67, (1955)*.

ELVEY, C. T., and ROACH, F. E., 'Aurora and Airglow', *Scientific American*, vol. 193, p. 140, (1955).

ROACH, F. E., 'A Review of Observational Results in Airglow Photometry', *Annales de Géophysique*, vol. 11, p. 100, (1955).*

SEATON, M. J., Theories of the Airglow Spectrum', *Annales de Géophysique*, vol. 11, p. 118, (1955).*

CHAPTER 14: AURORAE AND MAGNETIC STORMS

CHAPMAN, S., 'The Aurora in Middle and Low Latitudes', *Nature*, vol. 179, p. 7, (1957).

ELVEY, C. T., and ROACH, F. E., 'Aurorae and Airglow', *Scientific American*, vol. 193, p. 240, (1955).

FERRARO, V. C. A., 'The Aurorae', *Advances in Physics*, vol. 2, p. 265, (1953).*

HARANG, L., *The Aurorae*, (Chapman and Hall, London, 1951).*

MARTYN, D. F., 'The Theory of Magnetic Storms and Aurorae', *Nature*, vol. 167, p. 92, (1951).*

STÖRMER, C., *The Polar Aurora*, (Clarendon Press, Oxford, 1955).*

CHAPTER 15: METEORS

KAISER, T. R., (Ed.), *Meteors*, (Pergamon Press, London, 1955).*

LOVELL, A. C. B., *Meteor Astronomy*, (Clarendon Press, Oxford, 1954).*

LOVELL, A. C. B., and CLEGG, J. A., *Radio Astronomy*, (Chapman and Hall, London, 1952).

WATSON, FLETCHER, G., *Between the Planets*, (Clarendon Press, Oxford, 1956).

CHAPTER 16: COSMIC RADIATION

JÁNOSSY, L., *Cosmic Rays*, (Clarendon Press, Oxford, 1948).*

JÁNOSSY, L., *Cosmic Rays and Nuclear Physics*, (Pilot Press, London, 1948).

LEPRINCE-RINGUET, L., *Cosmic Rays*, (Prentice-Hall, New York, 1950).

WILSON, J. G., *About Cosmic Rays*, (Sigma Books, London, 1948).

WILSON, J. G., (Ed.), *Progress in Cosmic Ray Physics*, vol. 1, (1952), vol. 2 (1954), vol. 3 (1956), (North-Holland Publishing Co., Amsterdam).*

CHAPTER 17: GENESIS OF LIFE

BALDWIN, E., *Dynamic Aspects of Biochemistry*, (The University Press, Cambridge, 1952).*

BERNAL, J. D., *The Physical Basis of Life*, (Routledge, London, 1951).

BERNAL, J. D., 'The Origin of Life', *New Biology*, vol. 16, p. 28, (1954).

CALVIN, M., 'Chemical Evolution and the Origin of Life', *American Scientist*, vol. 44, p. 248, (1956).

FLEURY, P., COURTOIS, J., and DESJOBERT, A., 'Recherches sur le diose-phosphate. vi. Étude de l'hydrolyse en milieu acide', *Bull. Soc. Chim. France*, 694–700, (1948).*

HALDANE, J. B. S., 'The Origin of Life', *Rationalist Annual*, (1929).

LEVINTHAL, C., and CRANE, H. R., 'On the unwinding of DNA' *Proceedings of the National Academy of Sciences (Washington)*, vol. 42, p. 436, (1956).*

MILLER, S. L., 'Production of some Organic Compounds under Possible Primitive Earth Conditions', *Journal of the American Chemical Society*, vol. 77, p. 2351, (1955).*

OPARIN, A. I., *The Origin of Life*, (Macmillan, New York, 1938).

PIRIE, N. W., 'On Making and Recognizing Life', *New Biology*, vol. 16, p. 41, (1954).

PRINGLE, J. W. S., 'The Origin of Life', *Symposia of the Society of Experimental Biology*, 7, p. 1, (1953).

PRINGLE, J. W. S., 'The Evolution of Living Matter', *New Biology*, vol. 16, p. 54, (1954).

STAPLEDON, O. W., *First and Last Men*, (Methuen, London, 1930).

THODE, H. G., MACNAMARA J., and FLEMING, H. W., 'Sulphur Fractionation in Nature and Geological and Biochemical Time Scales' *Geochimica et Cosmochimica Acta*, vol. 3, p. 235, (1953).*

UREY, H. C., 'On the Early Chemical History of the Earth and on the Origin of Life', *Proc. Nat. Ac. of Sci.*, (Washington), vol. 38, p. 351, (1953).

WATSON, J. D., and CRICK, F. H. C., 'Molecular Structure of Nucleic Acids', *Nature*, vol. 171, p. 737, (1953).

APPENDICES

Appendix I

GRAVITATION AND THE MASS OF THE EARTH

According to Newton's law of gravitation, two bodies of masses M and m, with their centres distant r apart, attract each other with a force of magnitude GMm/r^2, where G is the 'universal' constant of gravitation, equal to $6 \cdot 67 \times 10^{-8}$ units in the c.g.s. system.

Let M be the mass of the Earth, and m the mass of a body falling freely with acceleration g near the Earth's surface. The force of gravitational attraction in the body is its weight, mg. Hence g and M are connected by the equation

$$g = \frac{GM}{a^2}$$

where a is the radius of the Earth.

K. E. B.

Appendix II

MOMENT OF INERTIA

Let m be the mass of a typical one of a large number of small parts of which a given body is composed, and let x be the distance of this part from a given line. Then the moment of inertia of the body about the line is defined as the sum of the values of mx^2 for all the parts.

Let M be the mass of a spherical body and a its radius. If the body is of constant density its moment of inertia about a diameter is $0 \cdot 4\ Ma^2$. The moment of inertia of the Earth is found to be $0 \cdot 334\ Ma^2$, the smaller coefficient implying a degree of concentration towards the centre.

K. E. B.

Appendix III

PRECESSION OF THE EQUINOXES

Stars are sometimes conceived as bright points dotted about on the inside of a large hollow spherical dome called the celestial sphere. Let l be the line in which the plane of the Earth's equator cuts the plane containing the apparent annual motion of the Sun. Then the two points in which l meets the celestial sphere are called the equinoctial points. An effect of the Moon is to cause these points to move relatively to distant stars through an angular distance of about 50 seconds in a year. This is the phenomenon called the precession of the equinoxes.

K. E. B.

Appendix IV

P AND S WAVES

Let ρ be the density of the material at given point of the Earth's interior, and let k and μ be the incompressibility and rigidity. Then the velocities α and β of P and S seismic waves, respectively, are given by

$$\alpha = \sqrt{\frac{k + \frac{4}{3}\mu}{\rho}}, \quad \beta = \sqrt{\frac{\mu}{\rho}}.$$

K. E. B.

Appendix V

TEMPERATURE SCALES

The temperature F in degrees Fahrenheit and the temperature C in degrees Centigrade are related by the equations

$$F = 32 + 1.8\,C,$$

$$C = \frac{5}{9}(F - 32).$$

M. S.

Appendix VI

ATOMIC AND MOLECULAR SPECTRA

An atom consists of a cloud of negatively charged particles, called electrons, bound to a relatively heavy positively charged nucleus, the binding being due to the attraction that exists between electrical charges of opposite sign. The cloud has many possible forms each with a specific energy. If it has the form with the least energy, the atom is said to be in the *ground state*; and if it has any other form, the atom is said to be in an *excited state*.

In general, an atom which has been raised to an excited state quickly returns to the ground state with the emission of light. The return may occur through a single transition or, if there are excited states of intermediate energies, through a succession of transitions. The frequency of the light waves given out in any transition is proportional to the difference between the energies of the two states directly involved. Excited atoms of a given species thus radiate only at certain frequencies. These frequencies are characteristic of the species.

A *spectroscope* is used for the analysis of radiation. This instrument makes use of the fact that in passing through a prism of glass or other transparent material, light is deviated to an extent which depends on the frequency, so that a narrow beam containing waves of different frequencies is split into a number of narrow beams, which on being allowed to fall on a photographic plate, are recorded as *lines*. The record gives the *spectrum* of the light from the source. By measuring the positions of the lines, it is possible to determine the corresponding frequencies.

A molecule is composed of two or more atoms united chemically. It is convenient to suppose first that the nuclei are held fixed in position. As before, the electron cloud has a variety of possible forms each with a specific energy, so that the spectrum of the imaginary fixed-nuclei molecule would be essentially similar to that of an atom. The nuclei of an actual molecule vibrate and rotate with respect to one another. Because of the vibration, each of the energies just mentioned is replaced by a set of moderately spaced energies which, of course, makes the spectrum richer; and because of the rotation, each energy of this new set is replaced by a further set of closely spaced energies, which leads to groups of spectral lines so close together that the groups are called *bands* from their appearance.

Instead of the frequency it is often useful to give the wavelength which is simply the velocity of light, 3×10^{10} (thirty thousand million) centimetres per second, divided by the frequency. The wave-length is usually expressed in *angstroms*. An angstrom is 1×10^{-8} (one hundredth of a millionth) of a centimetre. It is denoted by the letter A for brevity. The following are the approximate wave-length ranges of some colours: red, 7700 A to 6300 A; orange, 6300 A to 5900 A; yellow, 5900 A to 5600 A; green, 5600 A to 4900 A; blue, 4900 A to 4500 A; violet, 4500 A to 3600 A. To the long wave-length side of 7700 A lies the infra-red and to the short wave-length side of 3600 A lies the ultra-violet.

D.R.B.